SONGS FOR
Praise & Worship

© Copyright 1992 by Word Music (a division of Word, Incorporated)
All Rights Reserved. International Copyright Secured

96 RRD 10987654

WORD MUSIC

FOREWORD

God delights in the praises of His people. Scripture has instructed us that glorious praise not only is His due, but is the very prerequisite to knowing His presence. For He has promised that He will draw near to us as we offer up our praise to Him. Through the centuries, Christians have claimed this promise and have experienced the real presence of God in their lives.

The same is true for us today. For I am convinced that the Holy Spirit is waiting for hearts that hunger and thirst for an unprecedented visitation of God to our generation—displaying His glorious power and might to every culture and in every church. And I am equally convinced that the one pathway to having that take place is a reformation in the worship-life of the Church, just as dramatic and dynamic as the reformation in the theology of the Church was five centuries ago. I believe that reformation begins for each of us in our perceiving the true purpose and spiritual dynamic in worship. What has been defined for so long as an hour's exercise on Sunday is being redefined today, and at the heart of this redefinition is music.

Worship may be possible without song, but nothing contributes more to its beauty, majesty, dignity, or nobility, nor to its tenderness and intimacy. The breadth of style, the endless melodic possibilities, the delicate nuances of choral dynamics, the brilliant luster of instrumental arrangement, the soul-stirring anthems of anointed choirs, the rumbling magnificence of giant organs—all seem clearly to be a God-given means for our endless expansion in worship.

Over the last few decades, a new song has risen in the Church which has led, and continues to lead, Christians all across our world into a more intimate relationship with God. While I am a firm believer that Christians today should not make the mistake of abandoning the great hymns of the faith which form a crucial foundation for our experience in worship, there must also be a growing newness in our musical expression. New musical expression is fitting as we each discover new things about the manifold wisdom of the Lord our God.

That which you hold in your hands represents a giant step toward enabling the Church more fully to realize the potential of this new musical expression. It provides those concrete tools necessary to bring together singer and instrumentalist, choir and congregation, all worshippers from varied backgrounds and traditions, into common and creative worship through music. This volume is filled with a remarkable collection of new and cherished music which God is truly using to move churches throughout the world into a renewed and expanded expression of worship.

May this wonderful resource, *Songs for Praise and Worship*, become for you an instrument of true worship and joyous praise to our glorious Lord.

Jack W. Hayford
Pastor, Author, Songwriter

PREFACE

Over the last two decades, the Church has experienced growth in ways that have given Christians new expressions of worship. Modern day men and women have continued to search for those expressions that draw them into a closer, more intimate relationship with God. Literally millions of worshippers around the world have found that expression in a new song . . . a song of praise and worship offered up to God because of who He is and because of what He has done in our lives. We believe that as the Church moves into the twenty-first century, this new song will continue to spread throughout the Christian faith. With that vision in mind, Word Music is proud to introduce you to *Songs for Praise and Worship*.

Songs for Praise and Worship is a rich anthology of 253 songs and choruses. It contains the most popular and well-known songs from the catalogs of all the major praise and worship publishers, and from many other independent publishers as well. It may be used either as a stand-alone collection of today's most popular praise songs or as a supplement to a hymnal, so that the great hymns of our faith can be blended with these newer musical expressions.

Songs for Praise and Worship consists of a Pew Edition (for the congregation), a Singer's Edition (for use by a worship team or a choir), a Worship Planner's Edition (for the Pastor or Worship Leader), a Keyboard Edition (which provides the foundational accompaniment), and fifteen Instrumental Editions. The entire collection is fully orchestrated, and playable by any size ensemble.

Songs for Praise and Worship contains many unique features which will enable pastors, worship leaders, and ministers of music to plan, create, and implement more effective and meaningful times of worship. Our prayer is that God will use these resources to bring honor and glory to His name, to further broaden the use of praise and worship music, and to draw the Body of Christ together in unity and in life-changing worship.

The Publisher

ACKNOWLEDGEMENTS

SENIOR EDITOR
Ken Barker

ASSOCIATE EDITOR
Tom Fettke

EXECUTIVE COMMITTEE
Ken Barker-Chairman, LaMar Boschman, Don Cason, Tom Fettke, David Guthrie, Dr. Terry C. Terry and Robert Till

ADVISORY BOARD
George Baldwin, Tom Blackaby, Sammy Davenport, Paul Ferrin, John Finochio, Don McMinn, Gary Rhodes, Jeanne Rogers, Jim Whitmire and Steve Williamson

SCRIPTURE EDITOR
Dr. Kenneth L. Barker

CONSULTANTS
Michael Biggs, Keith Christopher, George Gower, Dina Koviac, Richard Muehleman, Mark Rhodes and Michal Rutledge

LOGO DESIGN
Dennis Hill

COPYRIGHT ADMINISTRATION
Susan Flowers, LuAnn Inman and Conan Mathson

PRODUCTION ASSISTANTS
Brenda Barker, Maxine Clark, Donna Kent, Barry Kerrigan, Mark Ladd, Michael Lawrence, David McDonald, Linda Rebuck, Brent Roberts, Sharon Smith, Alyssa Wilson and Wayne Yankie

MUSIC TYPOGRAPHY
MicroMusic, Inc., Irving, Texas; Reid Lancaster

WORD INCORPORATED
Roland Lundy, President; Tom Ramsey, Executive Vice-President, Word Record and Music Group; Don Cason, Vice President, Word Music

The Publisher gratefully acknowledges permission received from other publishers, organizations and individuals to reprint texts, music, and arrangements contained in this book.

CONTENTS

1   We Bring the Sacrifice of Praise

KIRK DEARMAN   KIRK DEARMAN

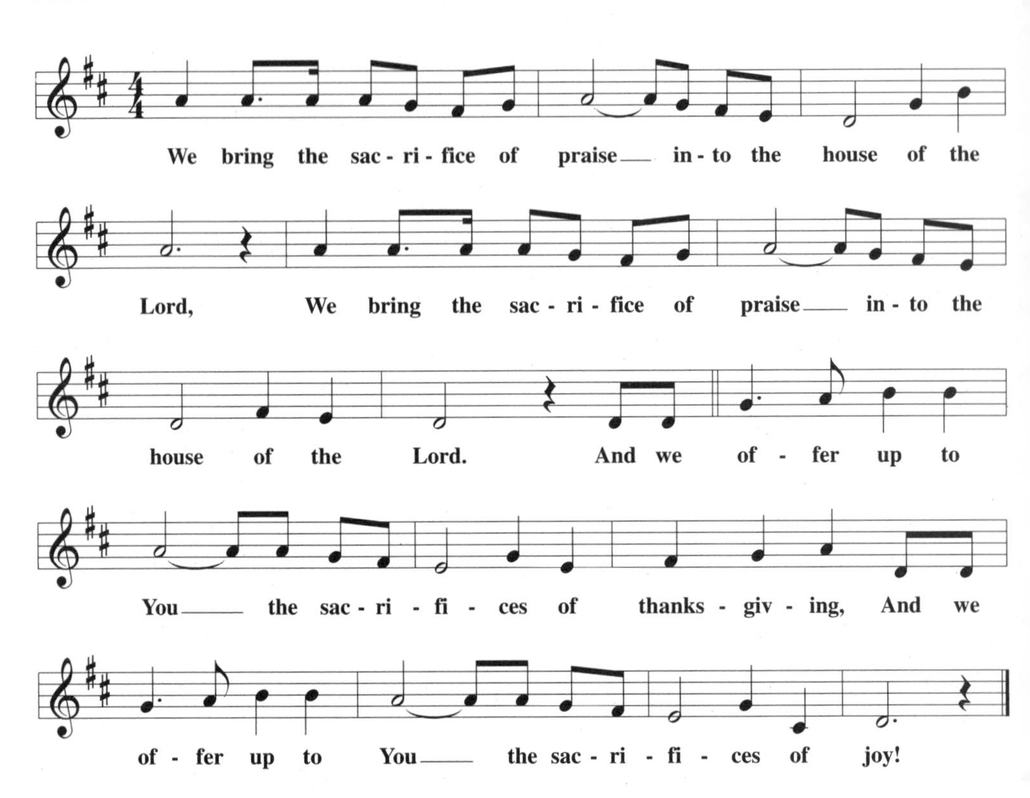

We bring the sac-ri-fice of praise into the house of the Lord, We bring the sac-ri-fice of praise into the house of the Lord. And we of-fer up to You the sac-ri-fi-ces of thanks-giv-ing, And we of-fer up to You the sac-ri-fi-ces of joy!

2   Ah, Lord God

KAY CHANCE   KAY CHANCE

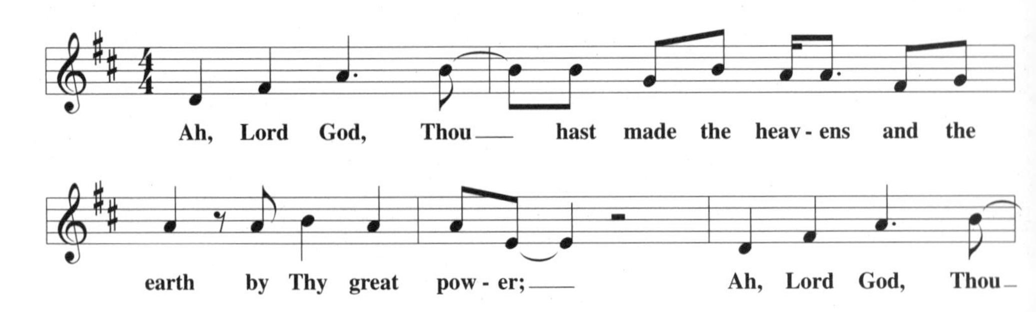

Ah, Lord God, Thou hast made the heav-ens and the earth by Thy great pow-er; Ah, Lord God, Thou

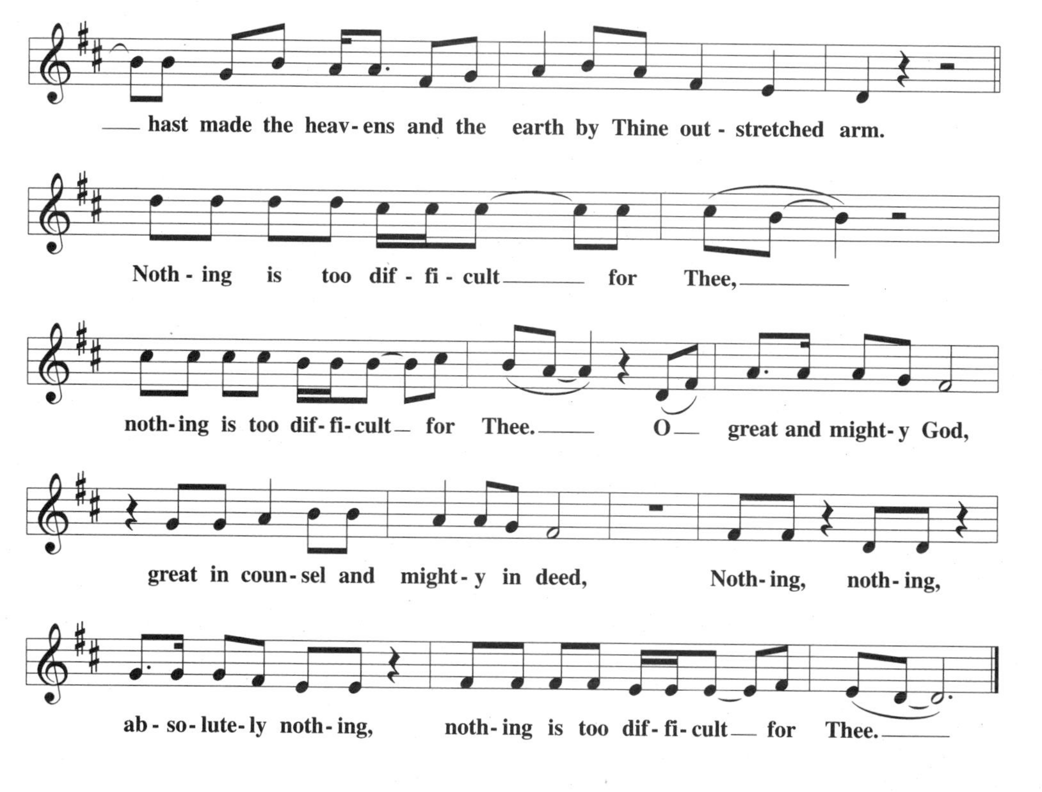

hast made the heav-ens and the earth by Thine out-stretched arm.

Noth-ing is too dif-fi-cult___ for Thee,___

noth-ing is too dif-fi-cult_ for Thee.___ O___ great and might-y God,

great in coun-sel and might-y in deed, Noth-ing, noth-ing,

ab-so-lute-ly noth-ing, noth-ing is too dif-fi-cult_ for Thee.___

What a Mighty God We Serve 3

AUTHOR UNKNOWN

COMPOSER UNKNOWN

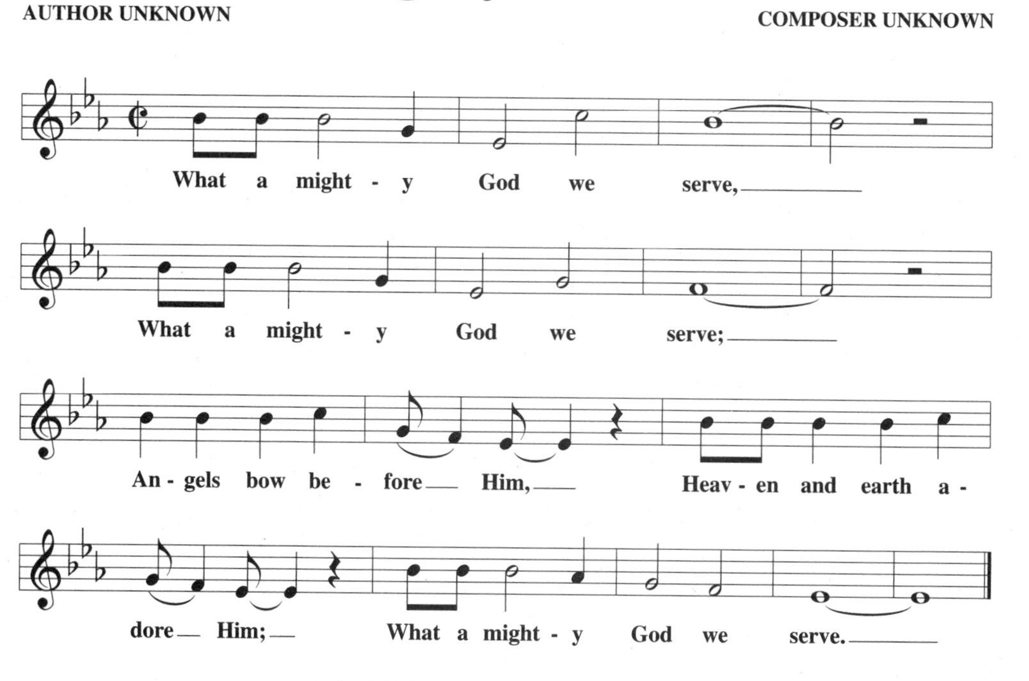

What a might-y God we serve,___

What a might-y God we serve;___

An-gels bow be-fore_ Him,___ Heav-en and earth a-

dore_ Him;___ What a might-y God we serve.___

4 Great and Mighty

MARLENE BIGLEY

MARLENE BIGLEY

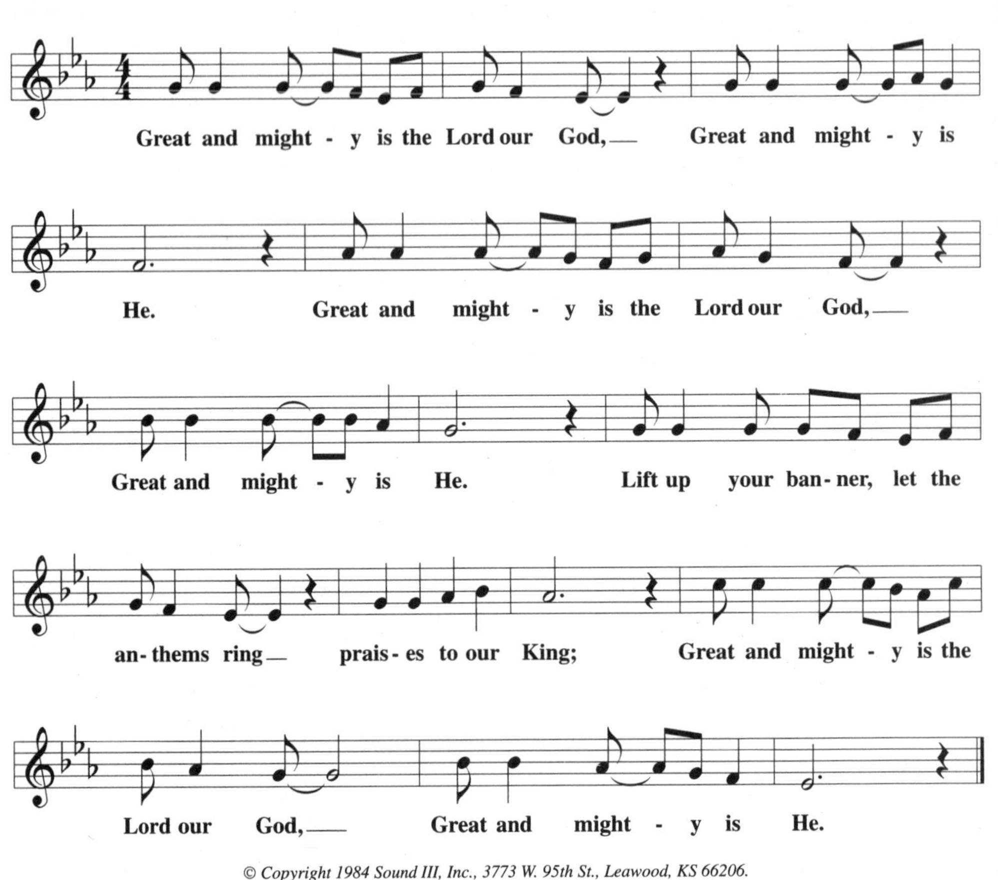

Great and might-y is the Lord our God,— Great and might-y is
He. Great and might-y is the Lord our God,—
Great and might-y is He. Lift up your ban-ner, let the
an-thems ring— prais-es to our King; Great and might-y is the
Lord our God,— Great and might-y is He.

5 Thou Art Worthy

PAULINE M. MILLS
Based on Rev. 4:11; 5:9

PAULINE M. MILLS

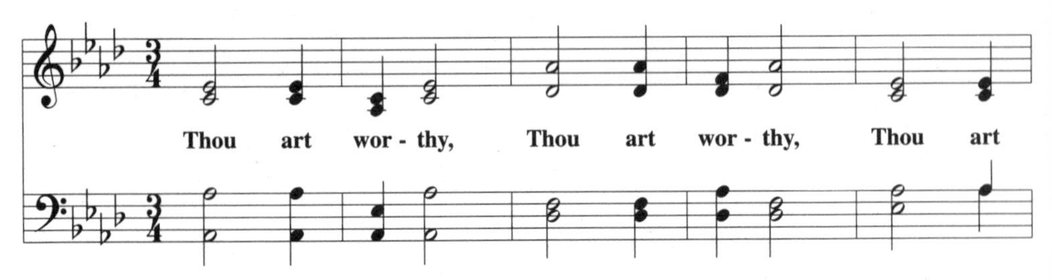

Thou art wor-thy, Thou art wor-thy, Thou art

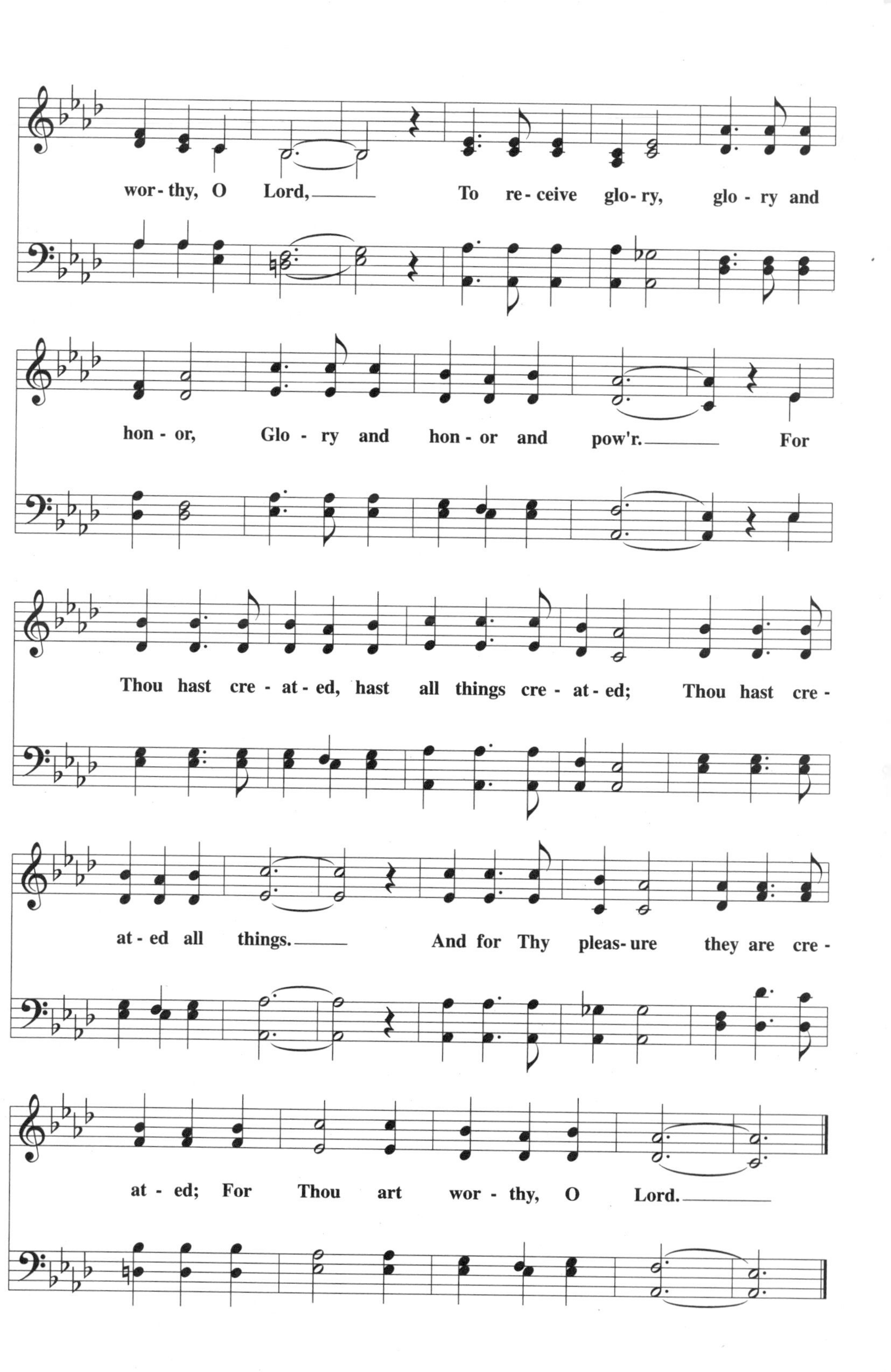

wor-thy, O Lord,_____ To re-ceive glo-ry, glo-ry and

hon-or, Glo-ry and hon-or and pow'r._____ For

Thou hast cre-at-ed, hast all things cre-at-ed; Thou hast cre-

at-ed all things._____ And for Thy pleas-ure they are cre-

at-ed; For Thou art wor-thy, O Lord._____

6 Father God

JACK W. HAYFORD

JACK W. HAYFORD

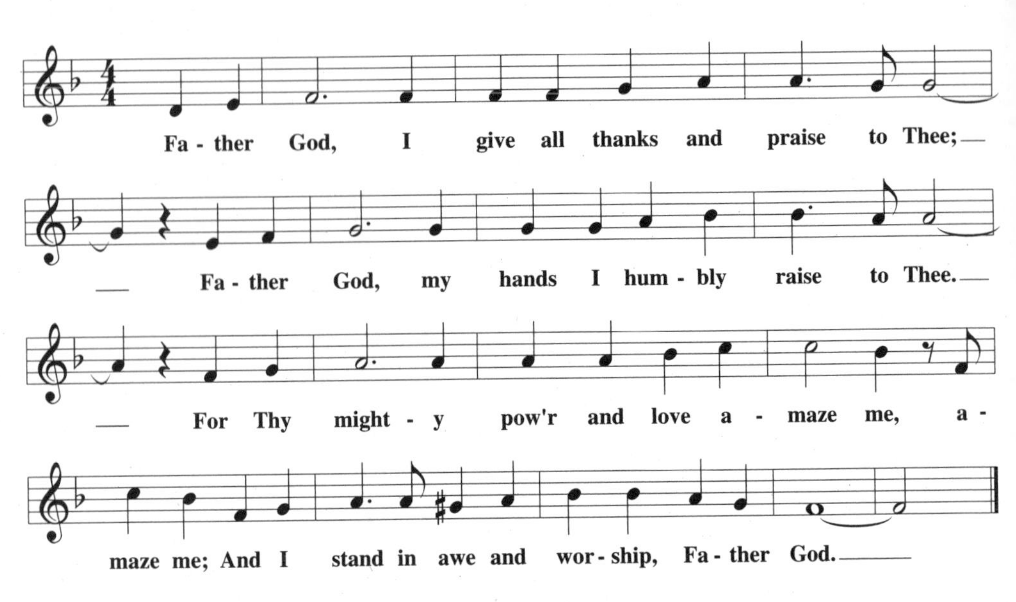

Fa - ther God, I give all thanks and praise to Thee; —

— Fa - ther God, my hands I hum - bly raise to Thee. —

— For Thy might - y pow'r and love a - maze me, a -

maze me; And I stand in awe and wor - ship, Fa - ther God. —

7 Blessed Be the Lord God Almighty

BOB FITTS

BOB FITTS

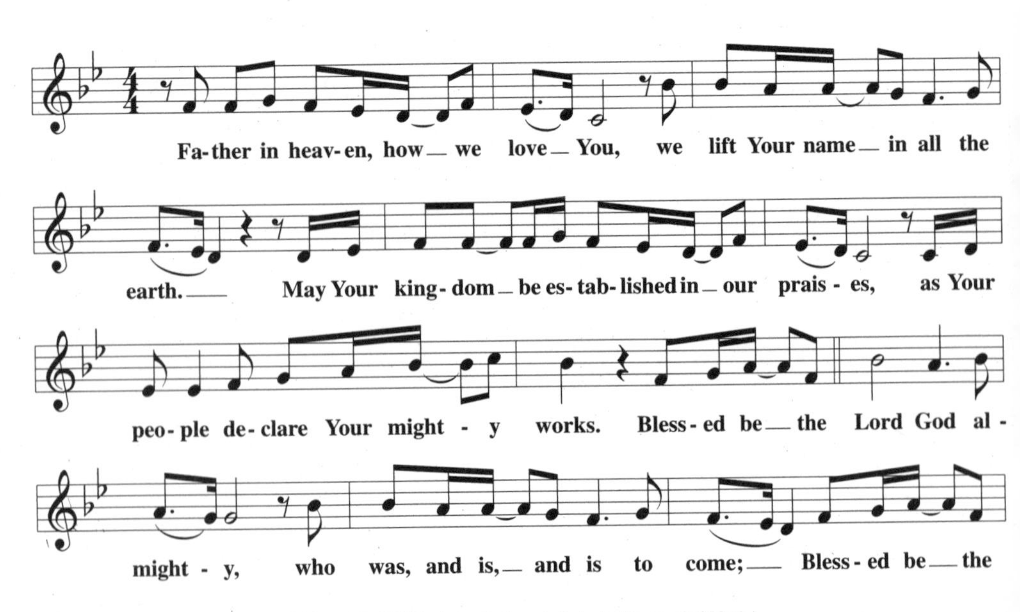

Fa - ther in heav - en, how — we love — You, we lift Your name — in all the

earth. — May Your king - dom — be es - tab - lished in — our prais - es, as Your

peo - ple de - clare Your might - y works. Bless - ed be — the Lord God al -

might - y, who was, and is, — and is to come; Bless - ed be — the

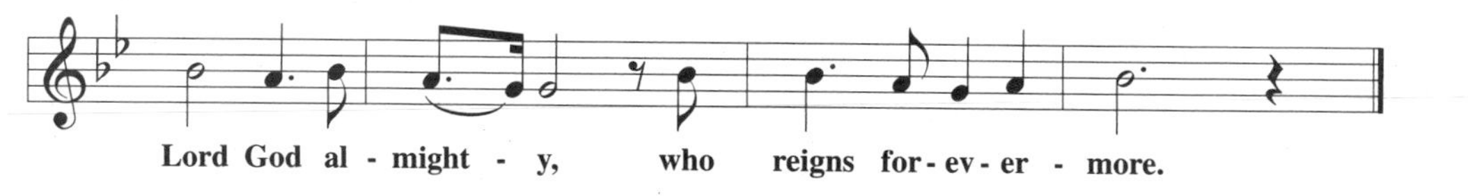

Lord God al - might - y, who reigns for - ev - er - more.

Bless His Holy Name

8

ANDRAÉ CROUCH
Based on Psalm 103

ANDRAÉ CROUCH

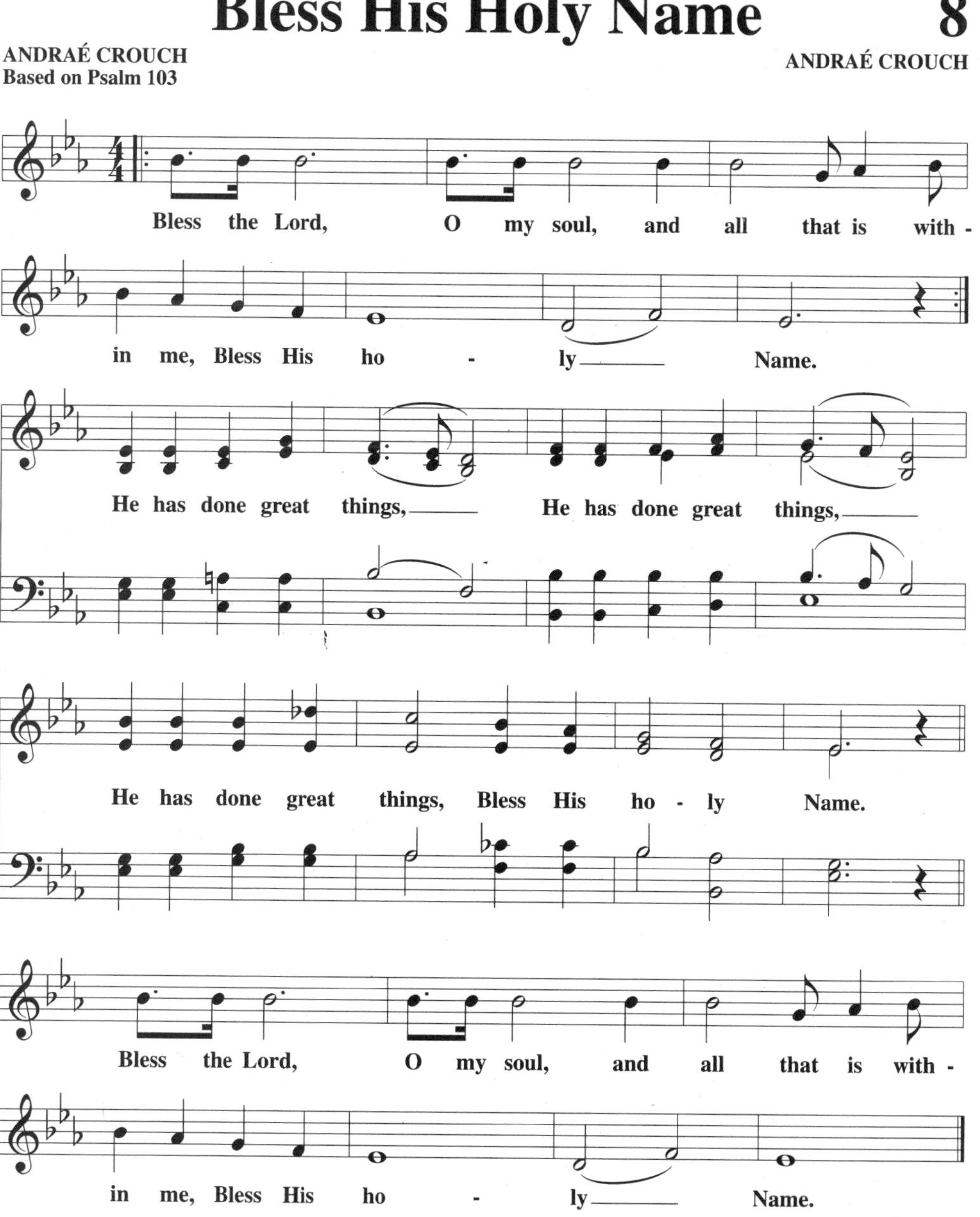

Bless the Lord, O my soul, and all that is with -

in me, Bless His ho - ly Name.

He has done great things, He has done great things,

He has done great things, Bless His ho - ly Name.

Bless the Lord, O my soul, and all that is with -

in me, Bless His ho - ly Name.

9   I Stand in Awe

MARK ALTROGGE   MARK ALTROGGE

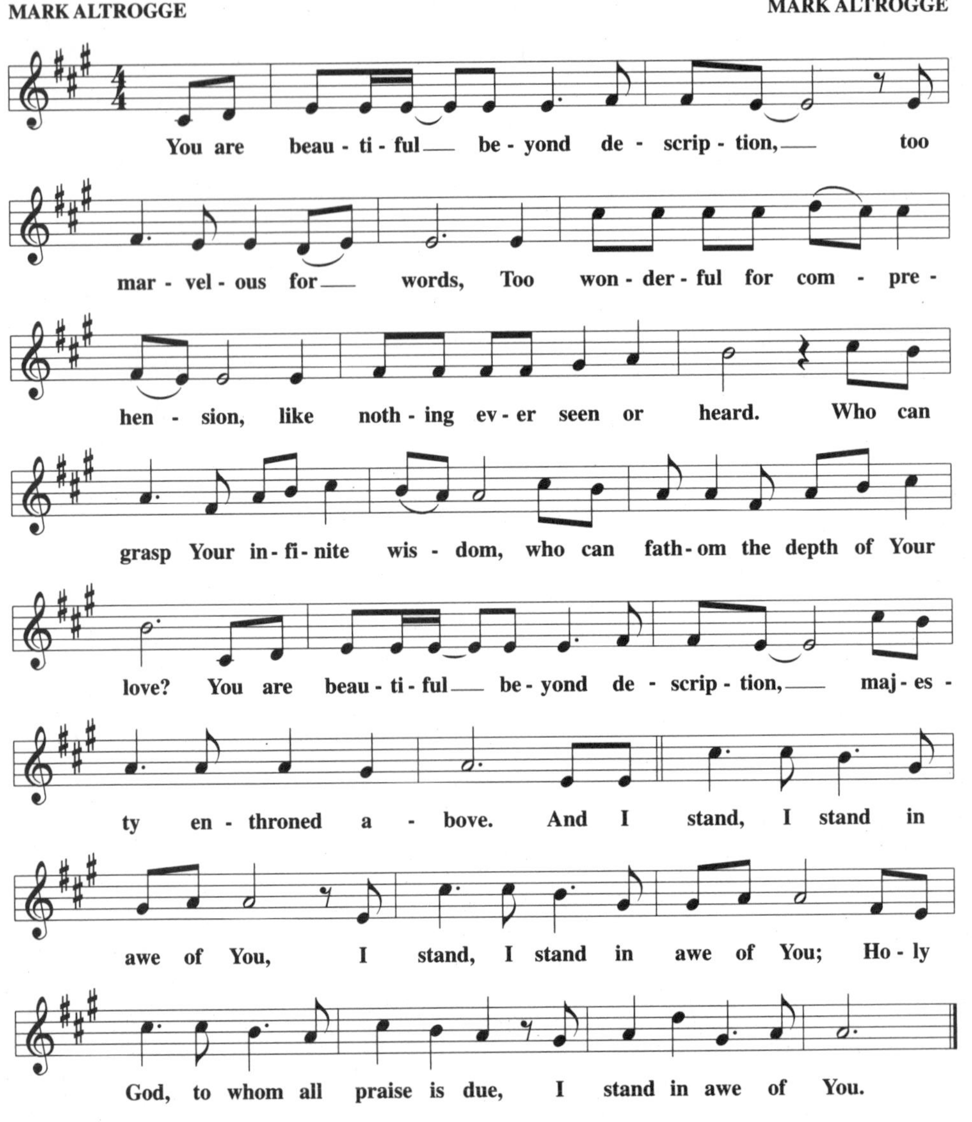

You are beau-ti-ful— be-yond de-scrip-tion,— too
mar-vel-ous for— words, Too won-der-ful for com-pre-
hen-sion, like noth-ing ev-er seen or heard. Who can
grasp Your in-fi-nite wis-dom, who can fath-om the depth of Your
love? You are beau-ti-ful— be-yond de-scrip-tion,— maj-es-
ty en-throned a-bove. And I stand, I stand in
awe of You, I stand, I stand in awe of You; Ho-ly
God, to whom all praise is due, I stand in awe of You.

10   Awesome Power

JOHN G. ELLIOTT   JOHN G. ELLIOTT

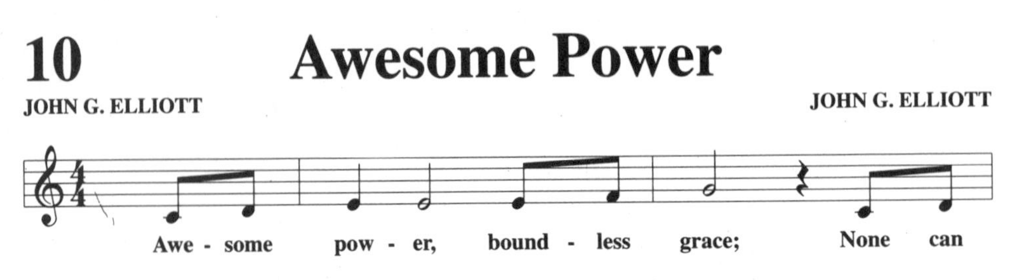

Awe-some pow-er, bound-less grace; None can

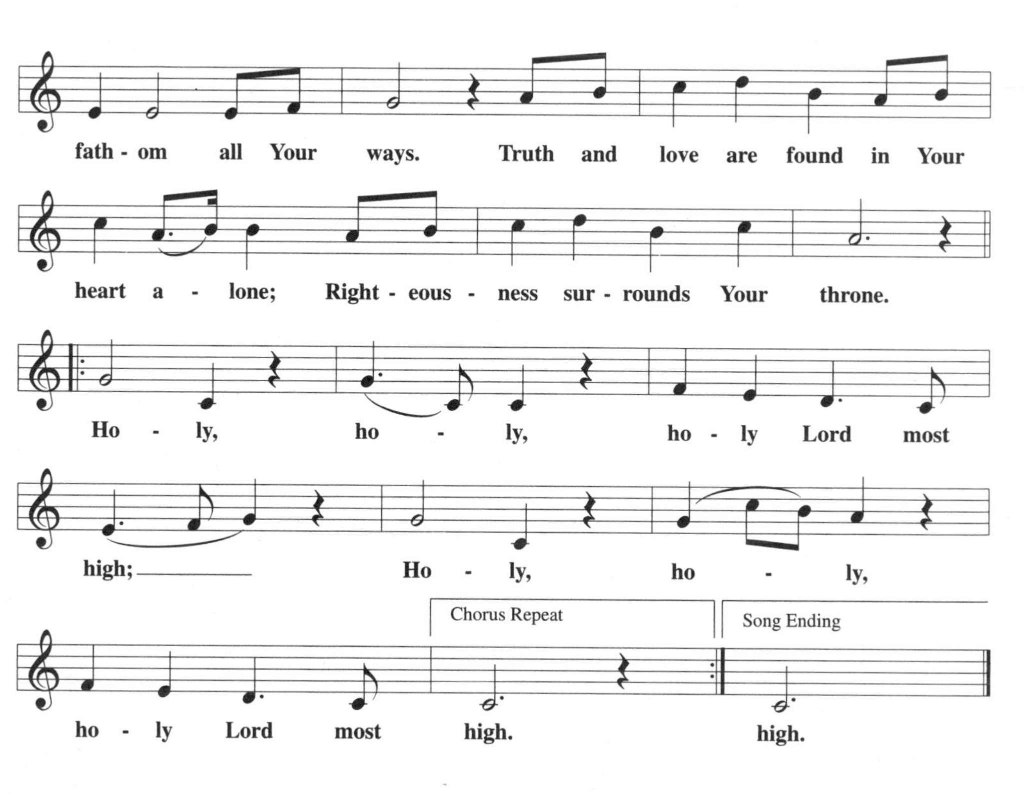

fath-om all Your ways. Truth and love are found in Your

heart a - lone; Right-eous - ness sur-rounds Your throne.

Ho - ly, ho - ly, ho - ly Lord most

high; Ho - ly, ho - ly,

Chorus Repeat | Song Ending

ho - ly Lord most high. high.

Awesome God 11

RICH MULLINS

RICH MULLINS

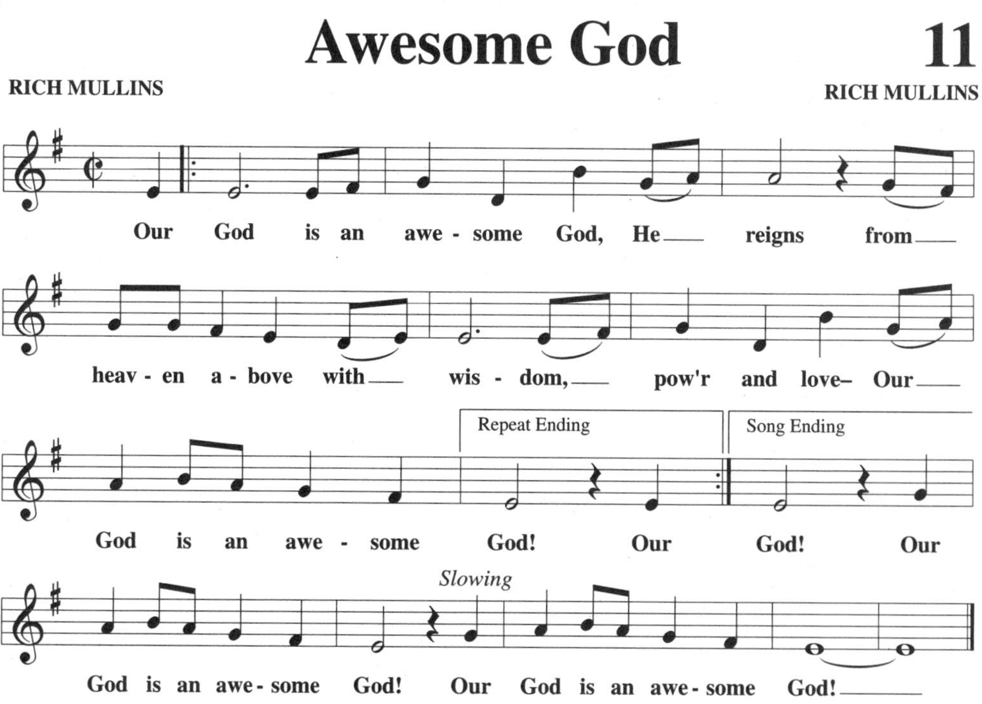

Our God is an awe - some God, He reigns from

heav - en a - bove with wis - dom, pow'r and love– Our

Repeat Ending | Song Ending

God is an awe - some God! Our God! Our

Slowing

God is an awe - some God! Our God is an awe - some God!

12 Mighty Is Our God

Words and Music by
EUGENE GRECO, GERRIT GUSTAFSON and DON MOEN

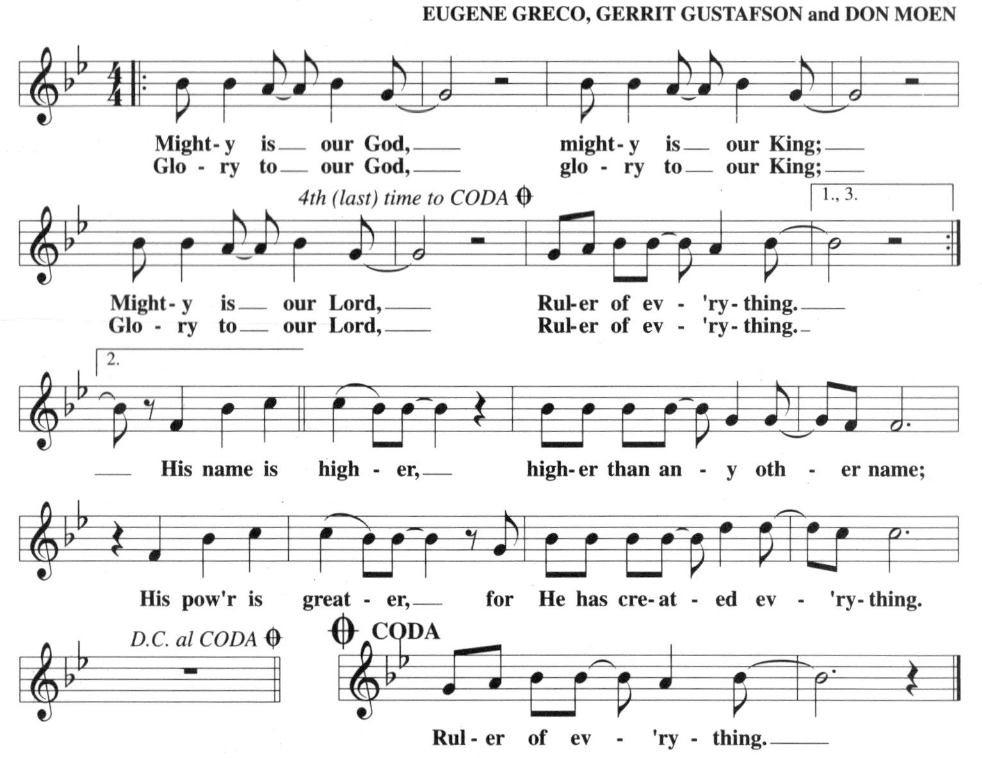

Might-y is— our God,— might-y is— our King;—
Glo-ry to— our God,— glo-ry to— our King;—

4th (last) time to CODA ⊕

1., 3.

Might-y is— our Lord,— Rul-er of ev-'ry-thing.—
Glo-ry to— our Lord,— Rul-er of ev-'ry-thing.—

2.
— His name is high-er,— high-er than an-y oth-er name;—

His pow'r is great-er,— for He has cre-at-ed ev-'ry-thing.

D.C. al CODA ⊕

⊕ CODA

Rul-er of ev-'ry-thing.—

13 How Excellent Is Thy Name

PAUL SMITH and MELODIE TUNNEY

DICK TUNNEY

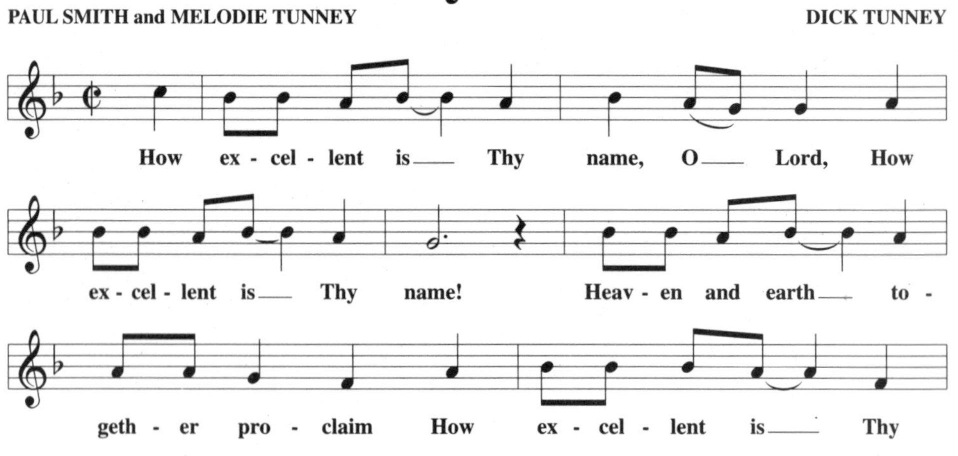

How ex-cel-lent is— Thy name, O— Lord, How

ex-cel-lent is— Thy name! Heav-en and earth— to-

geth-er pro-claim How ex-cel-lent is— Thy

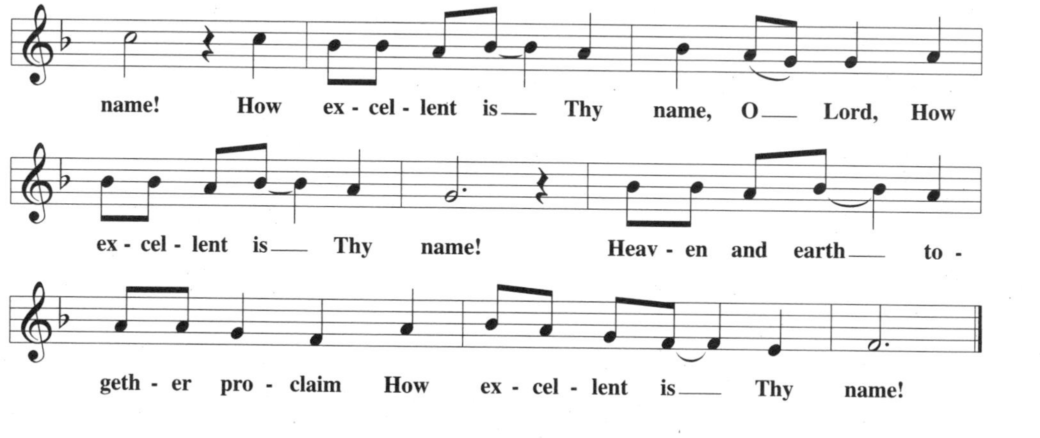

name! How ex - cel - lent is— Thy name, O— Lord, How
ex - cel - lent is— Thy name! Heav - en and earth— to -
geth - er pro - claim How ex - cel - lent is— Thy name!

How Majestic Is Your Name

14

MICHAEL W. SMITH   MICHAEL W. SMITH

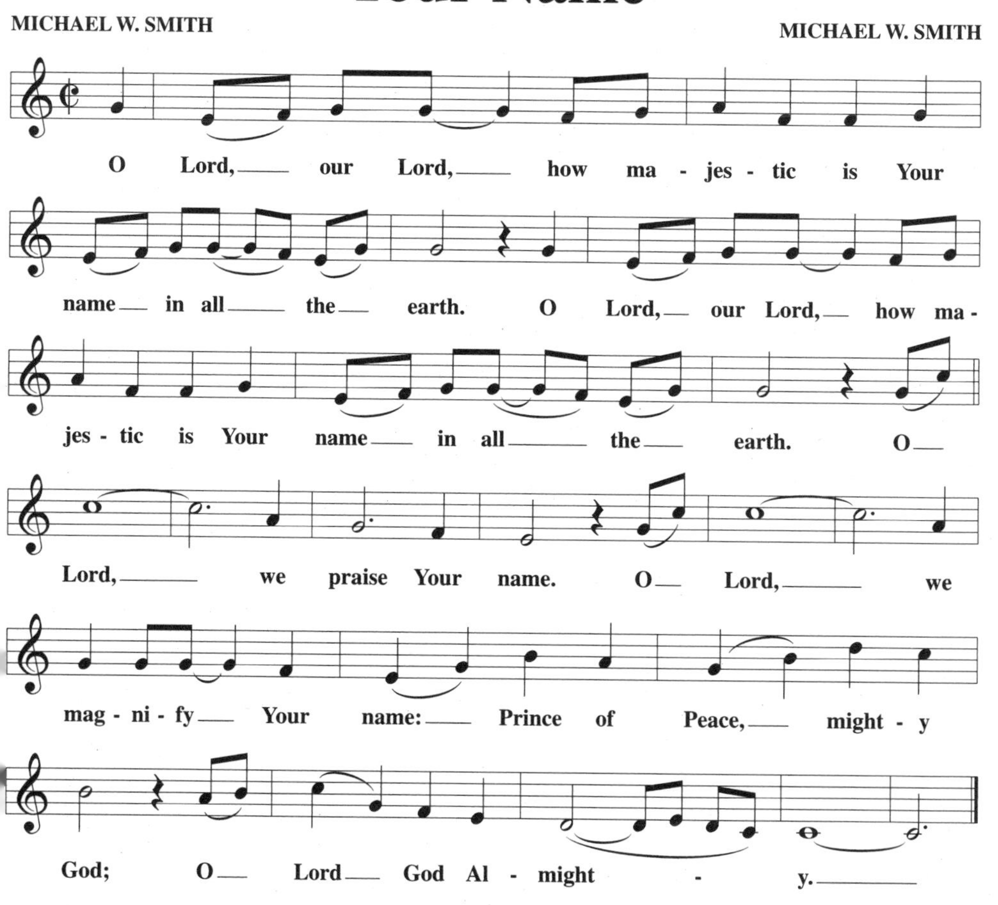

O Lord,— our Lord,— how ma - jes - tic is Your
name— in all— the— earth. O Lord,— our Lord,— how ma -
jes - tic is Your name— in all— the— earth. O—
Lord,— we praise Your name. O— Lord,— we
mag - ni - fy— Your name:— Prince of Peace,— might - y
God; O— Lord— God Al - might - y.

15 To Thee We Ascribe Glory

KIRK DEARMAN   KIRK DEARMAN

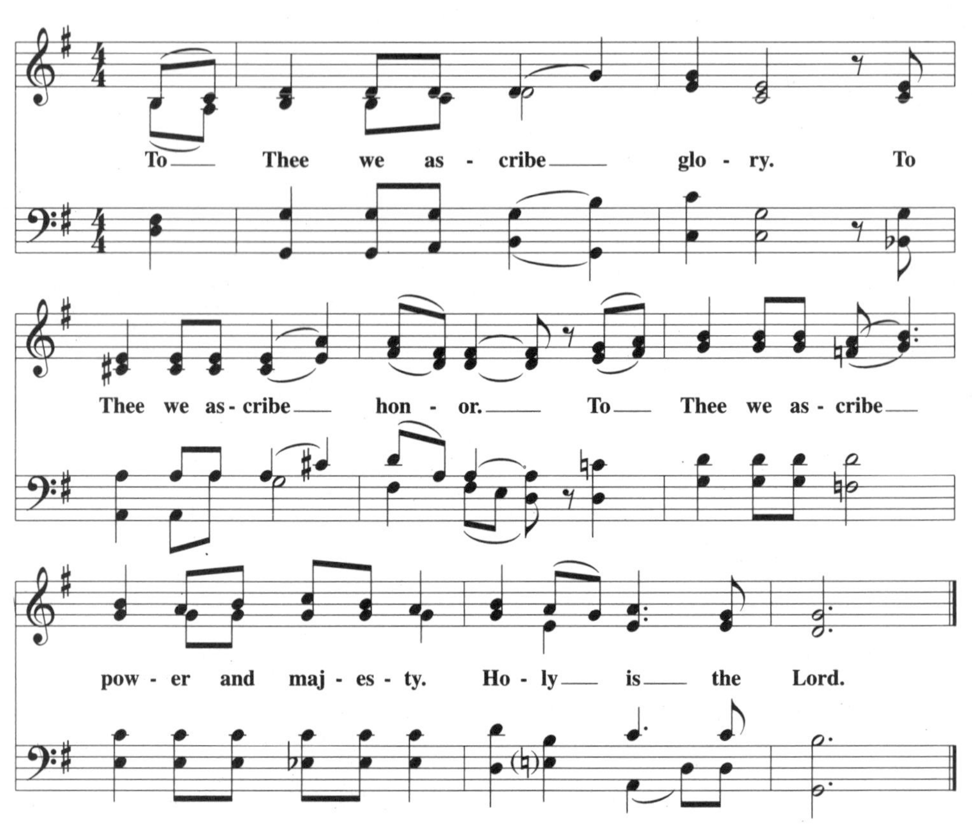

To— Thee we as - cribe— glo - ry. To

Thee we as - cribe— hon - or.— To— Thee we as - cribe—

pow - er and maj - es - ty. Ho - ly— is— the Lord.

16 The Majesty and Glory of Your Name

LINDA LEE JOHNSON
Based on Psalm 8   TOM FETTKE

Al - le - lu - ia,— Al - le - lu - ia!— The

maj - es - ty and glo - ry of Your name.— Al - le -

lu - ia,— Al - le - lu - ia!— The maj - es - ty and

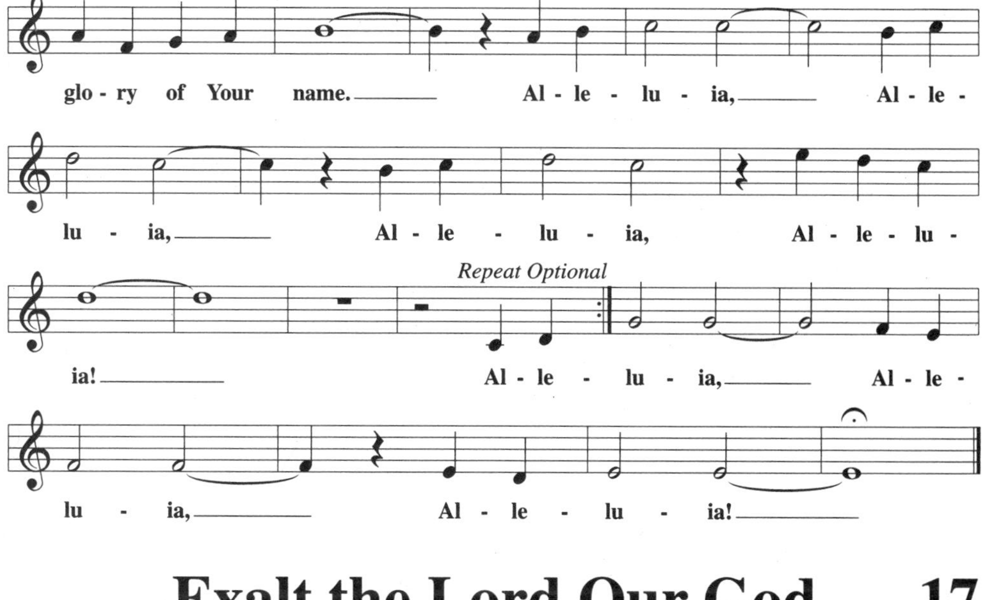

glo - ry of Your name. Al - le - lu - ia, Al - le -
lu - ia, Al - le - lu - ia, Al - le - lu -
ia! Al - le - lu - ia, Al - le -
lu - ia, Al - le - lu - ia!

Repeat Optional

Exalt the Lord Our God 17

DANIEL GARDNER   DANIEL GARDNER

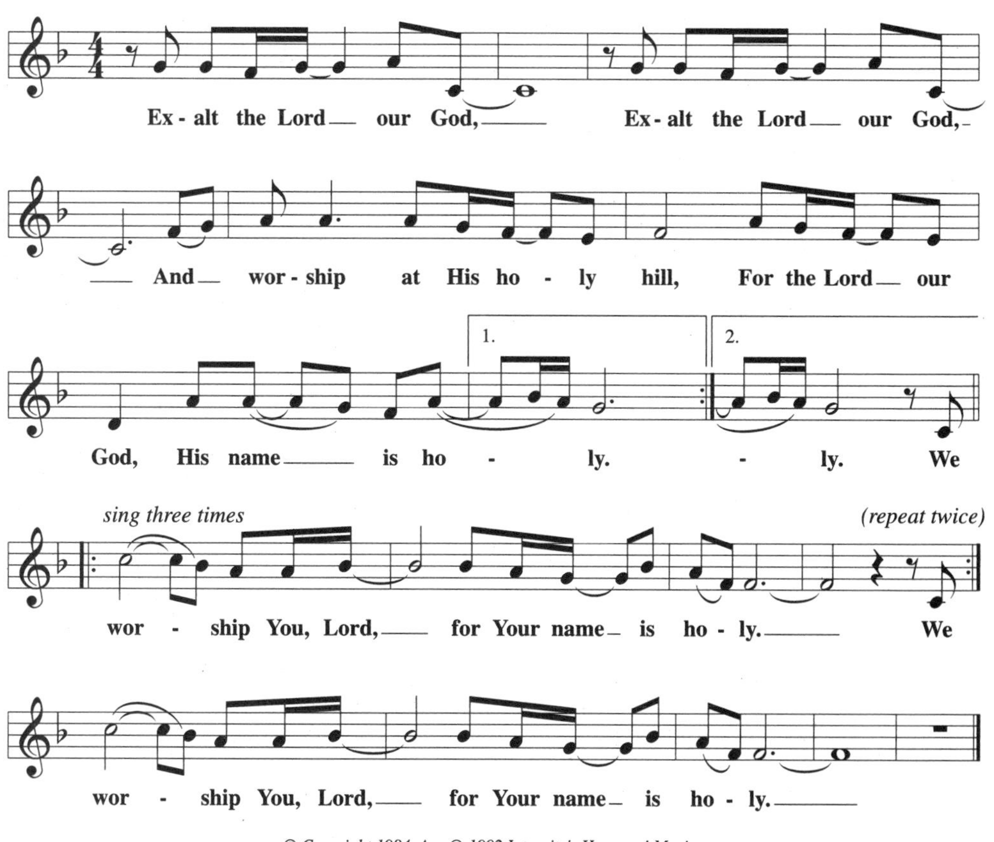

Ex - alt the Lord — our God, — Ex - alt the Lord — our God, —
— And — wor - ship at His ho - ly hill, For the Lord — our
God, His name is ho - ly. - ly. We
wor - ship You, Lord, — for Your name — is ho - ly. We
wor - ship You, Lord, — for Your name — is ho - ly.

sing three times   *(repeat twice)*

18 I Exalt Thee

PETE SANCHEZ, JR.

PETE SANCHEZ, JR.

For Thou, O Lord art high a - bove all the earth.

Thou art ex - alt - ed far a - bove all gods.

For Thou, O bove all gods. I ex -

alt Thee, I ex - alt Thee, I ex - alt Thee,

O Lord. I ex - Lord. Lord.

19 Glorify Thy Name

DONNA ADKINS

DONNA ADKINS

1. Fa - ther, we love You, we wor - ship and a - dore You,
2. Je - sus, we love You, we wor - ship and a - dore You,
3. Spir - it, we love You, we wor - ship and a - dore You,

Glo - ri - fy Thy name in all the earth.

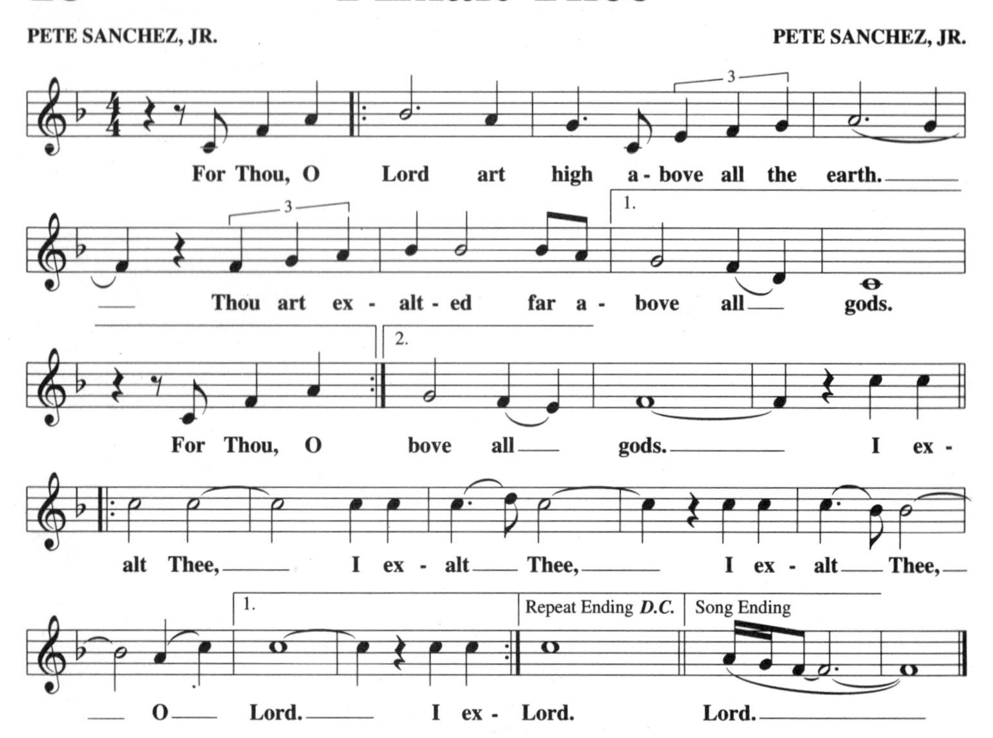

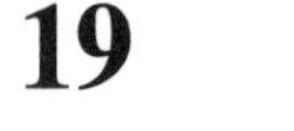

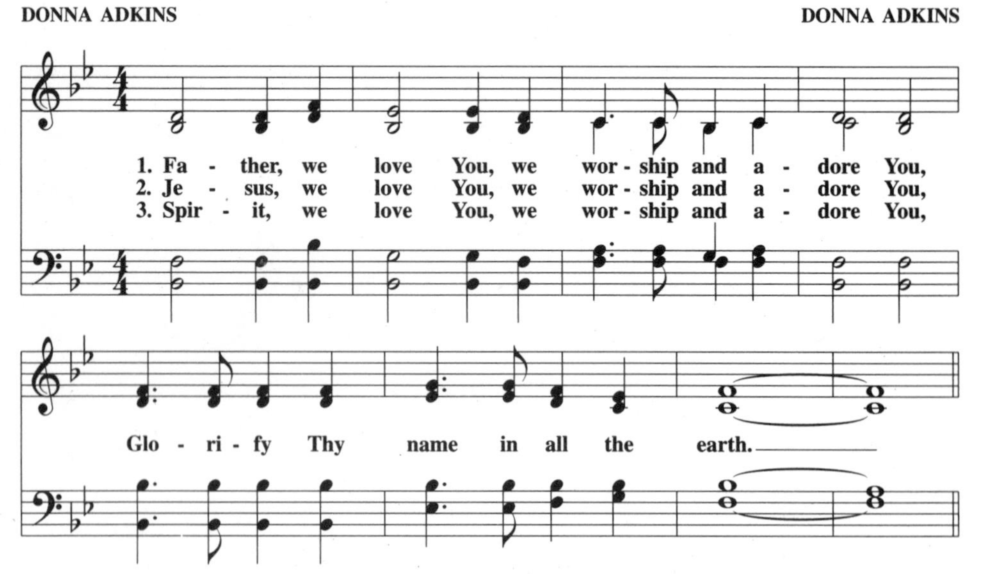

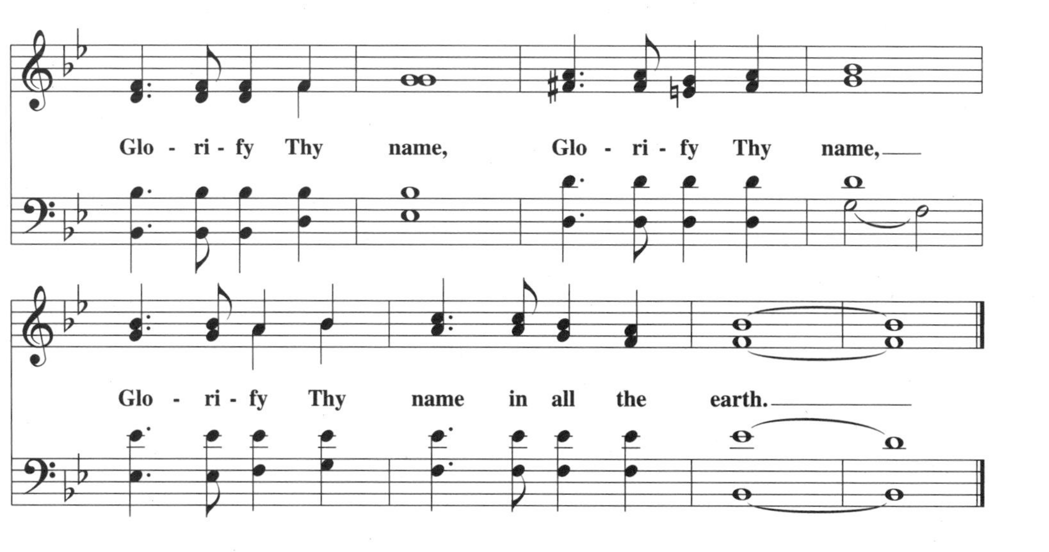

Glo - ri - fy Thy name, Glo - ri - fy Thy name, ___

Glo - ri - fy Thy name in all the earth. ___

Oh, the Glory
of Your Presence

20

STEVE FRY

STEVE FRY

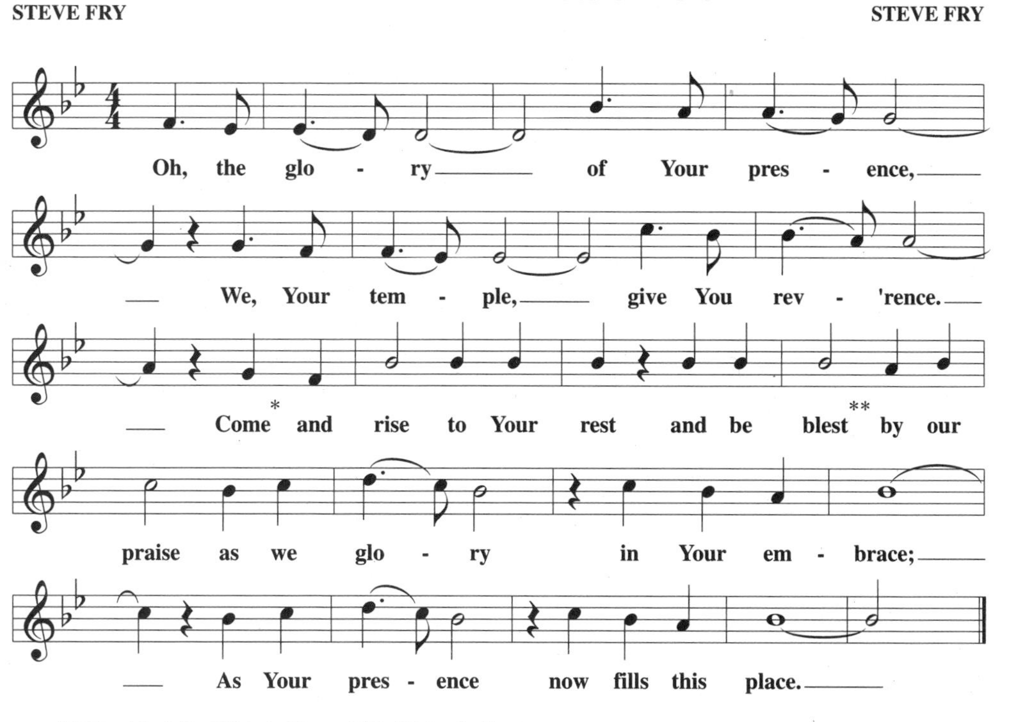

Oh, the glo - ry ___ of Your pres - ence, ___

___ We, Your tem - ple, ___ give You rev - 'rence. ___

___ Come and rise to Your rest and be blest by our

praise as we glo - ry in Your em - brace; ___

___ As Your pres - ence now fills this place. ___

* II Chronicles 6:41   ** Intent of the word "blest" is "praised."

21

I Will Worship You, Lord

DANIEL GARDNER

DANIEL GARDNER

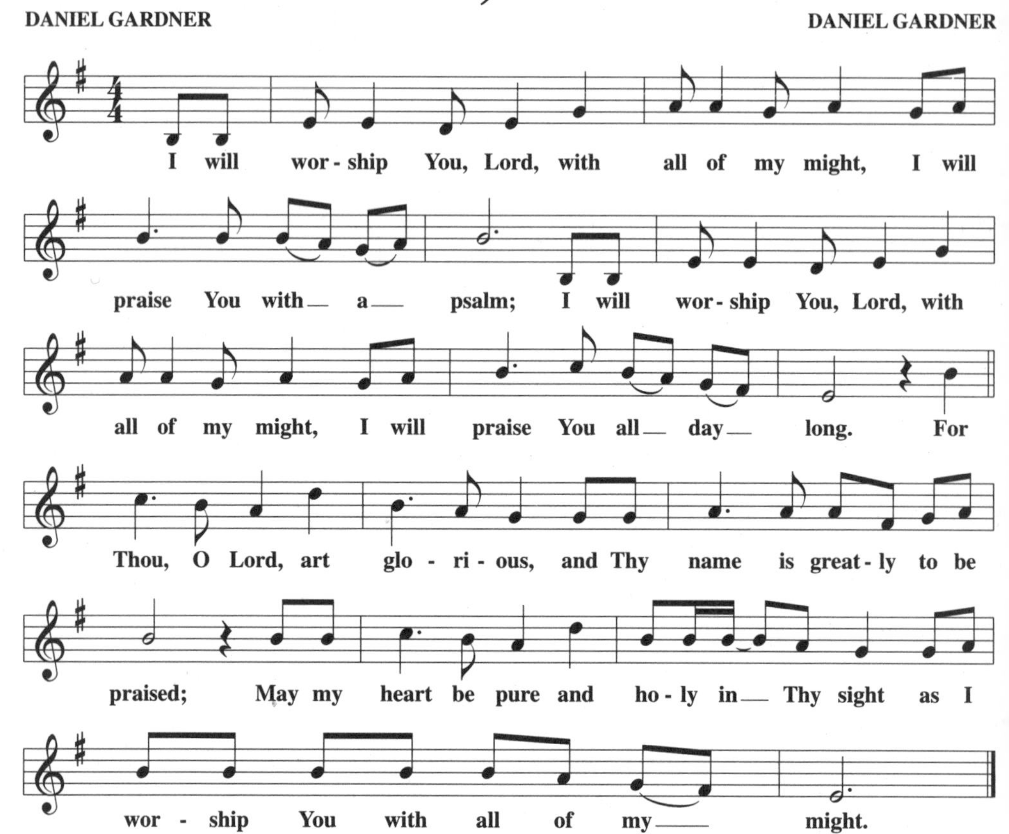

I will wor-ship You, Lord, with all of my might, I will praise You with a psalm; I will wor-ship You, Lord, with all of my might, I will praise You all day long. For Thou, O Lord, art glo-ri-ous, and Thy name is great-ly to be praised; May my heart be pure and ho-ly in Thy sight as I wor-ship You with all of my might.

22

Hallelujah! Our God Reigns

DALE GARRATT

DALE GARRATT

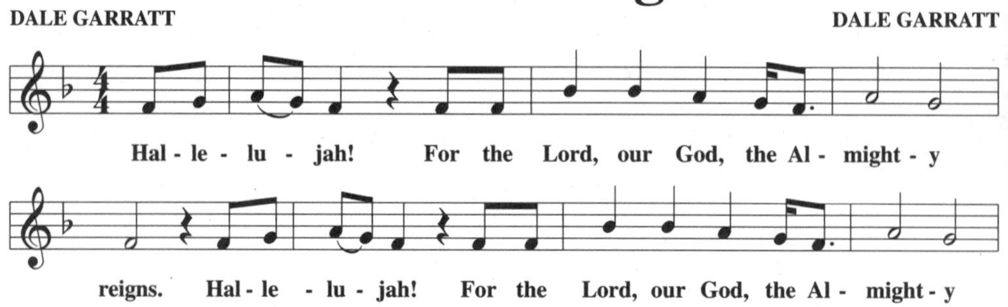

Hal-le-lu-jah! For the Lord, our God, the Al-might-y reigns. Hal-le-lu-jah! For the Lord, our God, the Al-might-y

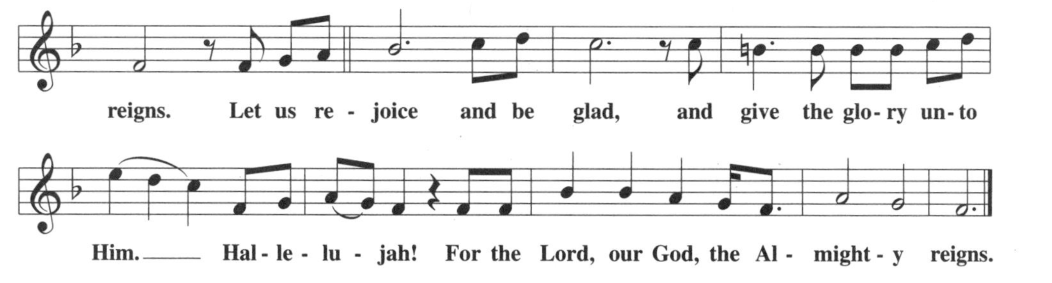

reigns. Let us re - joice and be glad, and give the glo - ry un - to

Him.___ Hal - le - lu - jah! For the Lord, our God, the Al - might - y reigns.

Sing unto the Lord

23

PSALM 96: 1, 4

UNKNOWN

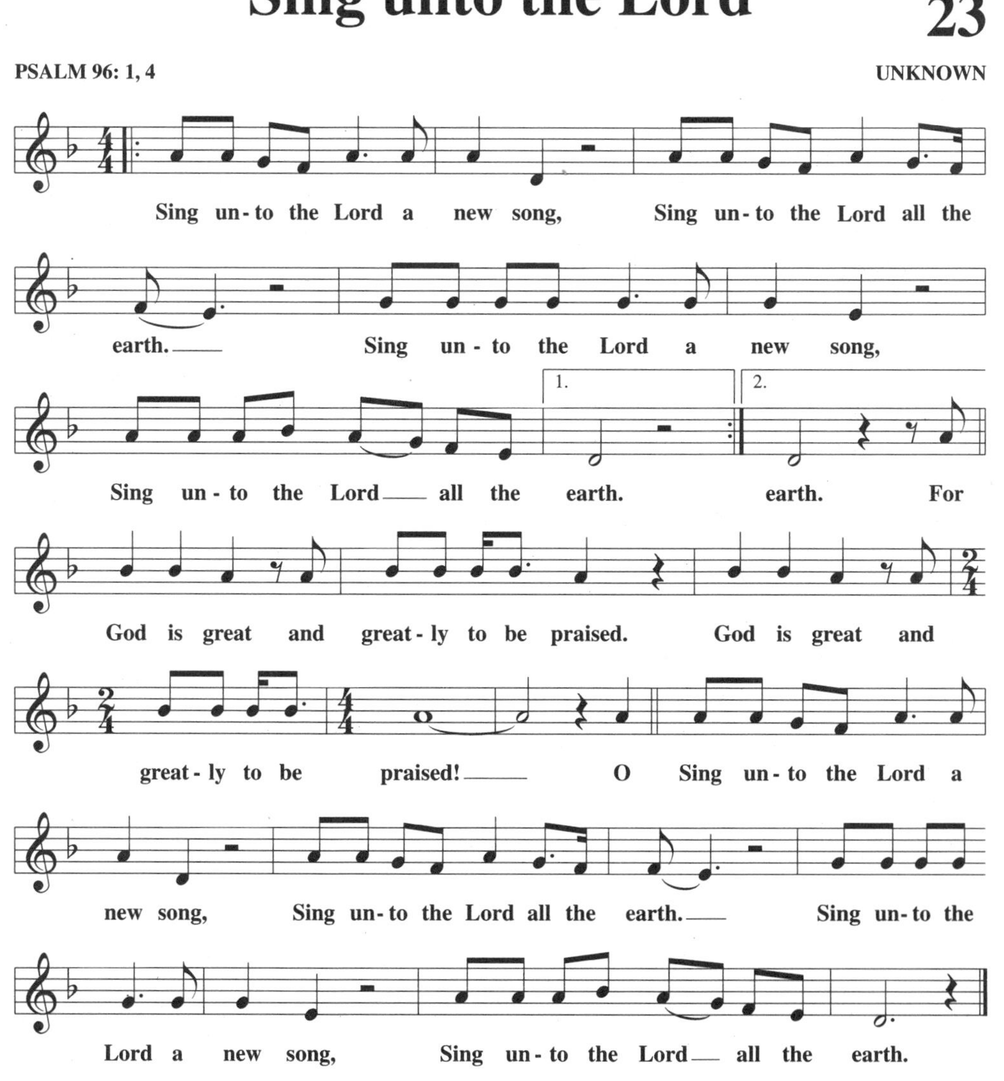

Sing un - to the Lord a new song, Sing un - to the Lord all the

earth.___ Sing un - to the Lord a new song,

Sing un - to the Lord___ all the earth. earth. For

God is great and great - ly to be praised. God is great and

great - ly to be praised!___ O Sing un - to the Lord a

new song, Sing un - to the Lord all the earth.___ Sing un - to the

Lord a new song, Sing un - to the Lord___ all the earth.

24 Come into the King's Chambers

DANIEL GARDNER

DANIEL GARDNER

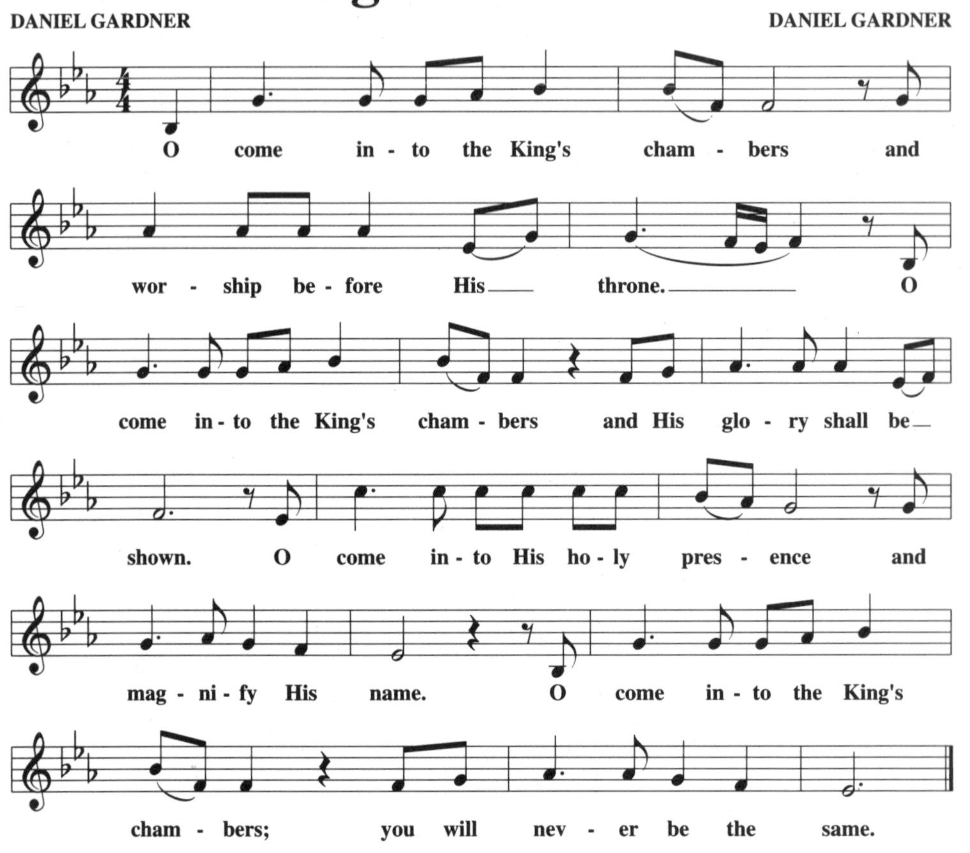

O come in-to the King's cham-bers and wor - ship be-fore His throne. O come in-to the King's cham-bers and His glo-ry shall be shown. O come in-to His ho-ly pres - ence and mag-ni-fy His name. O come in-to the King's cham-bers; you will nev-er be the same.

25 Antiphonal Praise
(We Worship You)

STEVE GREEN

STEVE GREEN

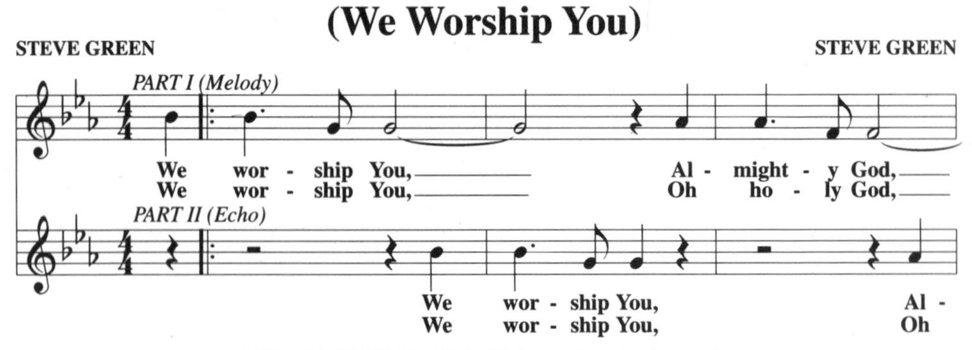

PART I (Melody)

We wor - ship You, Al - might - y God,
We wor - ship You, Oh ho - ly God,

PART II (Echo)

We wor - ship You, Al -
We wor - ship You, Oh

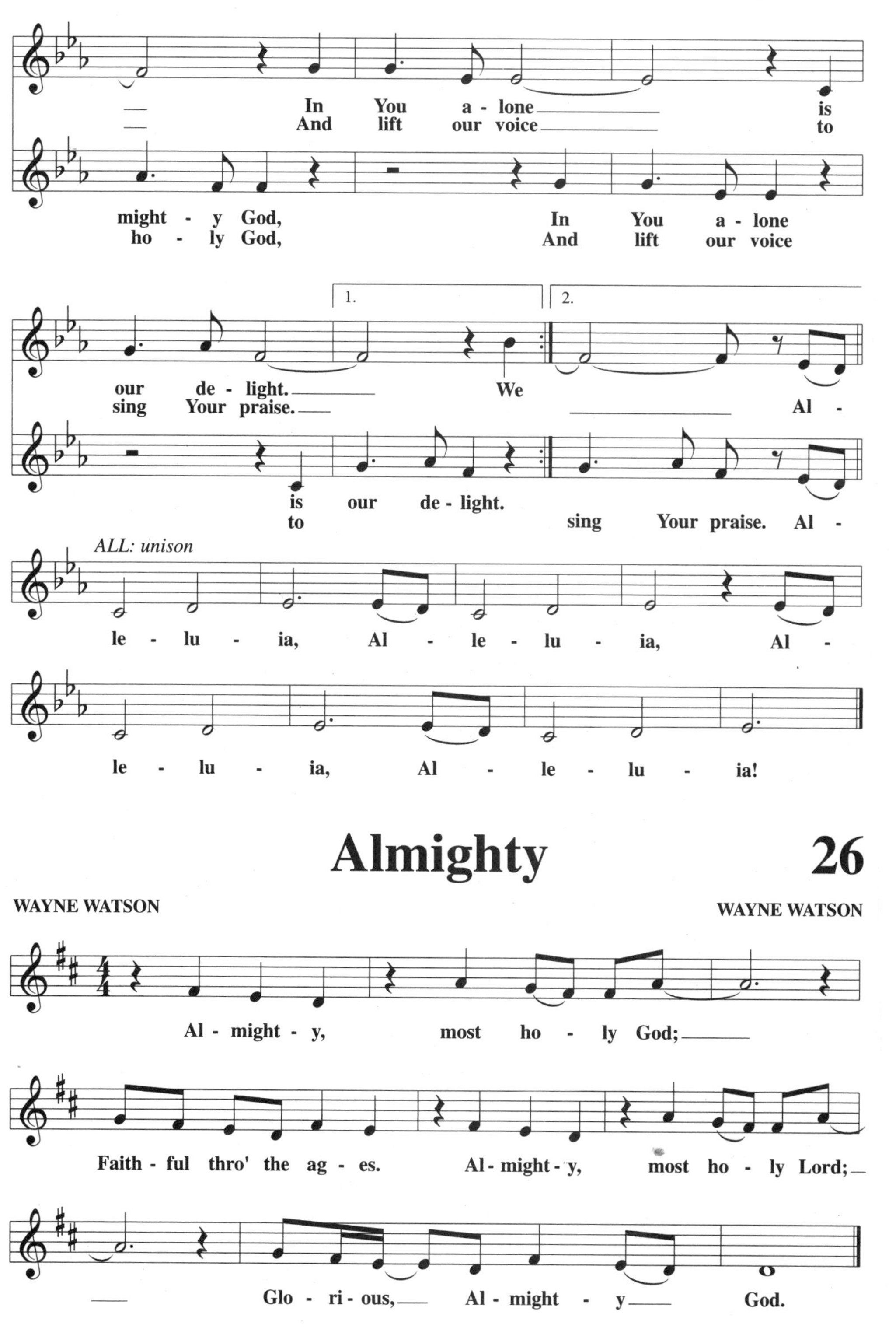

In You a - lone _____ is
And lift our voice _____ to

might - y God, In You a - lone
ho - ly God, And lift our voice

1.
our de - light. _____ We

2.
is our de - light. Al -
to sing Your praise. Al -

ALL: unison
le - lu - ia, Al - le - lu - ia, Al -

le - lu - ia, Al - le - lu - ia!

Almighty

26

WAYNE WATSON

WAYNE WATSON

Al - might - y, most ho - ly God; _____

Faith - ful thro' the ag - es. Al - might - y, most ho - ly Lord;

_____ Glo - ri - ous, _____ Al - might - y _____ God.

27 I Sing Praises

TERRY MAC ALMON

TERRY MAC ALMON

1. I sing prais-es to Your name, O— Lord,
2. I give glo-ry to Your name, O— Lord,

Prais-es to Your name, O— Lord, For Your name is great and
Glo-ry to Your name, O— Lord, For Your name is great and

great-ly to be praised; I sing prais-es to Your
great-ly to be praised; I give glo-ry to Your

name, O— Lord, Prais-es to Your name, O—
name, O— Lord, Glo-ry to Your name, O—

Lord, For Your name is great and great-ly to be praised.
Lord, For Your name is great and great-ly to be praised.

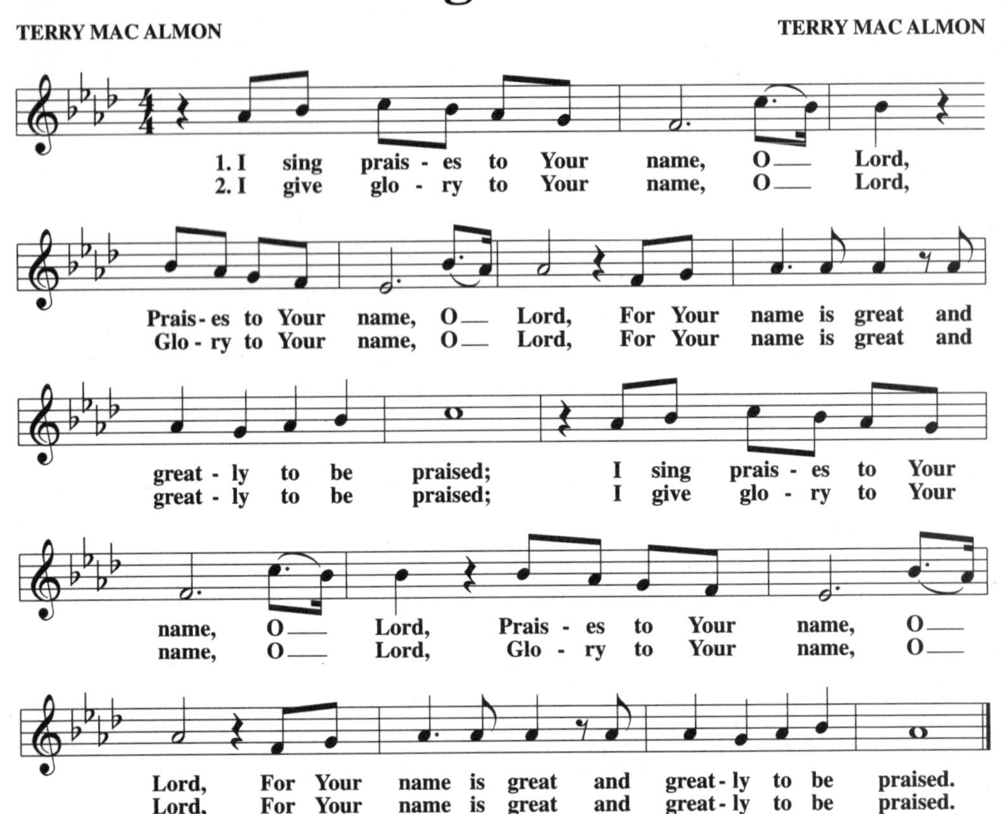

28 I Worship You, Almighty God

SONDRA CORBETT

SONDRA CORBETT

I wor-ship You, Al-might-y God, There is none like

You. I wor-ship You, O Prince of Peace, That is what I

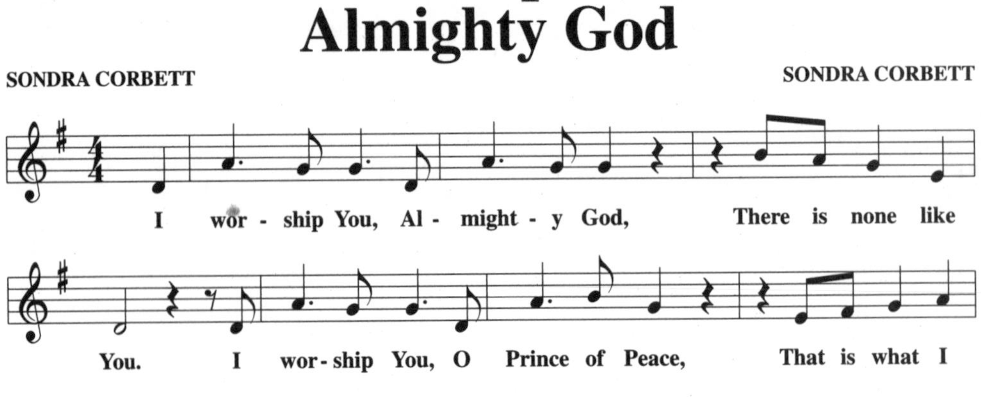

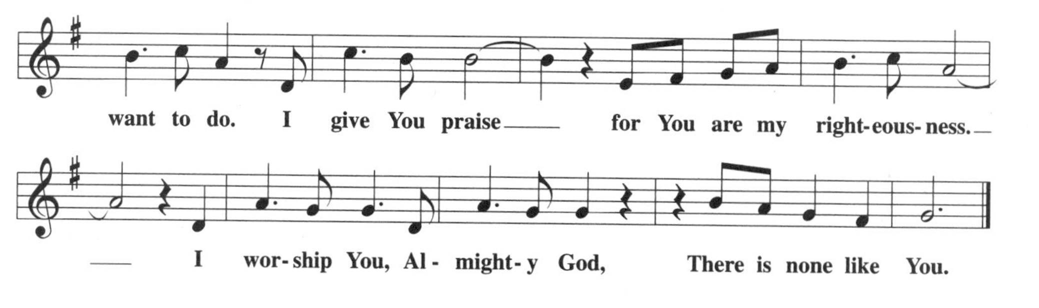

want to do. I give You praise—— for You are my right-eous-ness.——

—— I wor-ship You, Al-might-y God, There is none like You.

Our God Is Lifted Up 29

TIM SMITH   TIM SMITH

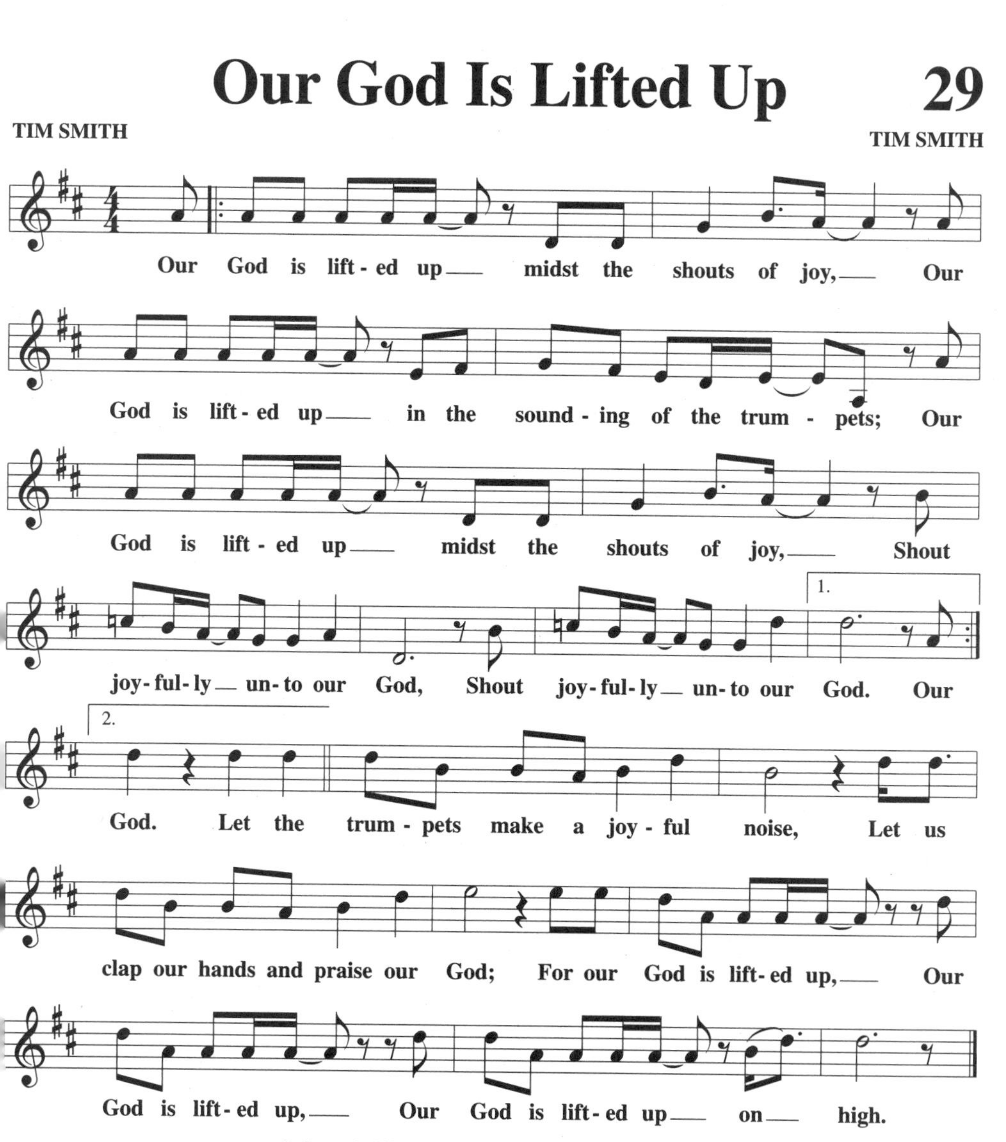

Our God is lift-ed up—— midst the shouts of joy,—— Our

God is lift-ed up—— in the sound-ing of the trum - pets; Our

God is lift-ed up—— midst the shouts of joy,—— Shout

1.
joy-ful-ly—— un-to our God, Shout joy-ful-ly—— un-to our God. Our

2.
God. Let the trum-pets make a joy-ful noise, Let us

clap our hands and praise our God; For our God is lift-ed up,—— Our

God is lift-ed up,—— Our God is lift-ed up—— on—— high.

30 Great Is the Lord

Words and Music by
MICHAEL W. SMITH and DEBORAH D. SMITH

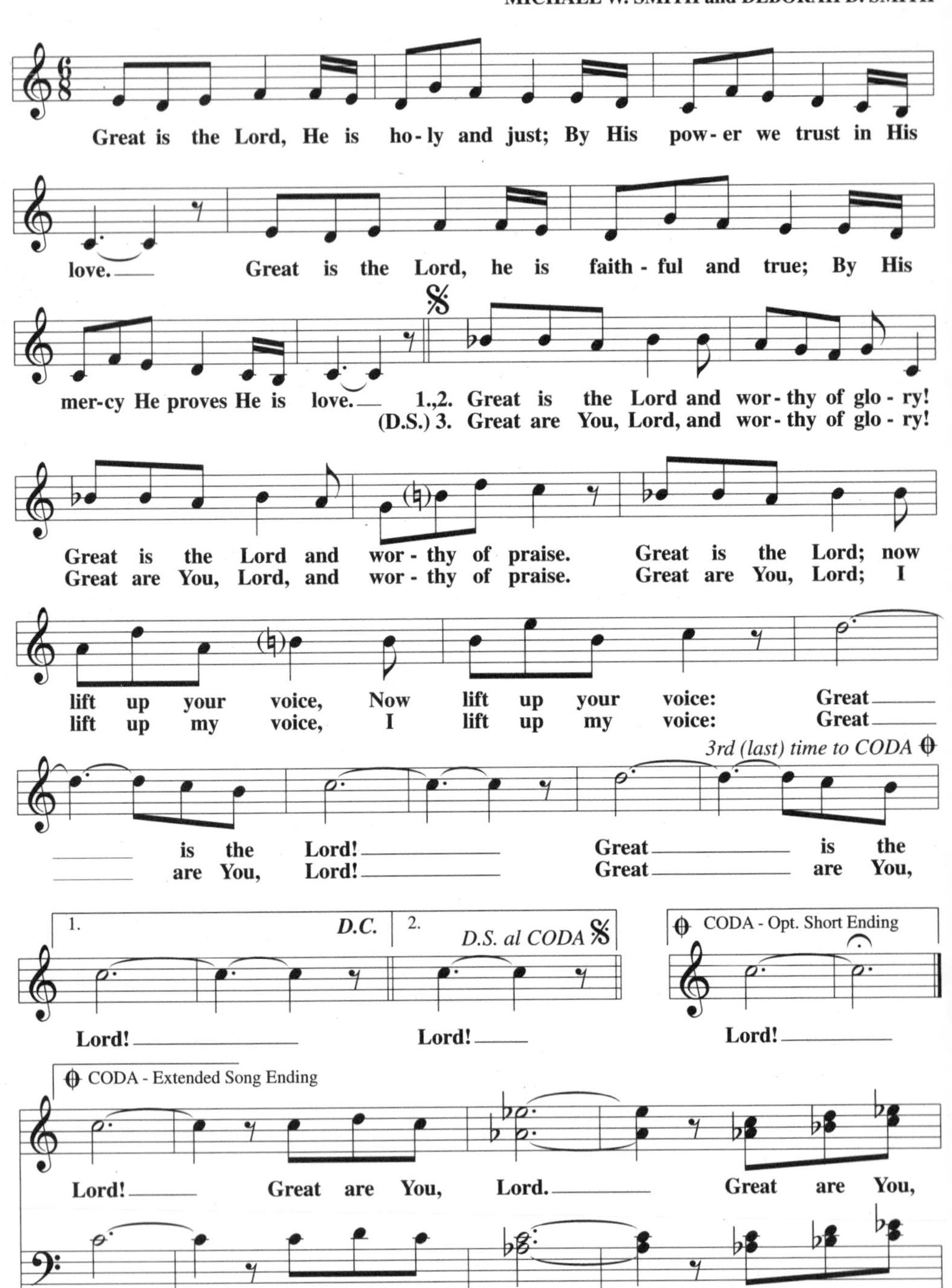

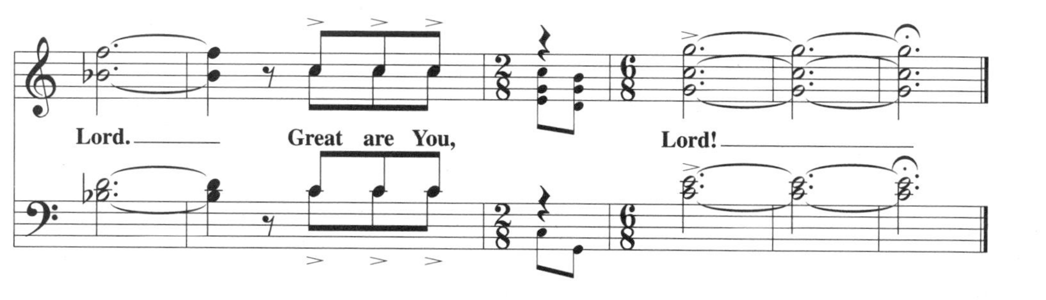

Lord._____ Great are You, Lord!_____

Stand Up

31

AUTHOR UNKNOWN

COMPOSER UNKNOWN

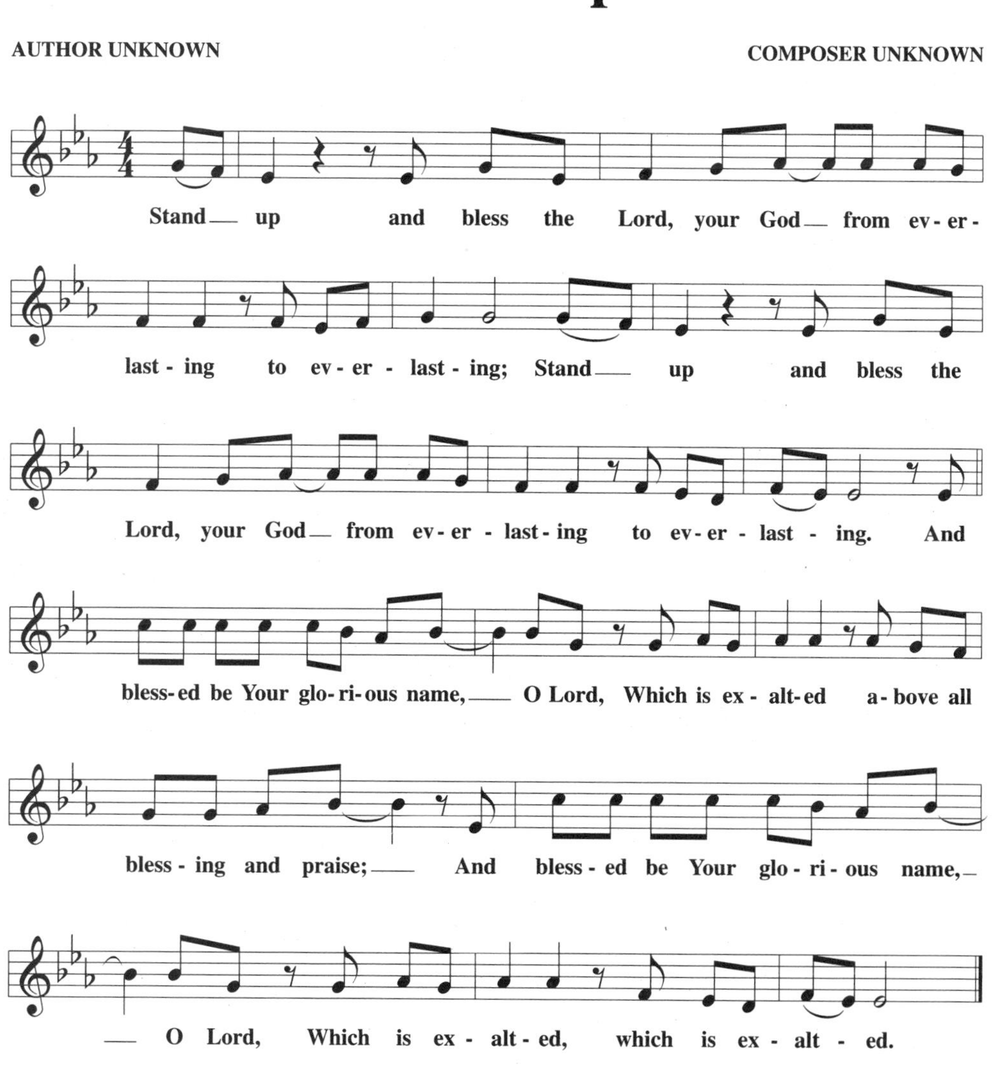

Stand — up and bless the Lord, your God — from ev - er -

last - ing to ev - er - last - ing; Stand — up and bless the

Lord, your God — from ev - er - last - ing to ev - er - last - ing. And

bless - ed be Your glo - ri - ous name, ____ O Lord, Which is ex - alt - ed a - bove all

bless - ing and praise; ____ And bless - ed be Your glo - ri - ous name, ____

____ O Lord, Which is ex - alt - ed, which is ex - alt - ed.

32 Bless the Lord, O My Soul

AUTHOR UNKNOWN

COMPOSER UNKNOWN
Arranged by Tom Fettke

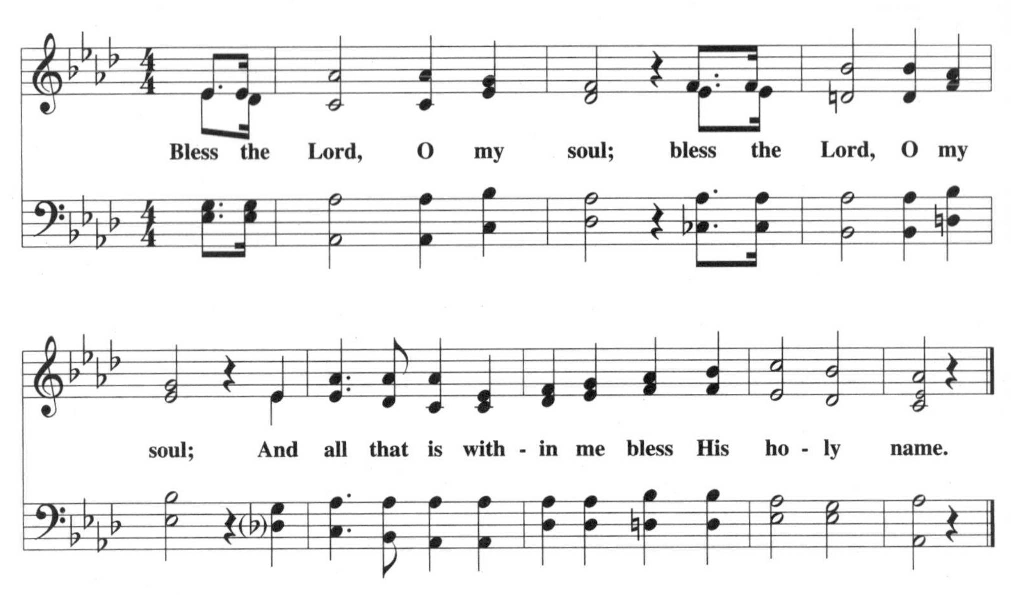

Bless the Lord, O my soul; bless the Lord, O my

soul; And all that is with-in me bless His ho-ly name.

33 Bless God

Words and Music by
CARMAN LICCIARDELLO and JOHN ROSASCO

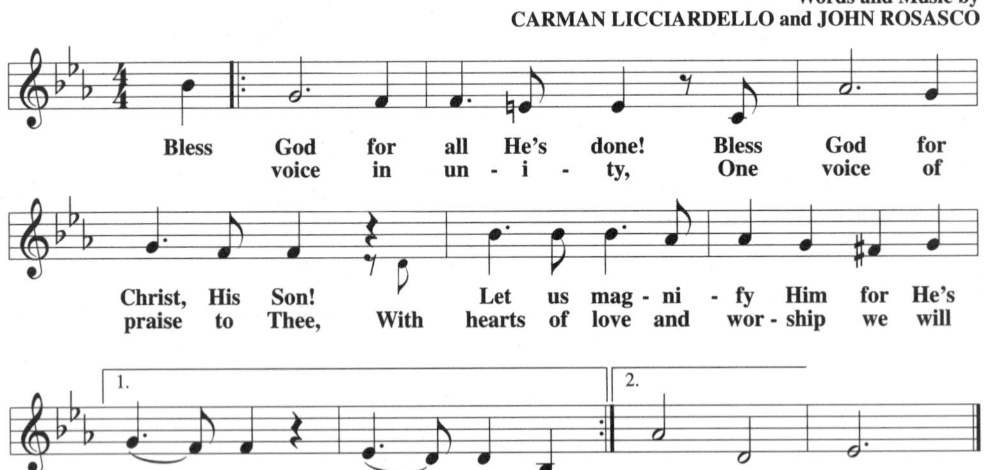

Bless God for all He's done! Bless God for
voice in un - i - ty, One voice of

Christ, His Son! With Let us mag - ni - fy Him for He's
praise to Thee, With hearts of love and wor - ship we will

1.
ho - ly, ho - ly! One

2.
sing, "Bless God!"

Come into the Holy of Holies

34

JOHN SELLERS

JOHN SELLERS

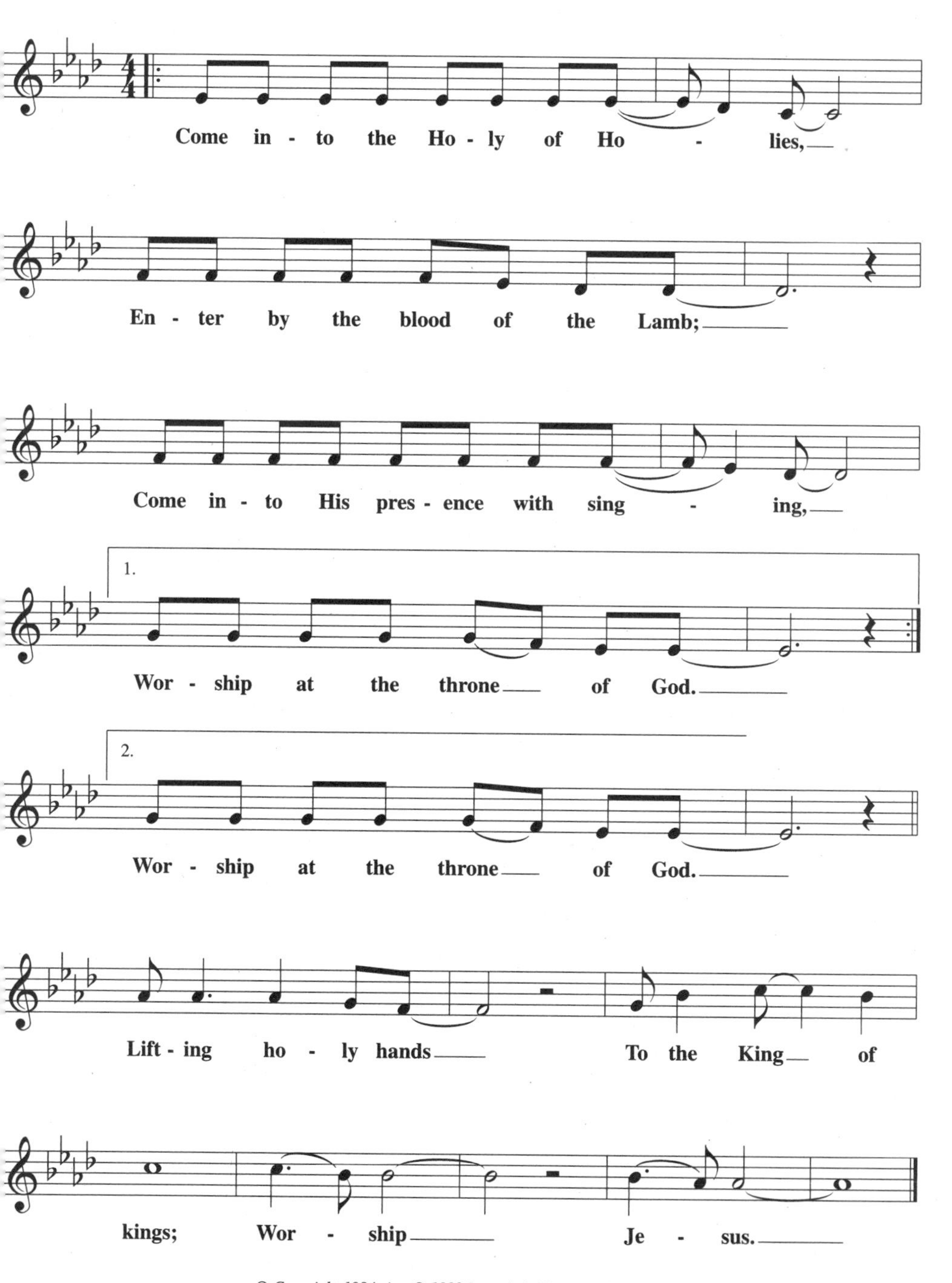

Come in-to the Ho-ly of Ho - lies,—

En - ter by the blood of the Lamb;—

Come in-to His pres-ence with sing - ing,—

1. Wor - ship at the throne— of God.—

2. Wor - ship at the throne— of God.—

Lift - ing ho - ly hands— To the King— of

kings; Wor - ship— Je - sus.—

35

Holy, Holy, Holy
Is the Lord of Hosts

NOLENE PRINCE

NOLENE PRINCE

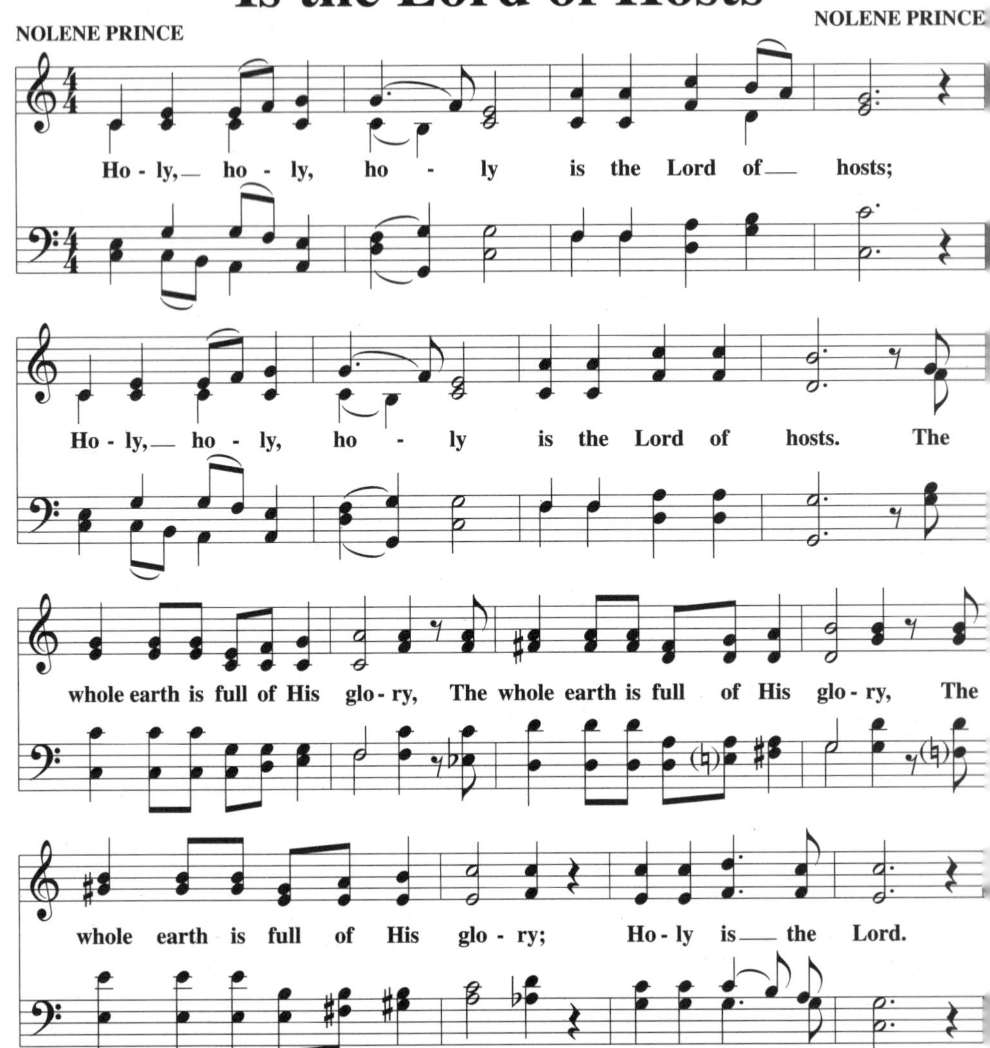

Ho - ly,— ho - ly, ho - ly is the Lord of— hosts;

Ho - ly,— ho - ly, ho - ly is the Lord of hosts. The

whole earth is full of His glo - ry, The whole earth is full of His glo - ry, The

whole earth is full of His glo - ry; Ho - ly is— the Lord.

36

Thou Art Worthy,
Great Jehovah

KAREN EAGAN

KAREN EAGAN

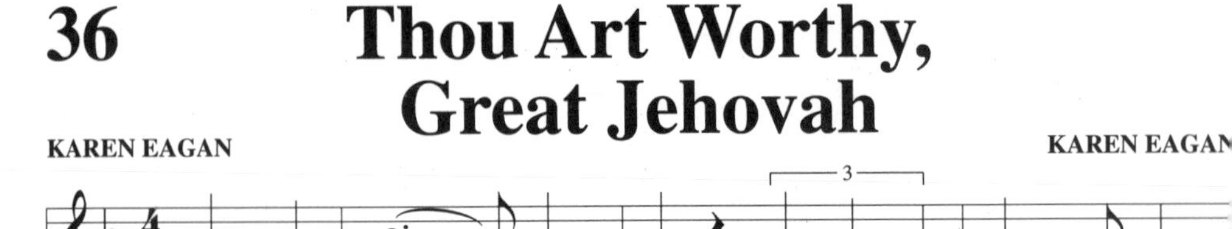

Thou art wor - thy,—— Great— Je - ho - vah.

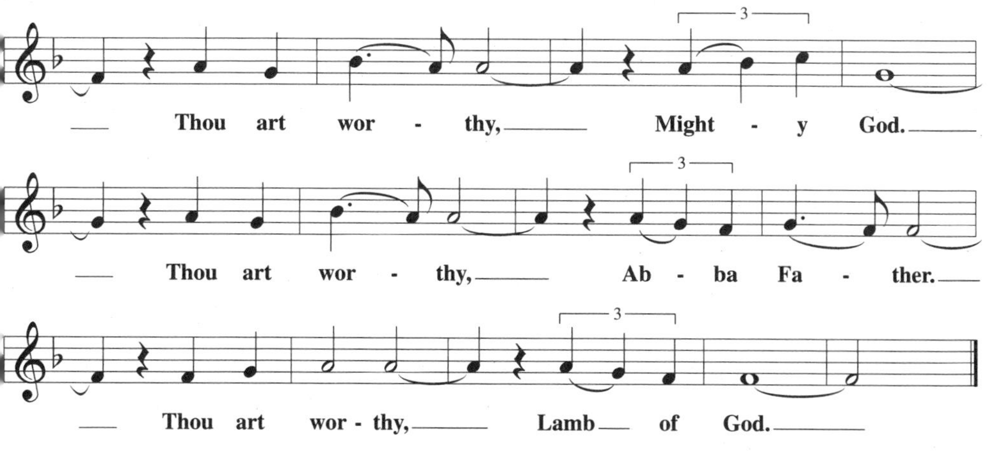

Thou art wor - thy, ___ Might - y God. ___

Thou art wor - thy, ___ Ab - ba Fa - ther. ___

Thou art wor - thy, ___ Lamb ___ of God. ___

Holy, Holy, Holy

(Hosanna)

37

PETER SCHOLTES

PETER SCHOLTES

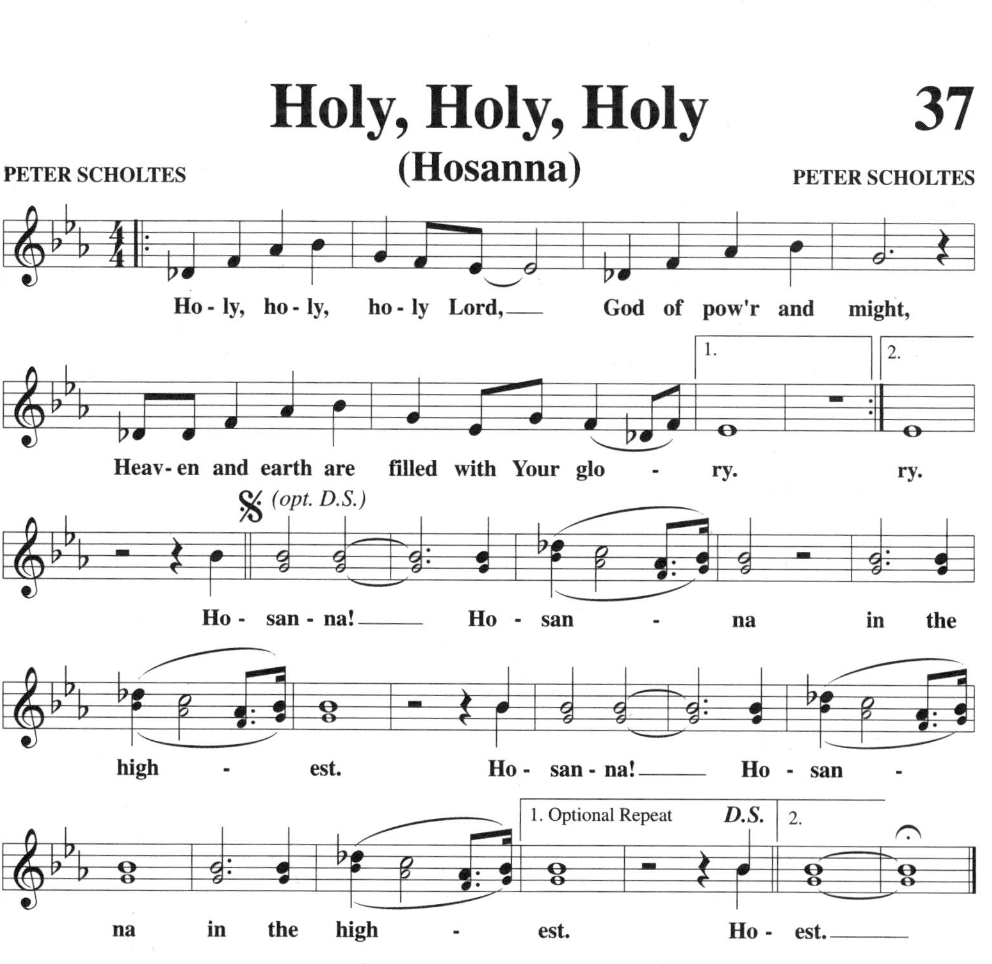

Ho - ly, ho - ly, ho - ly Lord, ___ God of pow'r and might,

Heav - en and earth are filled with Your glo - ry. ry.

(opt. D.S.)

Ho - san - na! ___ Ho - san - na in the

high - est. Ho - san - na! ___ Ho - san -

1. Optional Repeat   **D.S.**   2.

na in the high - est. Ho - est. ___

38 Bless the Lord

CHRIS CHRISTENSEN
Based on Psalms 30:5; 103:1-4

CHRIS CHRISTENSEN

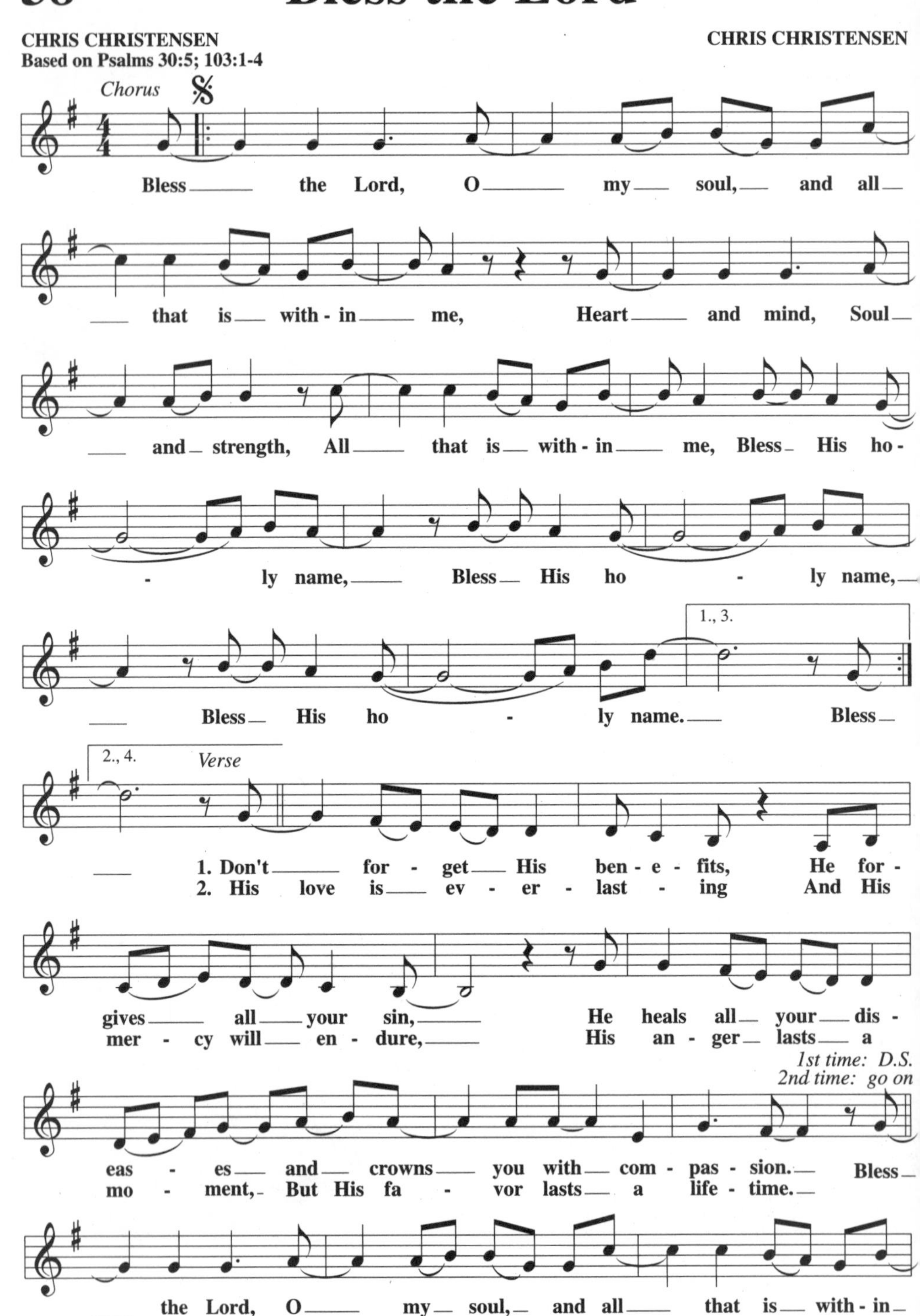

Chorus

Bless ____ the Lord, O ____ my ____ soul, ____ and all ____ that is ____ with - in ____ me, Heart ____ and mind, Soul ____ and ____ strength, All ____ that is ____ with - in ____ me, Bless ____ His ho - ly name, ____ Bless ____ His ho - ly name, ____ Bless ____ His ho - ly name. ____ Bless ____

1., 3.

2., 4. *Verse*

1. Don't ____ for - get ____ His ben - e - fits, He for -
2. His love is ____ ev - er - last - ing And His

1. gives ____ all ____ your sin, ____ He heals all ____ your ____ dis -
2. mer - cy will ____ en - dure, ____ His an - ger lasts ____ a

1st time: D.S.
2nd time: go on

1. eas - es ____ and ____ crowns ____ you with ____ com - pas - sion. ____ Bless ____
2. mo - ment, ____ But His fa - vor lasts ____ a life - time. ____

the Lord, O ____ my ____ soul, ____ and all ____ that is ____ with - in ____

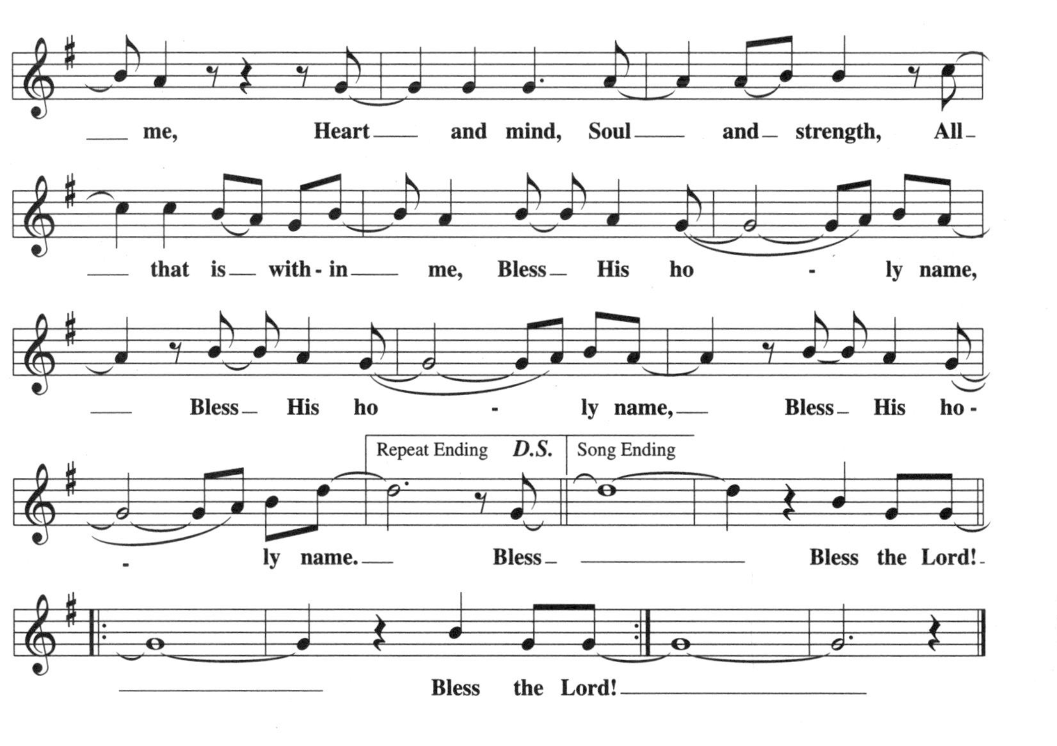

me, Heart and mind, Soul and strength, All

that is with-in me, Bless His ho - ly name,

Bless His ho - ly name, Bless His ho -

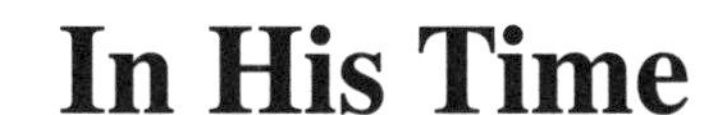

Repeat Ending | D.S. | Song Ending

ly name. Bless Bless the Lord!

Bless the Lord!

In His Time

39

DIANE BALL

DIANE BALL

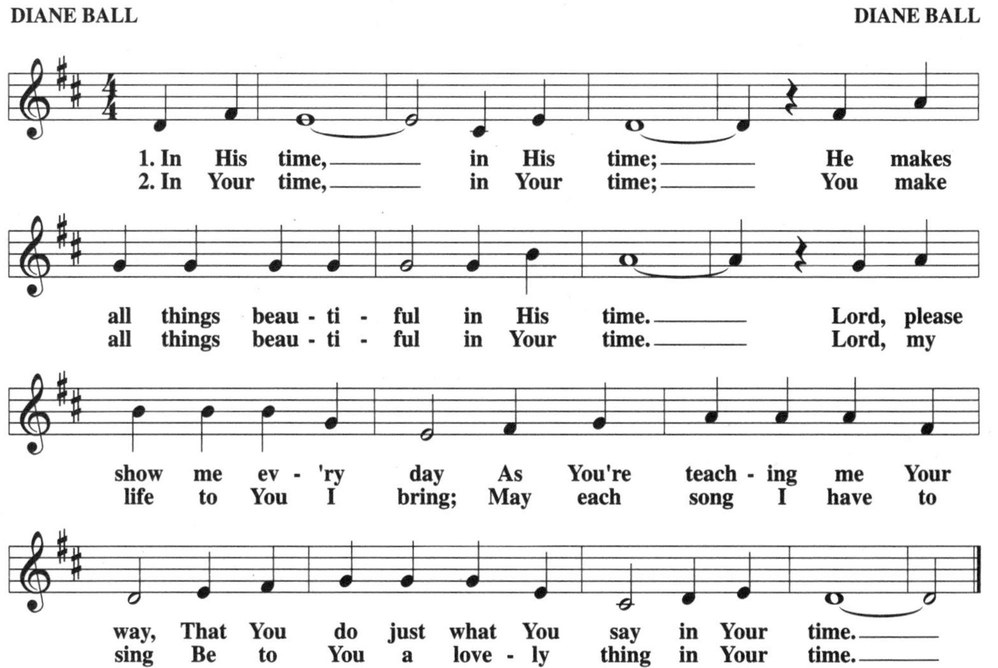

1. In His time, in His time; He makes
2. In Your time, in Your time; You make

all things beau - ti - ful in His time. Lord, please
all things beau - ti - ful in Your time. Lord, my

show me ev - 'ry day As You're teach - ing me Your
life to You I bring; May each song I have to

way, That You do just what You say in Your time.
sing Be to You a love - ly thing in Your time.

40 God Will Make a Way

DON MOEN

DON MOEN

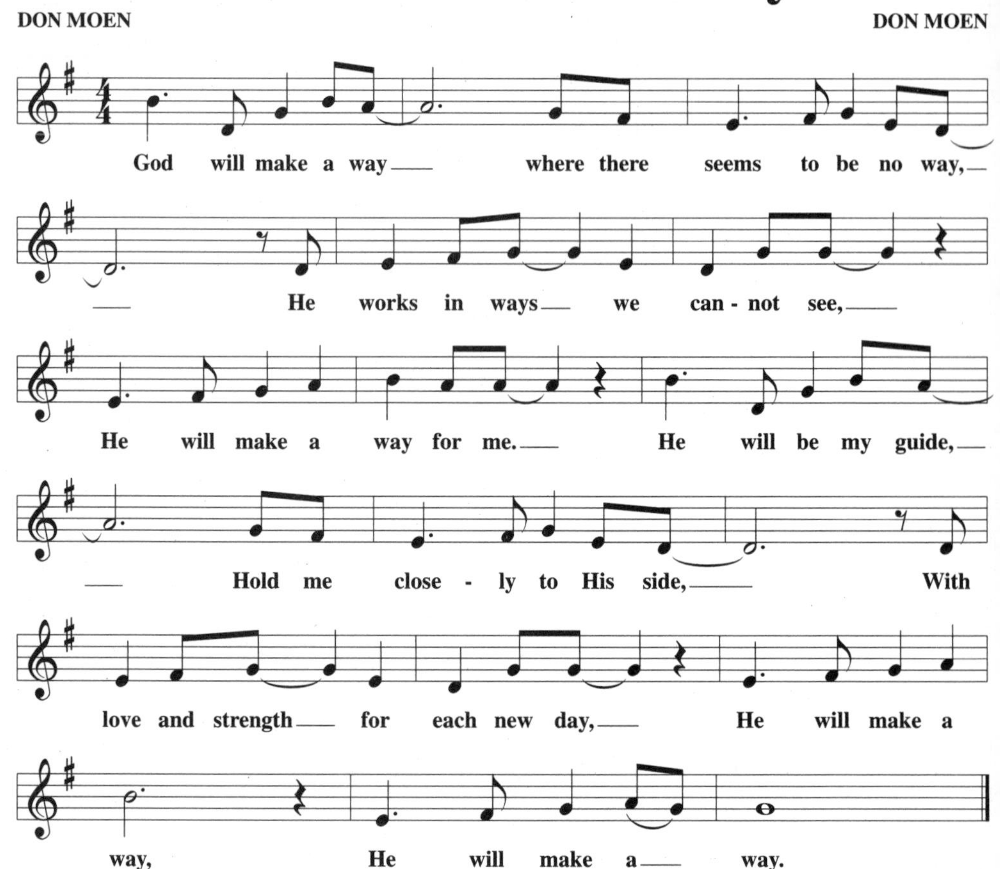

God will make a way where there seems to be no way,
He works in ways we can-not see,
He will make a way for me. He will be my guide,
Hold me close-ly to His side, With
love and strength for each new day, He will make a
way, He will make a way.

41 Hallowed Be Thy Name

Words and Music by
BABBIE MASON and ROBERT LAWSON
Arranged by Ken Barker

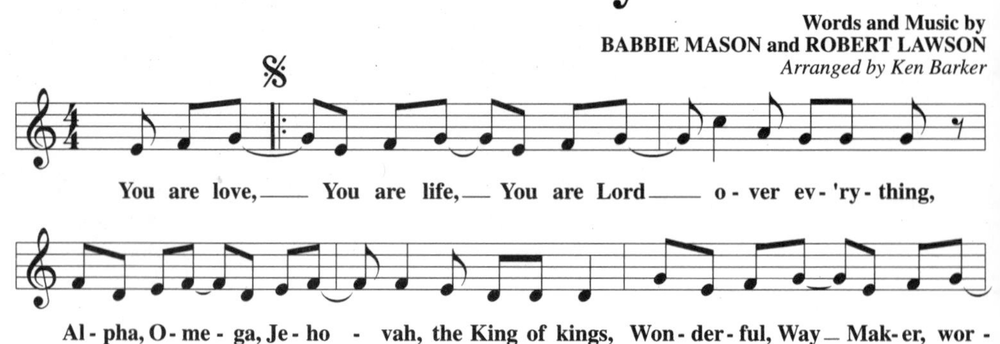

You are love, You are life, You are Lord o-ver ev-'ry-thing,
Al-pha, O-me-ga, Je-ho-vah, the King of kings, Won-der-ful, Way Mak-er, wor-

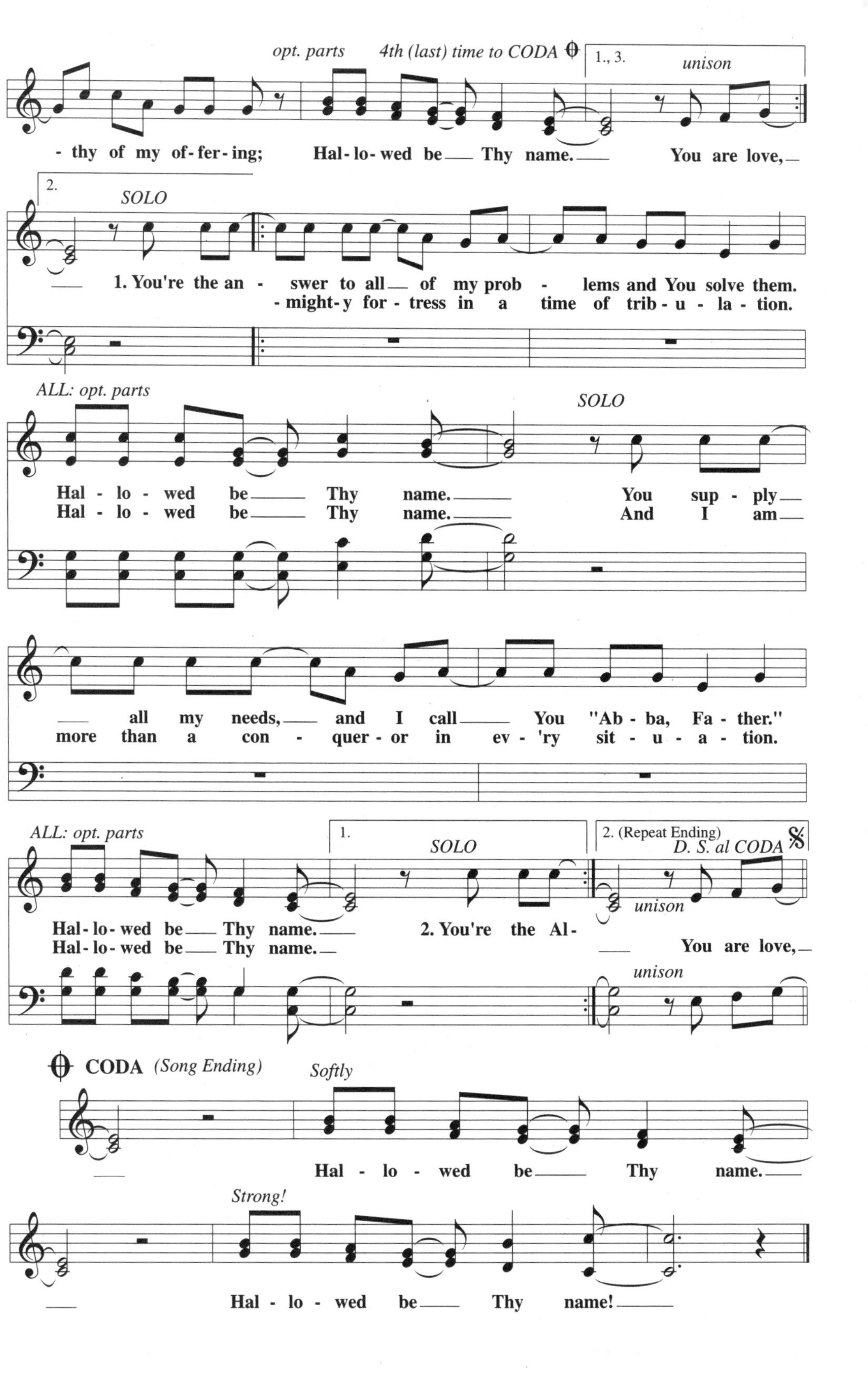
opt. parts
4th (last) time to CODA
1., 3.
unison
- thy of my of- fer- ing; Hal- lo- wed be Thy name. You are love,
2.
SOLO
1. You're the an - swer to all of my prob - lems and You solve them.
- might- y for - tress in a time of trib - u - la - tion.
ALL: opt. parts
SOLO
Hal - lo - wed be Thy name. You sup - ply
Hal - lo - wed be Thy name. And I am
all my needs, and I call You "Ab - ba, Fa - ther."
more than a con - quer - or in ev - 'ry sit - u - a - tion.
ALL: opt. parts
1.
SOLO
2. (Repeat Ending)
D. S. al CODA
unison
Hal- lo- wed be Thy name. 2. You're the Al-
Hal- lo- wed be Thy name. You are love,
unison
CODA (Song Ending)
Softly
Hal - lo - wed be Thy name.
Strong!
Hal - lo - wed be Thy name!

42 A Shield about Me

DONN THOMAS
Based on Psalm 3:3

DONN THOMAS and CHARLES WILLIAMS

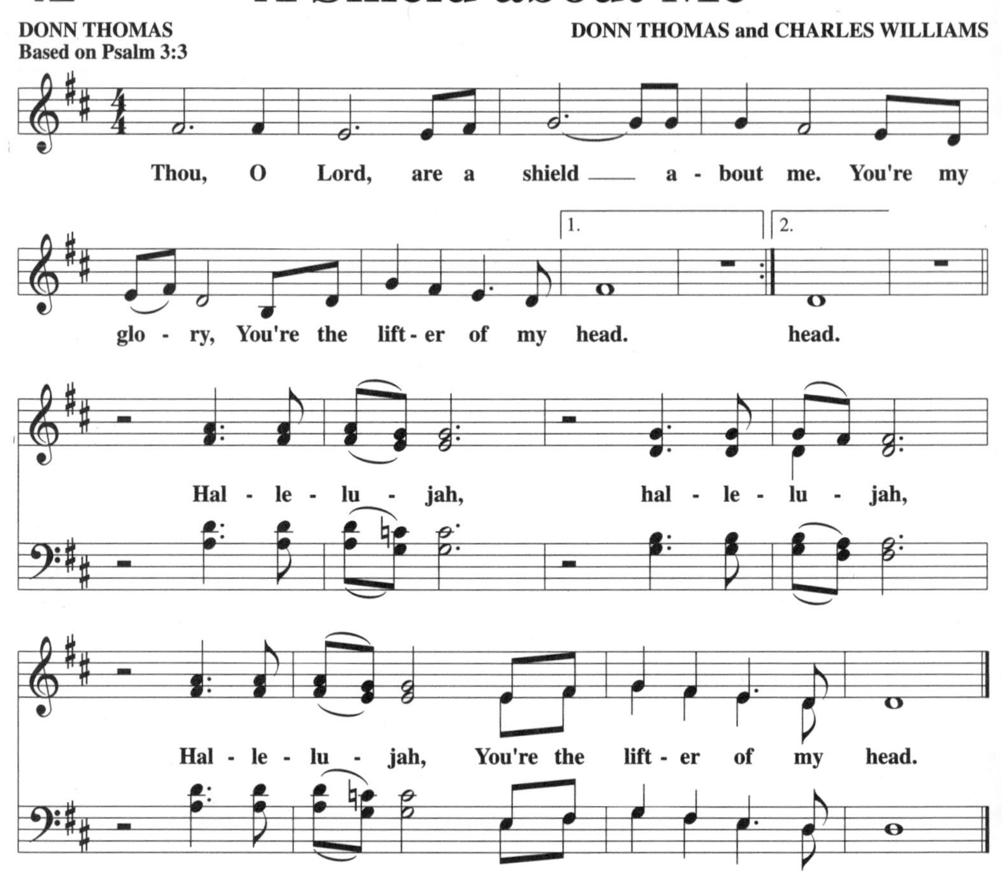

Thou, O Lord, are a shield a-bout me. You're my glo-ry, You're the lift-er of my head.

1. head.
2. head.

Hal-le-lu-jah, hal-le-lu-jah,

Hal-le-lu-jah, You're the lift-er of my head.

43 You Have Been Good

TWILA PARIS

TWILA PARIS

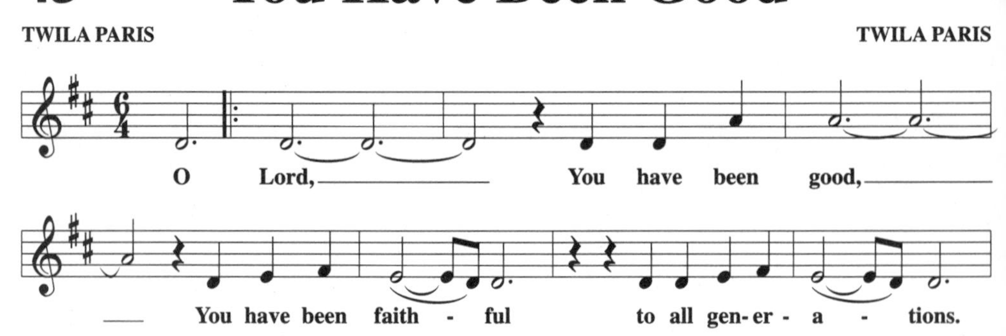

O Lord, You have been good, You have been faith-ful to all gen-er-a-tions.

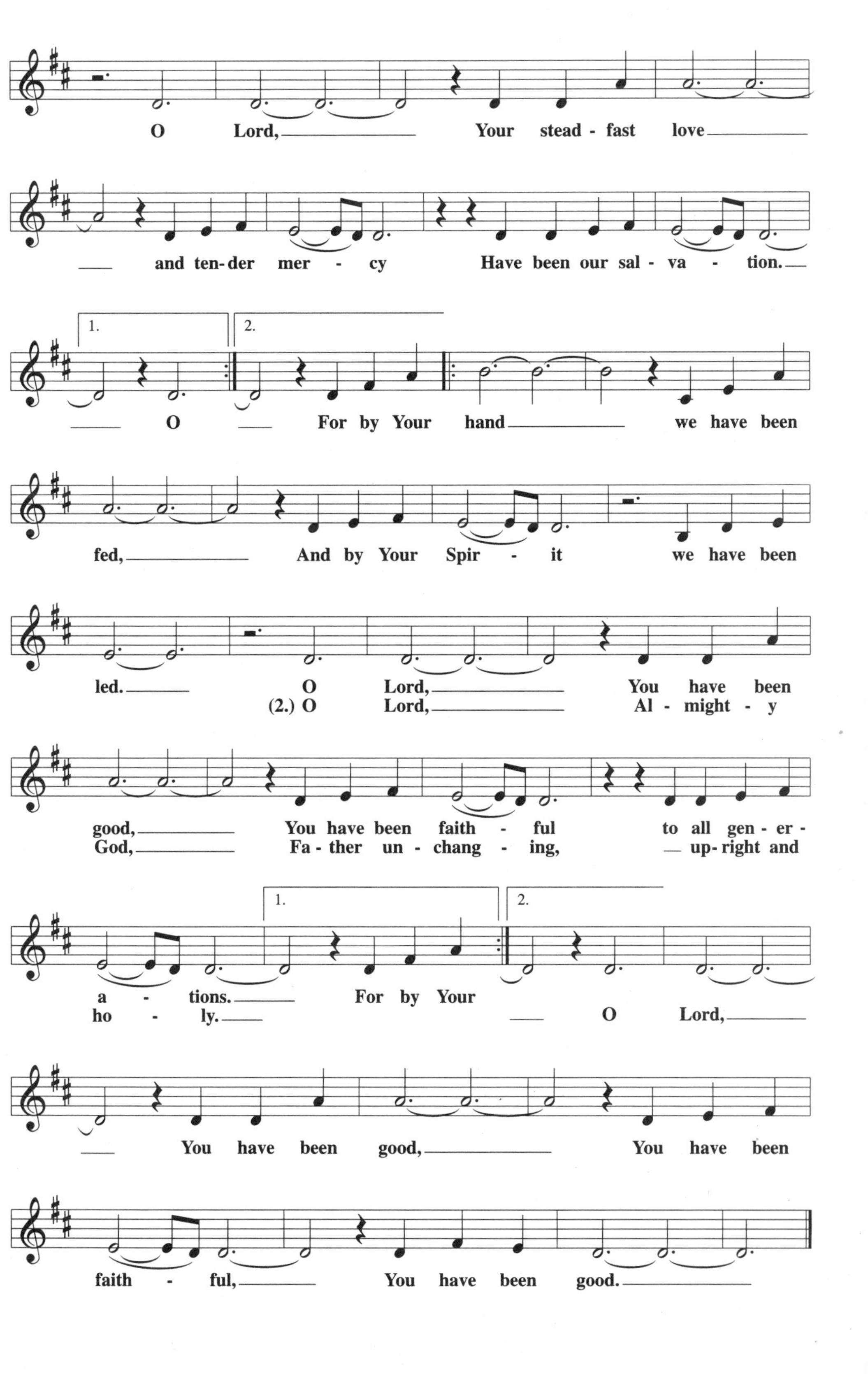

O Lord,———————— Your stead-fast love————

———— and ten-der mer - cy Have been our sal - va - tion.————

1. ———— O ———— 2. For by Your hand———————— we have been

fed,———————— And by Your Spir - it we have been

led.———— O Lord,———————— You have been
(2.) O Lord,———————— Al - might - y

good,———————— You have been faith - ful to all gen - er -
God,———————— Fa - ther un - chang - ing, — up-right and

1. a - tions.———————— For by Your 2. ———— O Lord,————

———— You have been good,———————— You have been

faith - ful,———————— You have been good.————————

44 God Is My Refuge

JUDY HORNER MONTEMAYOR

JUDY HORNER MONTEMAYOR

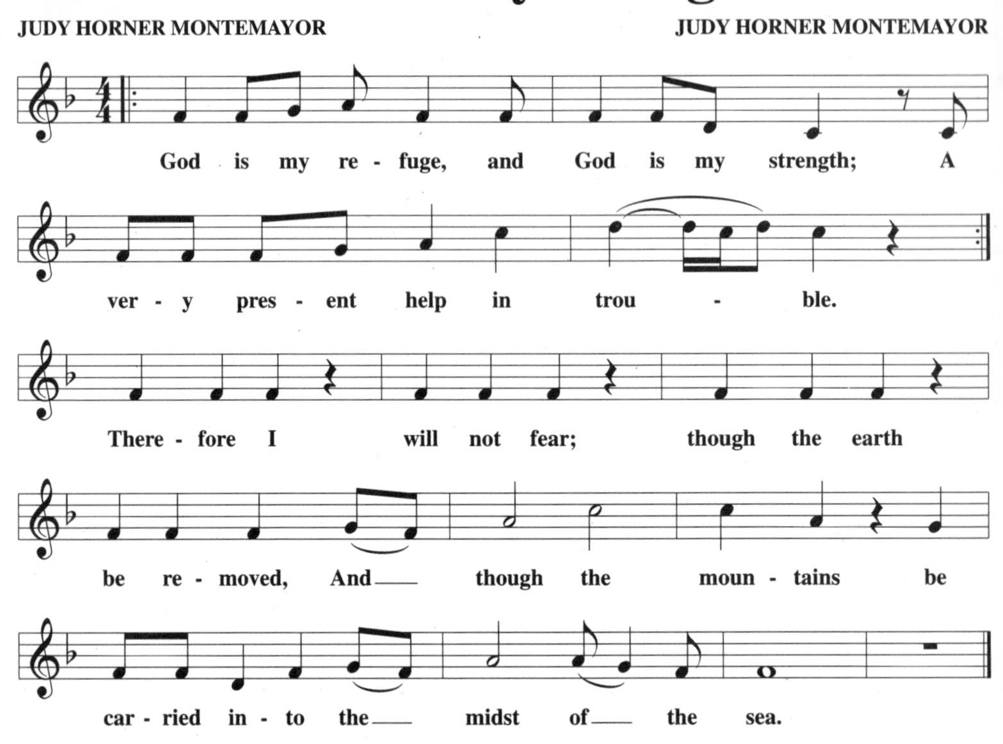

God is my re - fuge, and God is my strength; A

ver - y pres - ent help in trou - ble.

There - fore I will not fear; though the earth

be re - moved, And though the moun - tains be

car - ried in - to the midst of the sea.

45 Be Exalted, O God
(I Will Give Thanks)

BRENT CHAMBERS

BRENT CHAMBERS

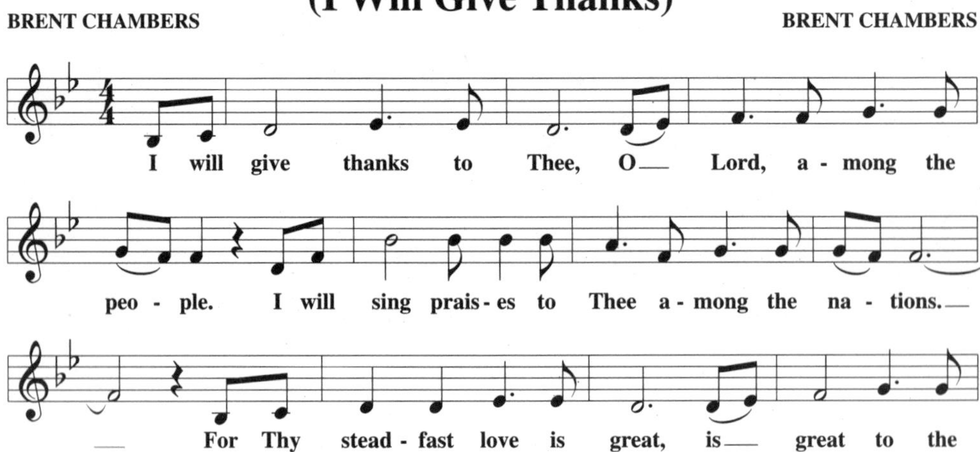

I will give thanks to Thee, O— Lord, a - mong the

peo - ple. I will sing prais - es to Thee a - mong the na - tions.—

— For Thy stead - fast love is great, is— great to the

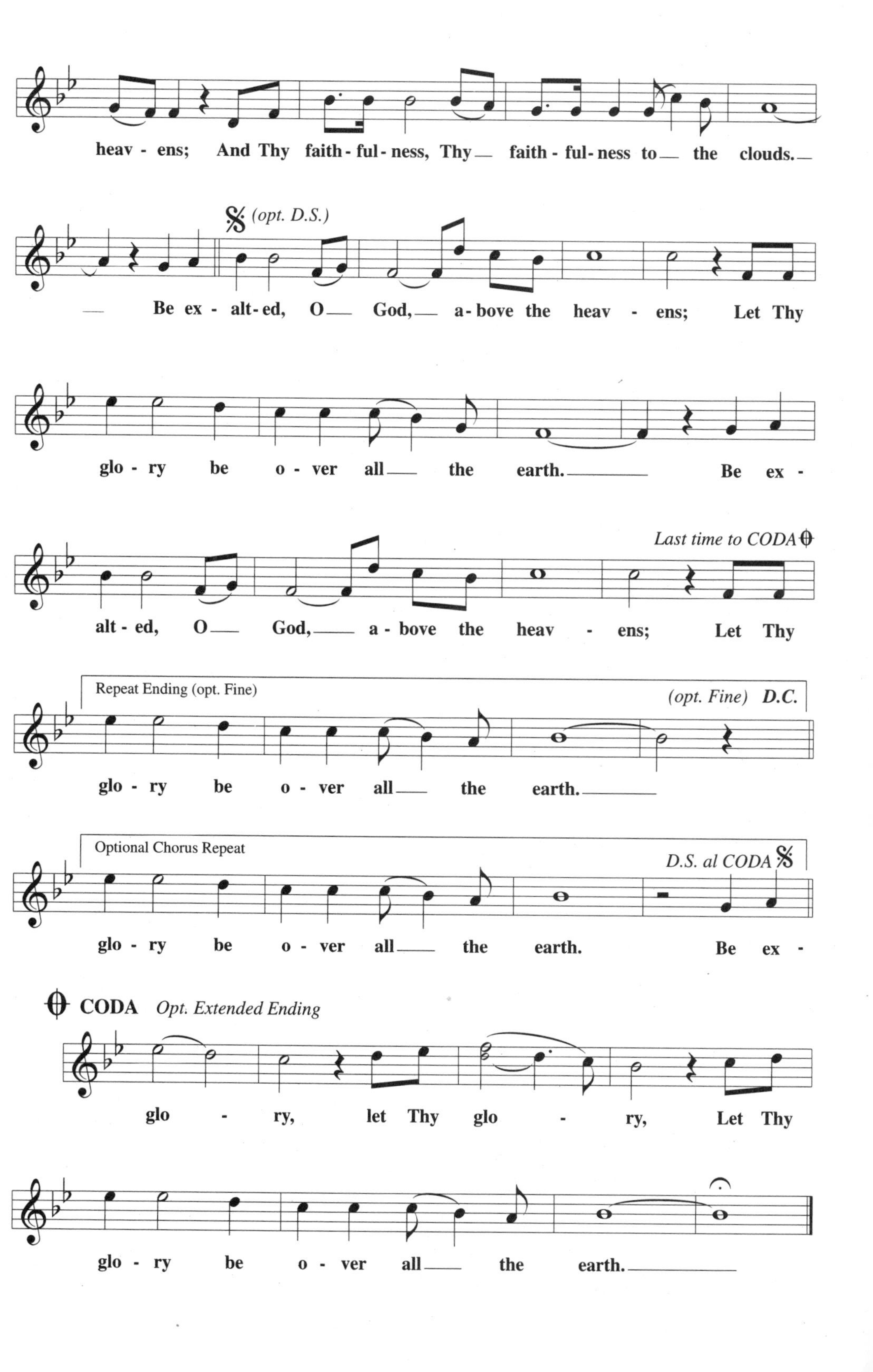
heav - ens; And Thy faith - ful - ness, Thy faith - ful - ness to the clouds.
(opt. D.S.)
Be ex - alt - ed, O God, a - bove the heav - ens; Let Thy
glo - ry be o - ver all the earth. Be ex -
Last time to CODA
alt - ed, O God, a - bove the heav - ens; Let Thy
Repeat Ending (opt. Fine)
(opt. Fine) D.C.
glo - ry be o - ver all the earth.
Optional Chorus Repeat
D.S. al CODA
glo - ry be o - ver all the earth. Be ex -
CODA Opt. Extended Ending
glo - ry, let Thy glo - ry, Let Thy
glo - ry be o - ver all the earth.

46 In His Presence

Words and Music by
DICK and MELODIE TUNNEY

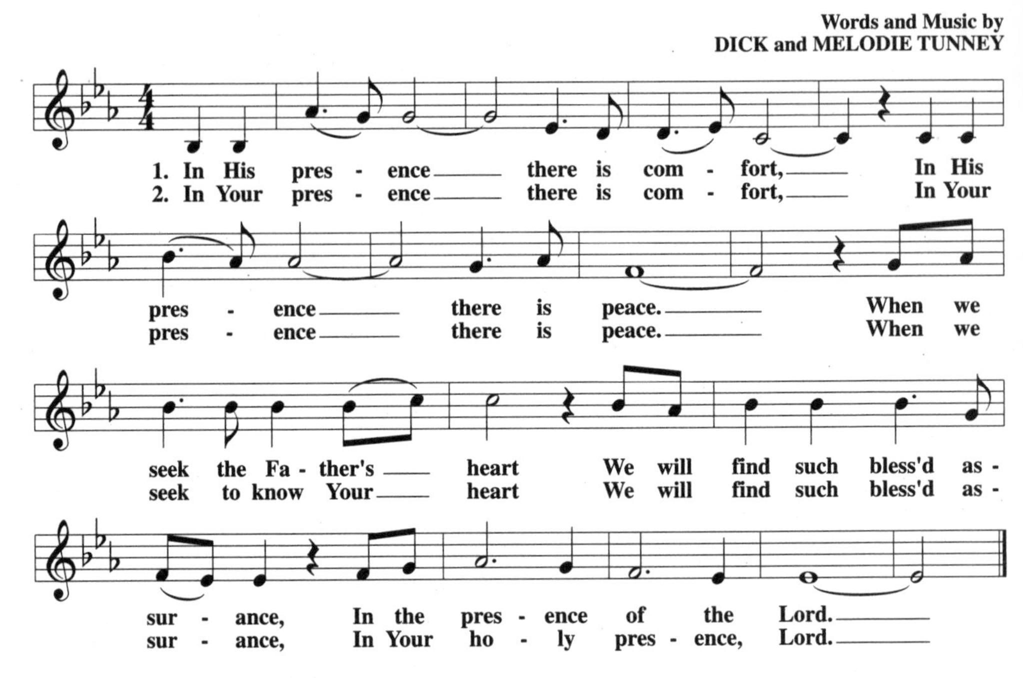

1. In His pres - ence____ there is com - fort,____ In His
2. In Your pres - ence____ there is com - fort,____ In Your

pres - ence____ there is peace.____ When we
pres - ence____ there is peace.____ When we

seek the Fa - ther's____ heart We will find such bless'd as -
seek to know Your____ heart We will find such bless'd as -

sur - ance, In the pres - ence of the Lord.____
sur - ance, In Your ho - ly pres - ence, Lord.____

47 I Will Bless the Lord

FRANK HERNANDEZ   **FRANK HERNANDEZ**

MELODY

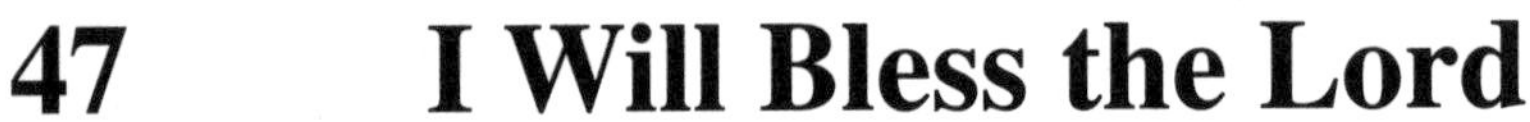

I will bless the____ Lord and

OPTIONAL ECHO (trio or solo)

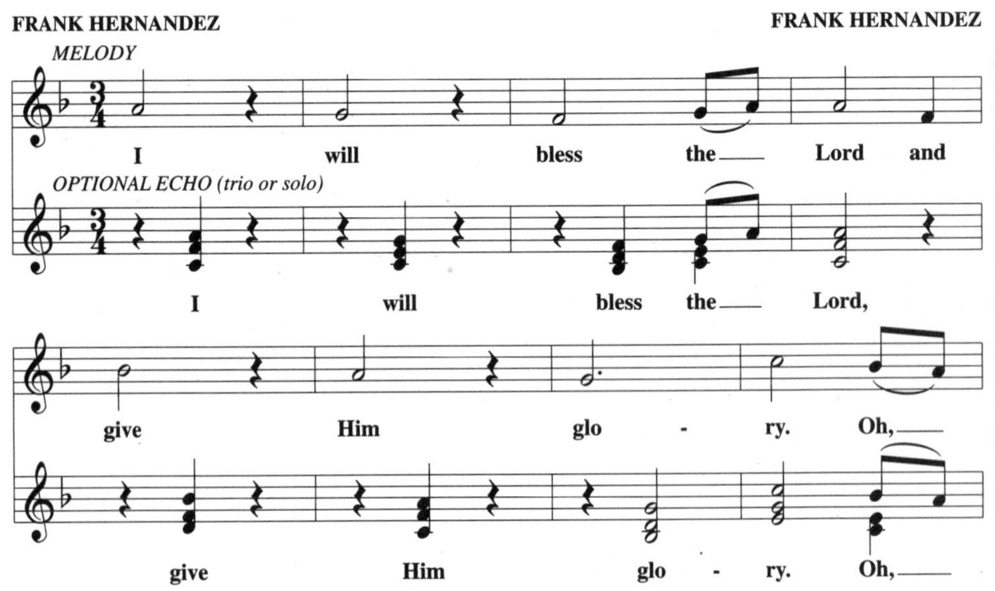

I will bless the____ Lord,

give Him glo - ry. Oh,____

give Him glo - ry. Oh,____

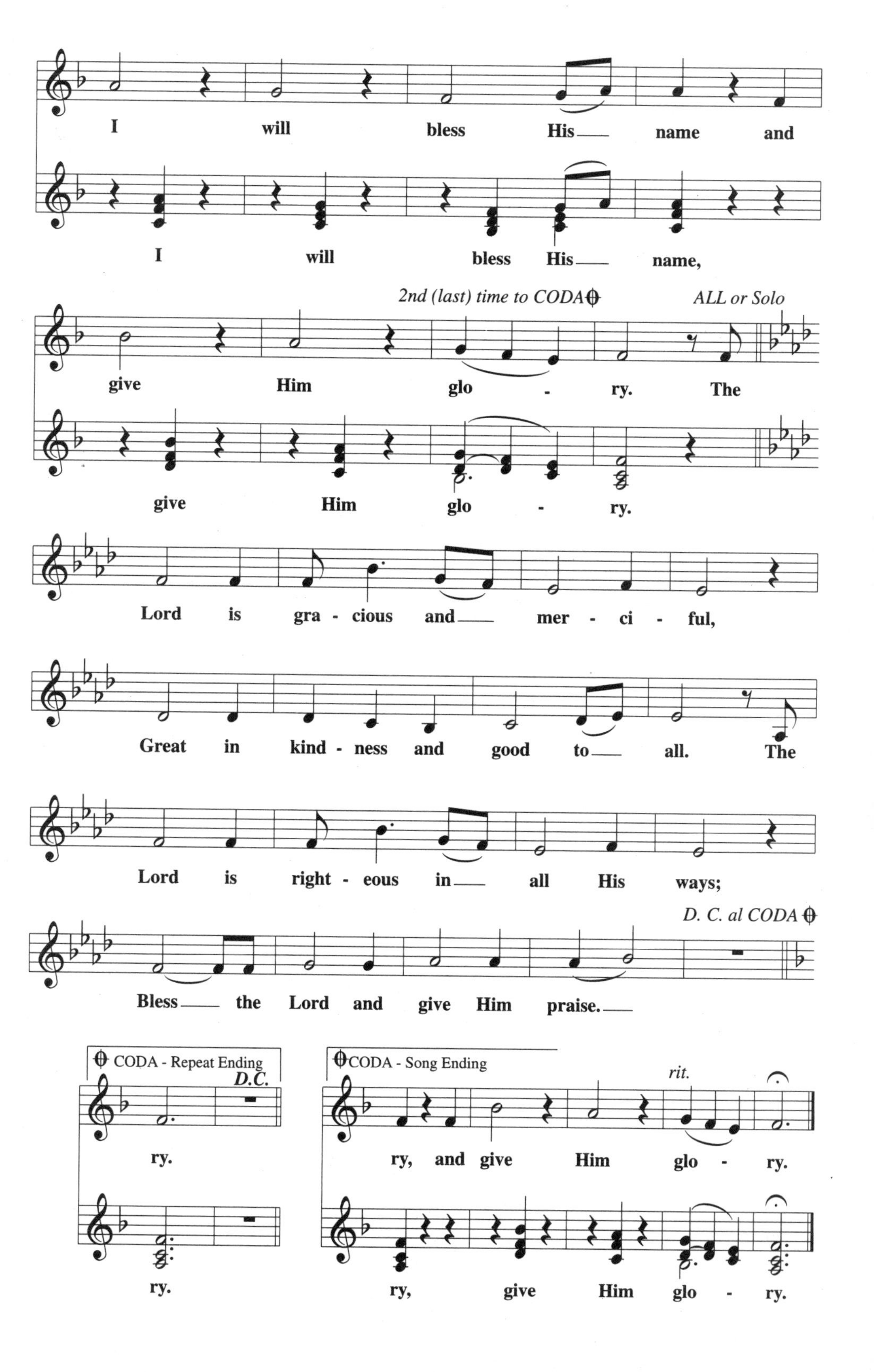
I will bless His name and
I will bless His name,
2nd (last) time to CODA
ALL or Solo
give Him glo - ry. The
give Him glo - ry.
Lord is gra - cious and mer - ci - ful,
Great in kind - ness and good to all. The
Lord is right - eous in all His ways;
D. C. al CODA
Bless the Lord and give Him praise.
CODA - Repeat Ending
D.C.
ry.
ry.
CODA - Song Ending
rit.
ry, and give Him glo - ry.
ry, give Him glo - ry.

48 Behold, What Manner of Love

Adapted from 1 John 3:1

PATRICIA VAN TINE

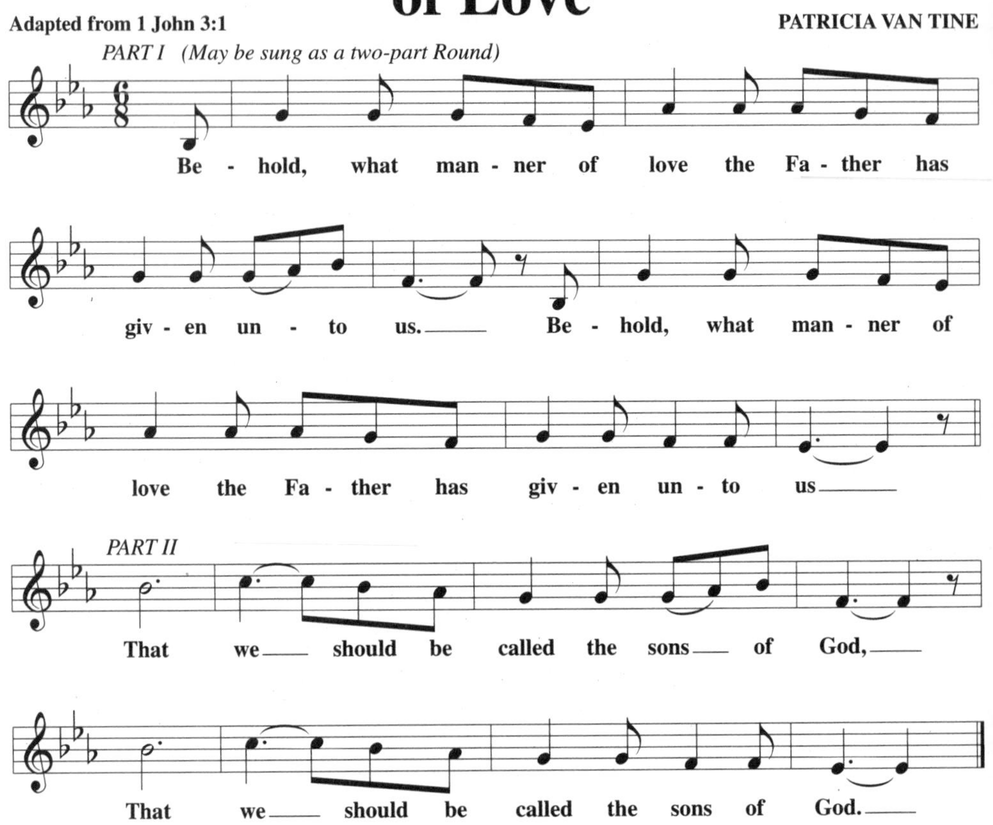

PART I *(May be sung as a two-part Round)*

Be - hold, what man - ner of love the Fa - ther has
giv - en un - to us.___ Be - hold, what man - ner of
love the Fa - ther has giv - en un - to us___

PART II

That we___ should be called the sons___ of God,___
That we___ should be called the sons of God.___

49 Be Still and Know

Verses 1 and 2, ANONYMOUS
Verses 3 and 4, TOM FETTKE

ANONYMOUS
Arranged by Lee Herrington and Tom Fettke

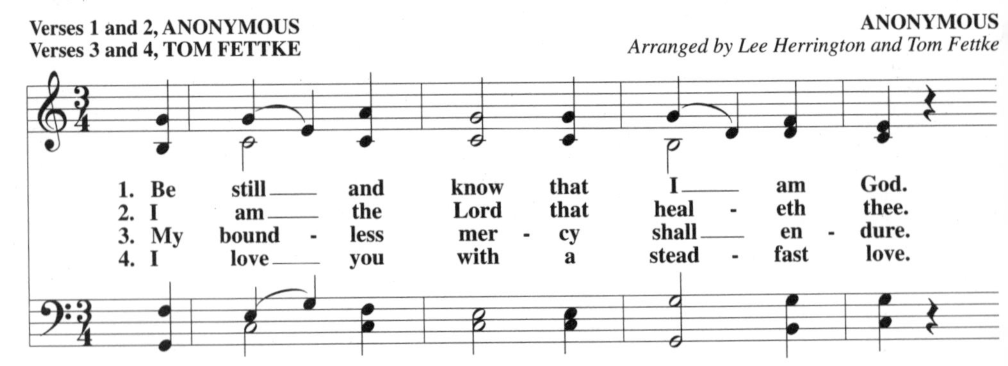

1. Be still___ and know that I___ am God.
2. I am___ the Lord that heal - eth thee.
3. My bound - less mer - cy shall___ en - dure.
4. I love___ you with a stead - fast love.

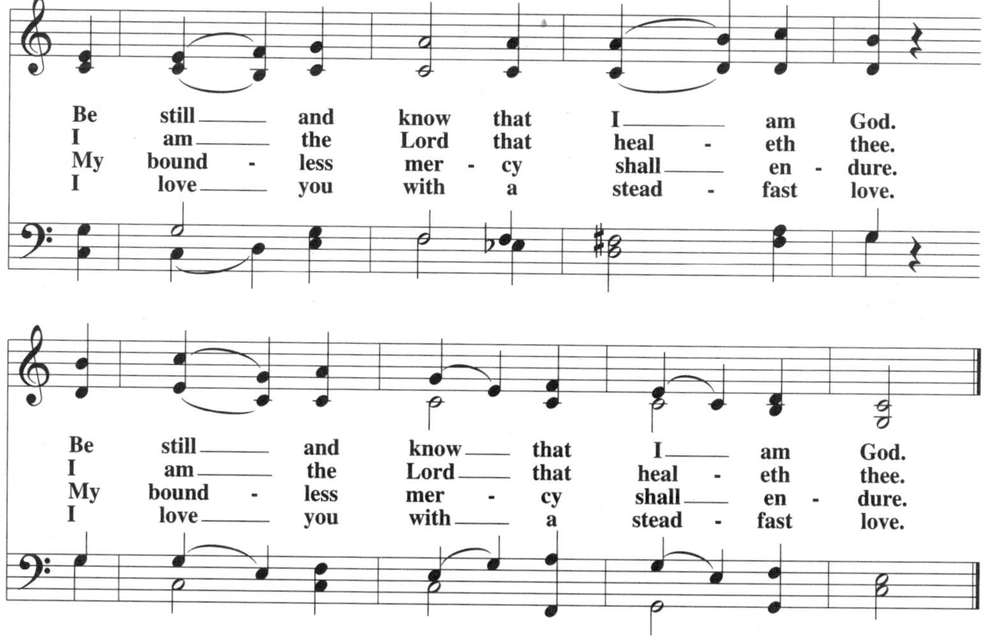

Be still____ and know that I____ am God.
I am____ the Lord that heal - eth thee.
My bound - less mer - cy shall____ en - dure.
I love____ you with a stead - fast love.

Be still____ and know____ that I____ am God.
I am____ the Lord____ that heal - eth thee.
My bound - less mer - cy shall____ en - dure.
I love____ you with a stead - fast love.

Think about His Love 50

WALT HARRAH   WALT HARRAH

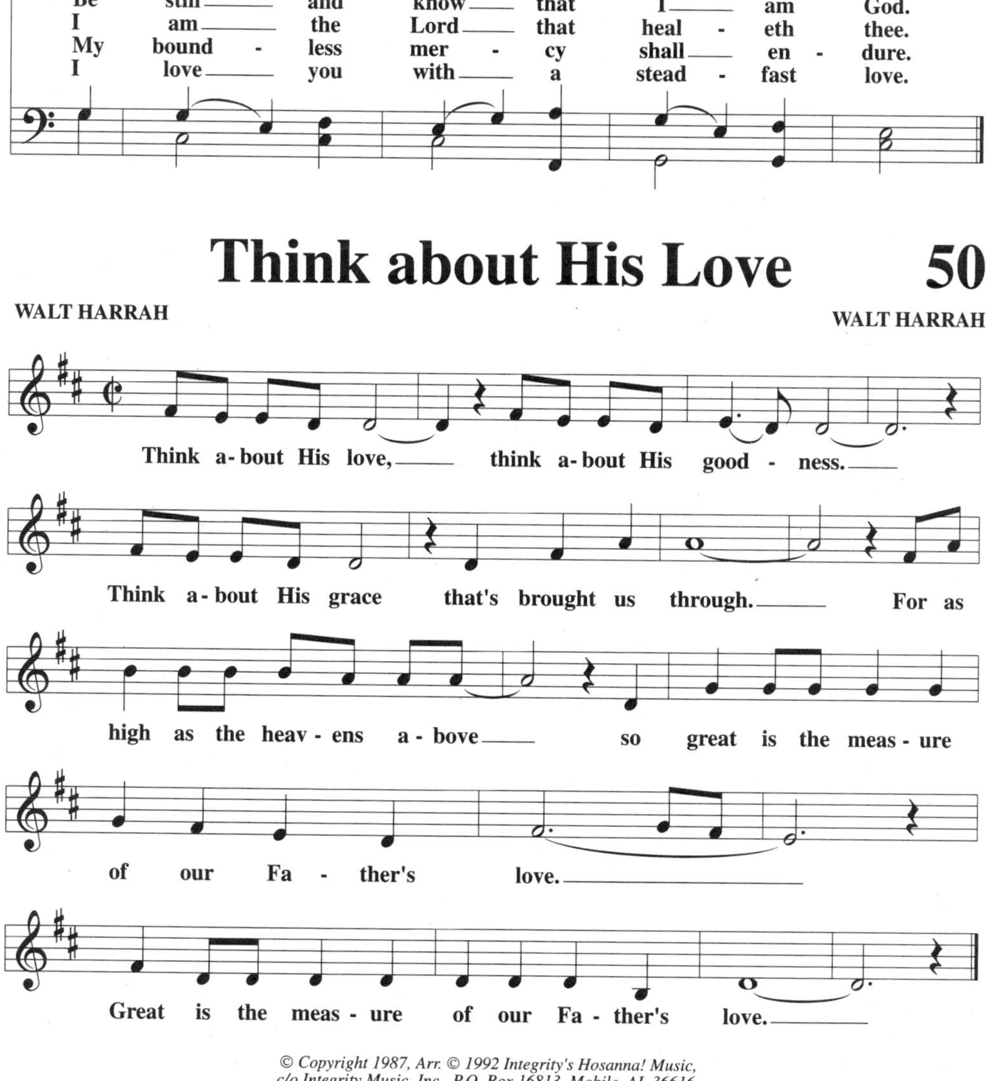

Think a-bout His love,____ think a-bout His good - ness.____

Think a-bout His grace that's brought us through.____ For as

high as the heav-ens a - bove____ so great is the meas - ure

of our Fa - ther's love.____

Great is the meas - ure of our Fa - ther's love.____

51   Your Mercy Flows

WES SUTTON

WES SUTTON

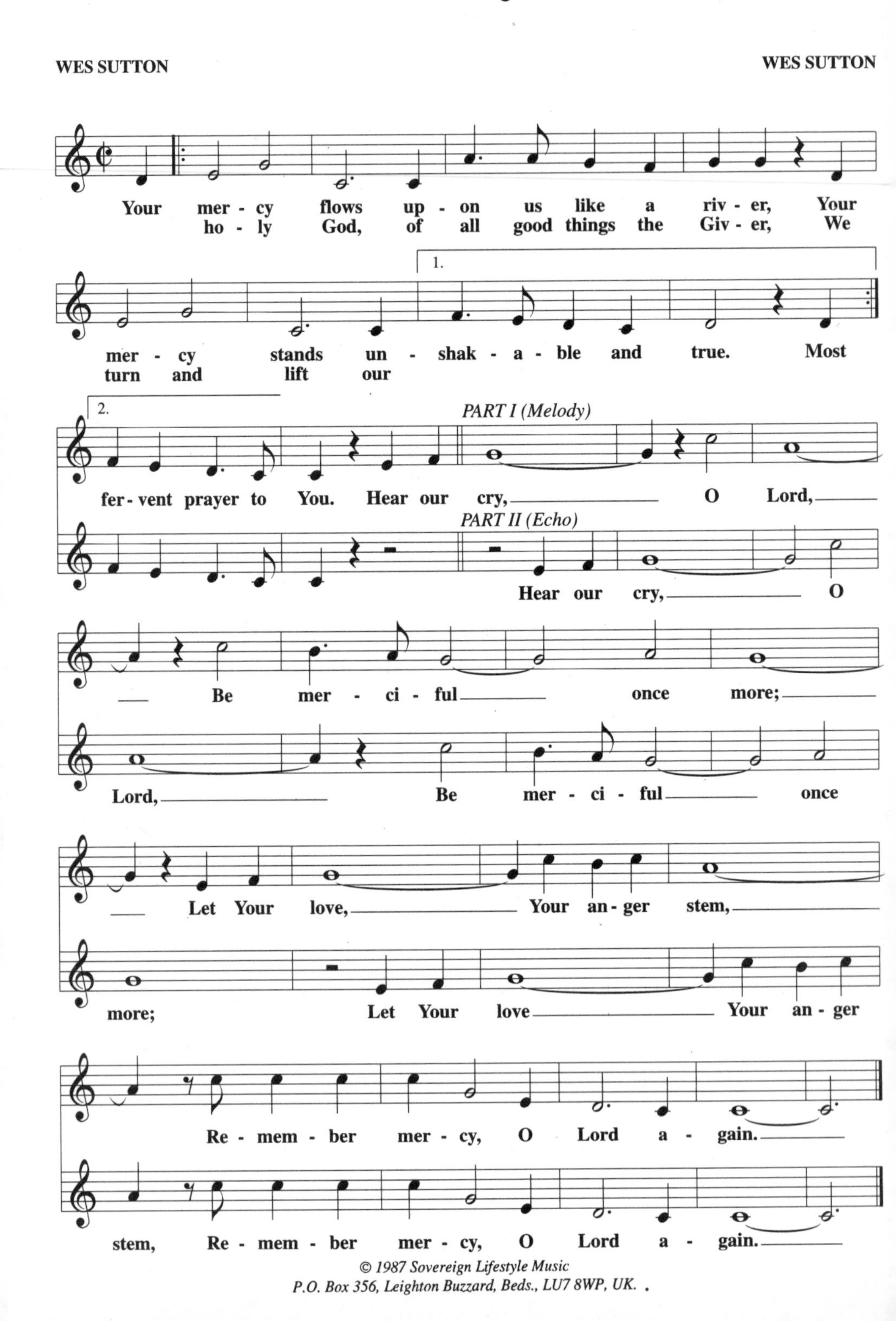

Your mer - cy flows up - on us like a riv - er, Your
ho - ly God, of all good things the Giv - er, We

1.
mer - cy stands un - shak - a - ble and true. Most
turn and lift our

2.
fer - vent prayer to You. Hear our cry,_____ O Lord,_____

PART I (Melody)

PART II (Echo)
Hear our cry,_____ O

Be mer - ci - ful_____ once more;_____
Lord,_____ Be mer - ci - ful_____ once

Let Your love,_____ Your an - ger stem,_____
more; Let Your love_____ Your an - ger

Re - mem - ber mer - cy, O Lord a - gain._____
stem, Re - mem - ber mer - cy, O Lord a - gain._____

I Will Sing of the Mercies 52

Adapted from Psalm 89:1

JAMES H. FILLMORE

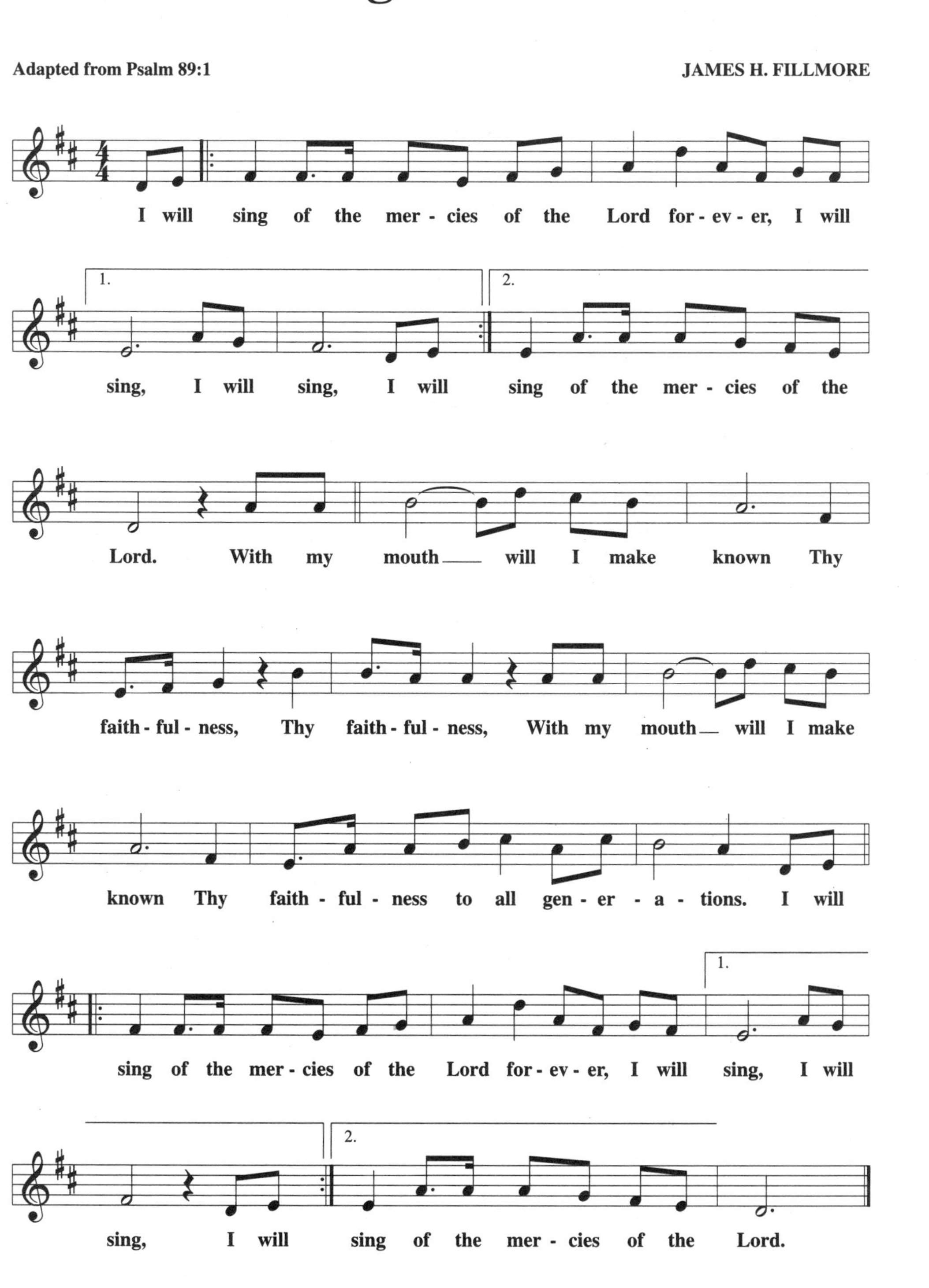

53 The Lord Reigneth

LaMAR BOSCHMAN

LaMAR BOSCHMAN

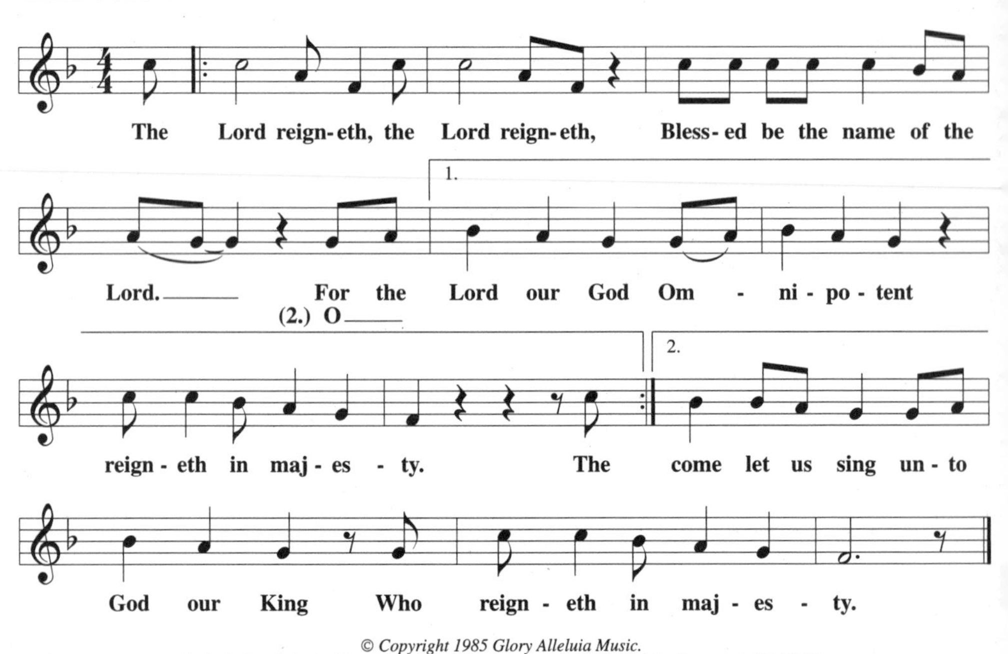

The Lord reign-eth, the Lord reign-eth, Bless-ed be the name of the

Lord. _____ For the Lord our God Om - ni - po - tent

(2.) O _____

reign - eth in maj - es - ty. The

come let us sing un - to

God our King Who reign - eth in maj - es - ty.

54 Jesus Is My Lord

AUTHOR UNKNOWN

COMPOSER UNKNOWN

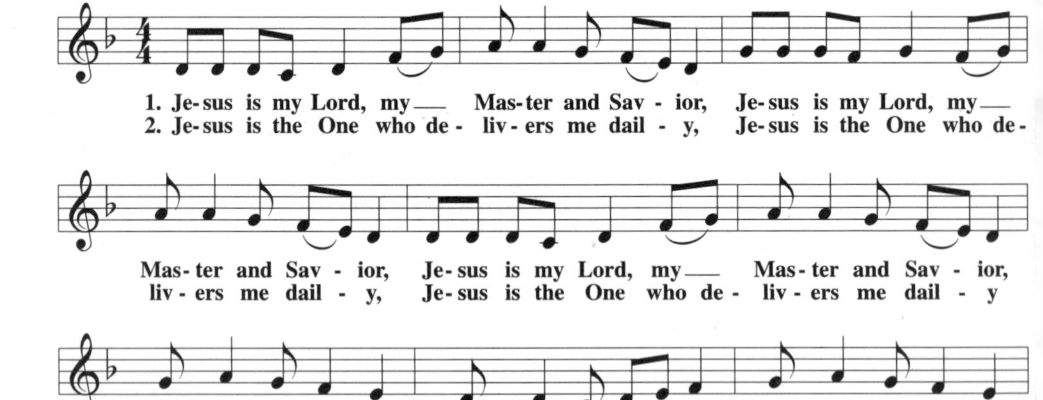

1. Je-sus is my Lord, my ___ Mas-ter and Sav - ior, Je-sus is my Lord, my ___
2. Je-sus is the One who de - liv-ers me dail - y, Je-sus is the One who de-

Mas-ter and Sav - ior, Je-sus is my Lord, my ___ Mas-ter and Sav - ior,
liv-ers me dail - y, Je-sus is the One who de - liv-ers me dail - y

now and for - ev - er - more, Hal - le - lu - jah, now and for - ev - er -
from all my sin and shame, Hal - le - lu - jah, from all my sin and

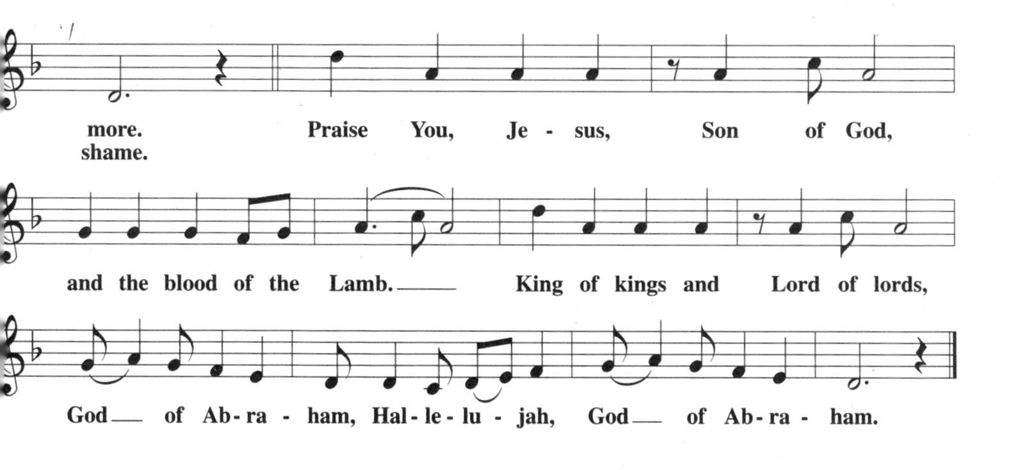

more.
shame.

Praise You, Je - sus, Son of God,

and the blood of the Lamb.— King of kings and Lord of lords,

God— of Ab - ra - ham, Hal - le - lu - jah, God— of Ab - ra - ham.

You Are Crowned with Many Crowns 55

JOHN SELLERS

JOHN SELLERS

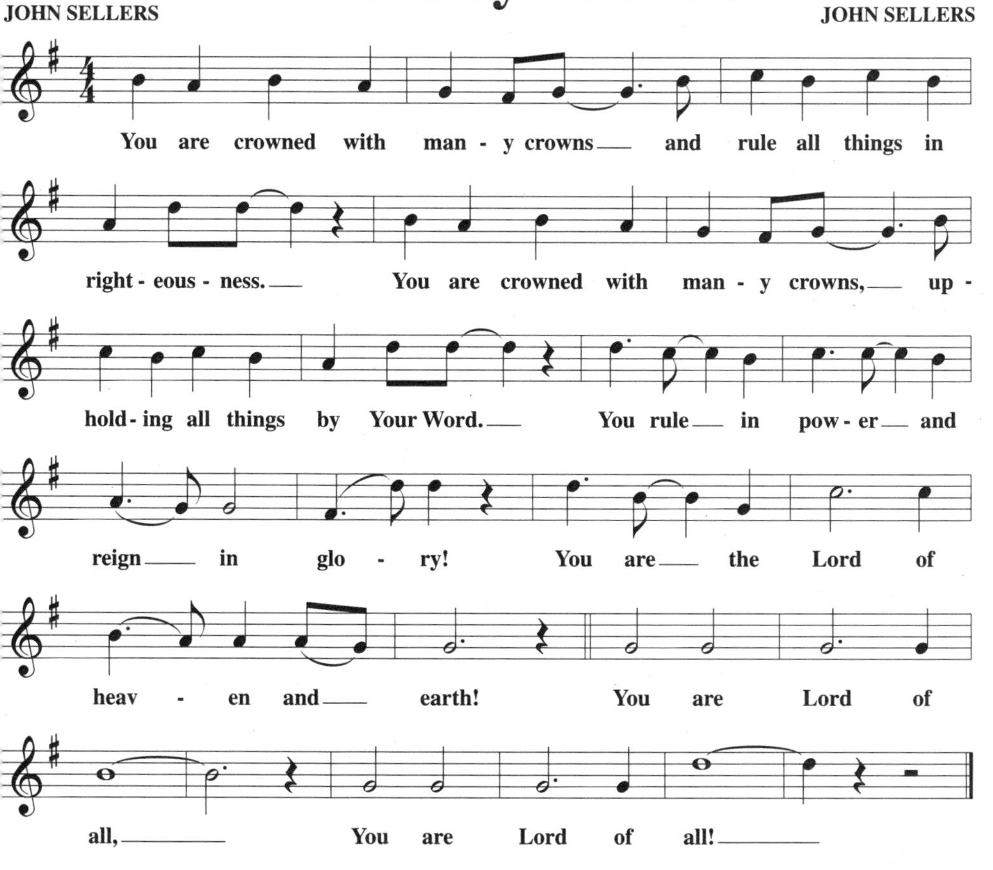

You are crowned with man - y crowns— and rule all things in

right - eous - ness.— You are crowned with man - y crowns,— up -

hold - ing all things by Your Word.— You rule— in pow - er— and

reign— in glo - ry! You are— the Lord of

heav - en and— earth! You are Lord of

all,— You are Lord of all!—

56 Jesus, Lord to Me

Words and Music by
GREG NELSON and GARY McSPADDEN

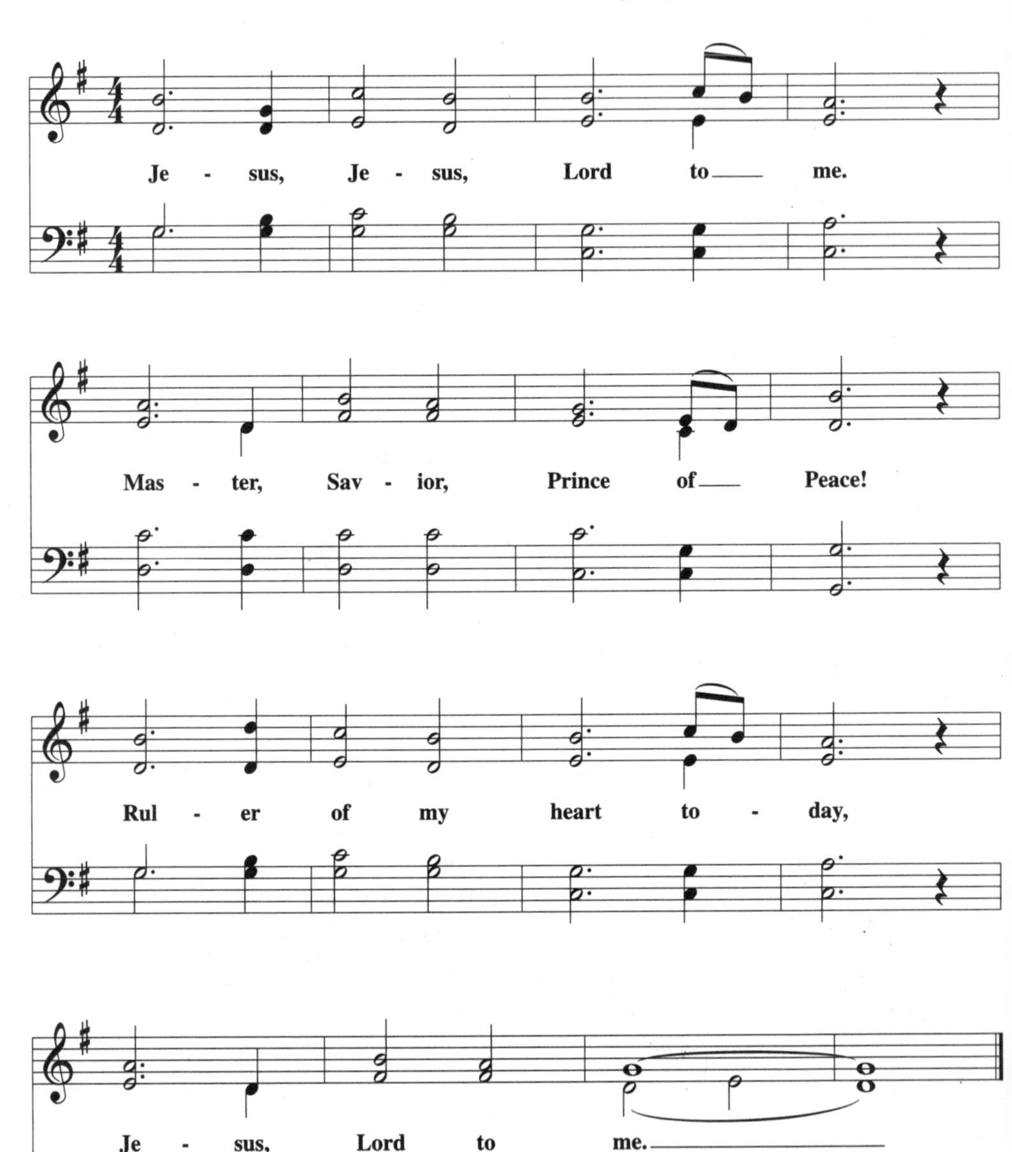

Lion of Judah

57

TED SANDQUIST

TED SANDQUIST

1., 4. Li - on of Ju - dah on the throne,
2. Li - on of Ju - dah come to earth,
3. Li - on of Ju - dah come a - gain,

I shout Your name, let it be known That You are
I want to thank You for Your birth; _ For the
Take up Your throne, Je - ru - sa - lem. _ Bring re -

(cues: third verse)

King of kings, You are the Prince of
Liv - ing Word, for Your death on the
lease to this earth, And the con - sum - ma -

(cues: second verse)

peace, May Your king - dom's reign nev - er
tree, For Your res - ur - rec - tion vic - to -
tion of Your king - dom's reign, let it

cease. Hail to the King! Hail to the
ry. Hal - le - lu - jah! Hal - le - lu -
come. Mar - an - a - tha! Mar - an - a -

| Repeat Ending *D.C.* | Song Ending | Optional Extended Ending |

King! Hail to the
jah!
tha!

King! Hail to the King! You are my King!

58 Great Is the Lord Almighty!

DENNIS L. JERNIGAN

DENNIS L. JERNIGAN

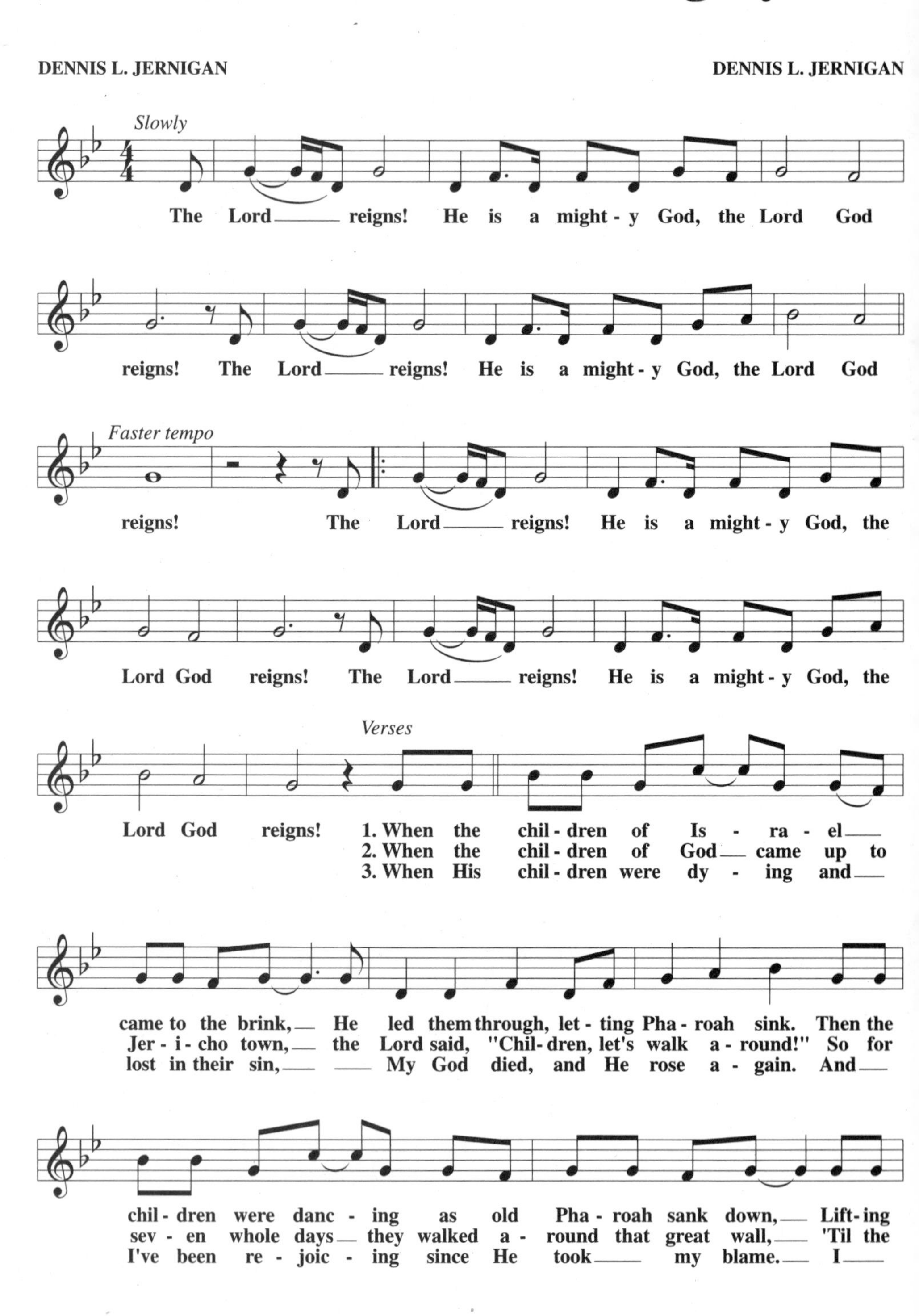

The Lord reigns! He is a might-y God, the Lord God

reigns! The Lord reigns! He is a might-y God, the Lord God

reigns! The Lord reigns! He is a might-y God, the

Lord God reigns! The Lord reigns! He is a might-y God, the

Lord God reigns!
1. When the chil-dren of Is - ra - el
2. When the chil-dren of God came up to
3. When His chil-dren were dy - ing and

came to the brink, He led them through, let-ting Pha-roah sink. Then the
Jer - i - cho town, the Lord said, "Chil-dren, let's walk a - round!" So for
lost in their sin, My God died, and He rose a - gain. And

chil-dren were danc-ing as old Pha-roah sank down, Lift-ing
sev - en whole days they walked a - round that great wall, 'Til the
I've been re - joic - ing since He took my blame. I

Chorus

up a might - y, joy - ful sound, sing-ing, "Great is the Lord Al- might-y, He is
Lord said, "Shout, and watch it fall, chil- dren!"
thank You, Je - sus, praise Your name! _____

Lord, He is God in-deed! Great is the Lord Al- might- y, He is God su- preme! __

Great is the Lord Al- might- y, He is Lord, He is God in- deed! Great is the

1., 2.   3.

Lord,   Great is the Lord!" _____ The _____

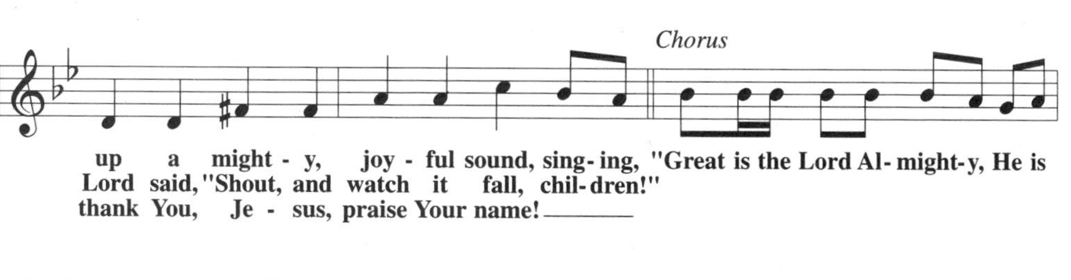

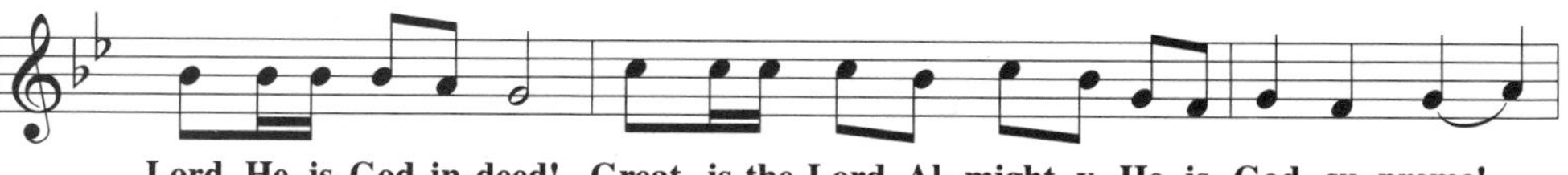

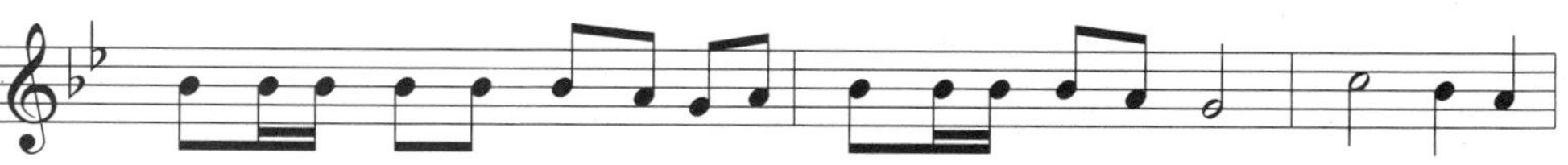

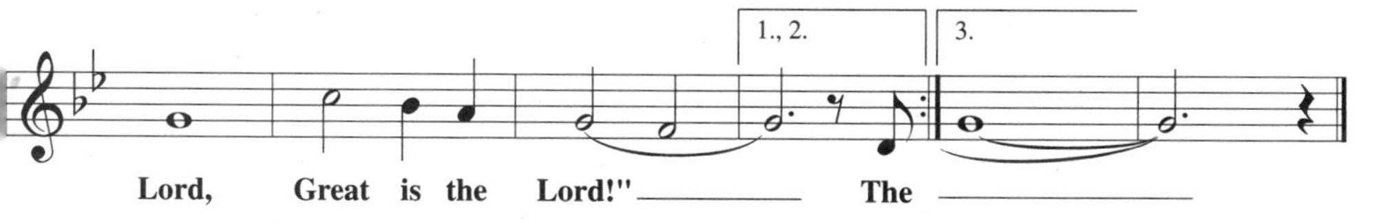

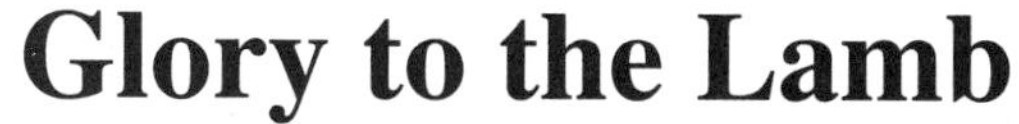

Glory to the Lamb   59

LARRY DEMPSEY   **LARRY DEMPSEY**

1. Glo - ry, glo - ry, glo - ry to the Lamb.
2. Wor - thy, wor - thy, wor - thy is the Lamb.
3. Ho - ly, ho - ly, ho - ly is the Lamb.

Glo - ry, glo - ry, glo - ry to the Lamb.
Wor - thy, wor - thy, wor - thy is the Lamb. For He is
Ho - ly, ho - ly, ho - ly is the Lamb.

glo - ri- ous and wor-thy to be praised, the Lamb up-on the throne; _____ And

un - to Him we lift our voice in praise, the Lamb up-on the throne.

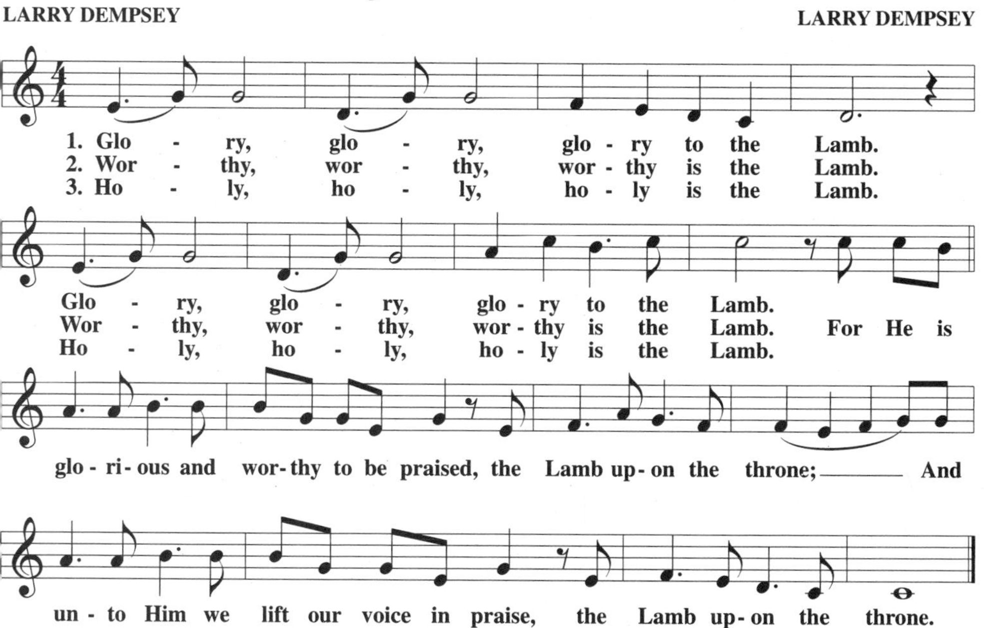

60
To Him Who Sits on the Throne

DEBBYE GRAAFSMA

DEBBYE GRAAFSMA

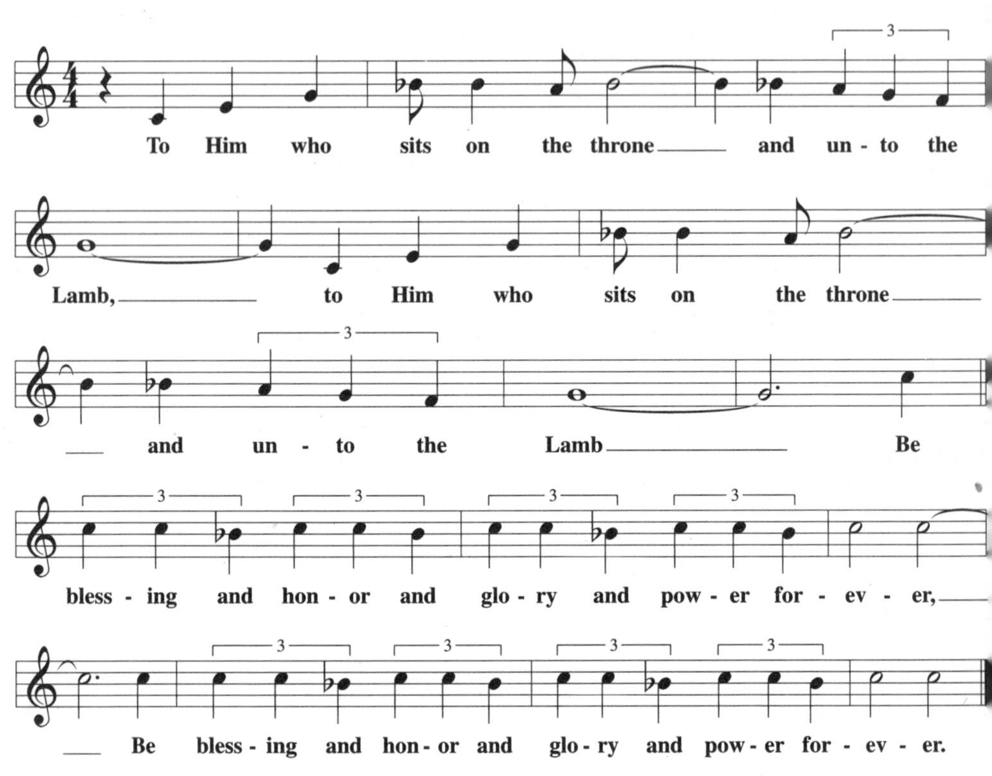

To Him who sits on the throne and un-to the Lamb, to Him who sits on the throne and un-to the Lamb Be bless-ing and hon-or and glo-ry and pow-er for-ev-er, Be bless-ing and hon-or and glo-ry and pow-er for-ev-er.

61
You Are My God

MACON DELAVAN

MACON DELAVAN

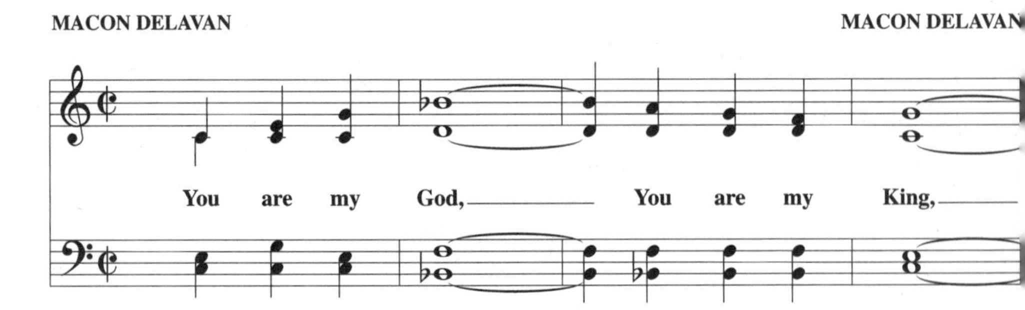

You are my God, You are my King,

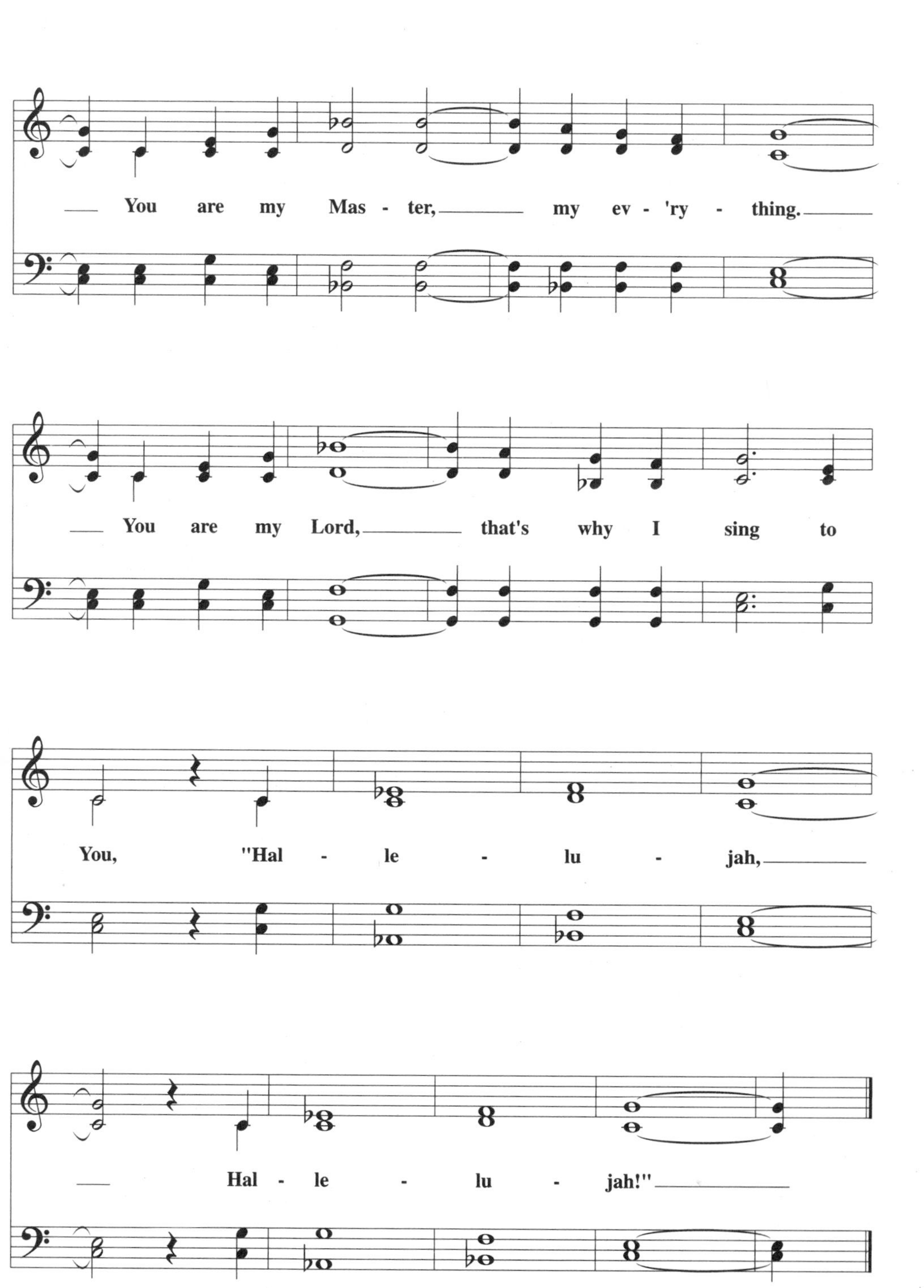
You are my Mas - ter, my ev - 'ry - thing.
You are my Lord, that's why I sing to
You, "Hal - le - lu - jah,
Hal - le - lu - jah!"

62 Here Comes Jesus

GARY ROBERTS

GARY ROBERTS

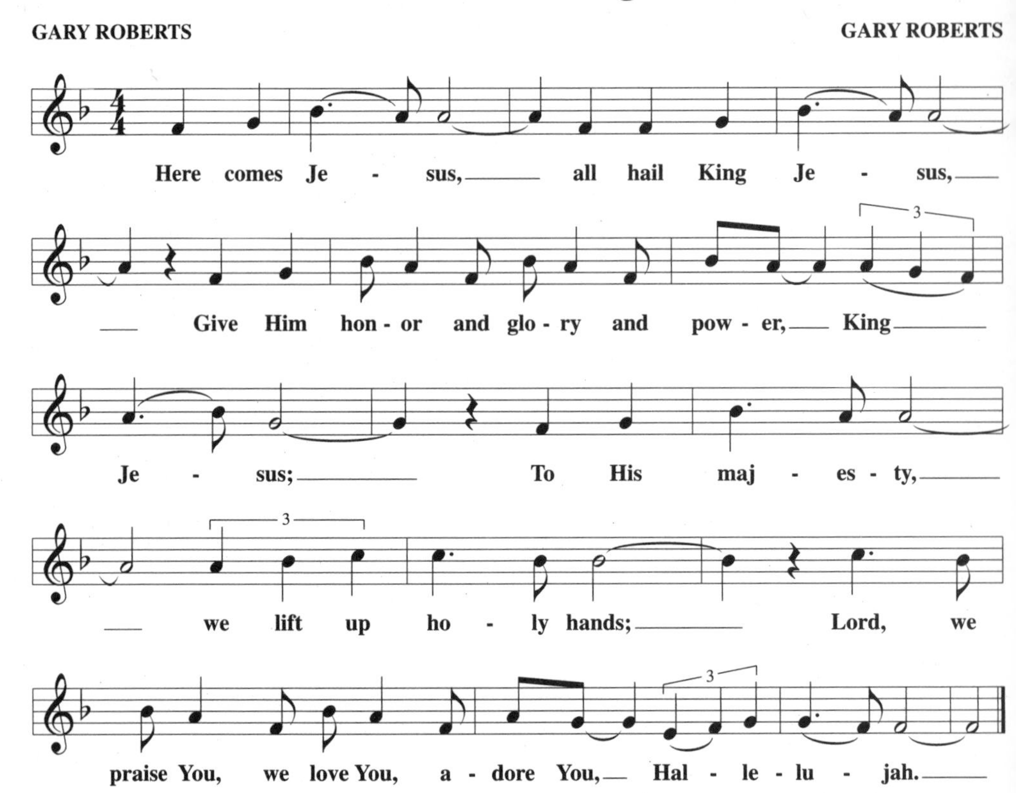

Here comes Je - sus,____ all hail King Je - sus,____ Give Him hon - or and glo - ry and pow - er,____ King Je - sus;____ To His maj - es - ty,____ we lift up ho - ly hands;____ Lord, we praise You, we love You, a - dore You,____ Hal - le - lu - jah.____

63 All Hail, King Jesus

DAVE MOODY

DAVE MOODY

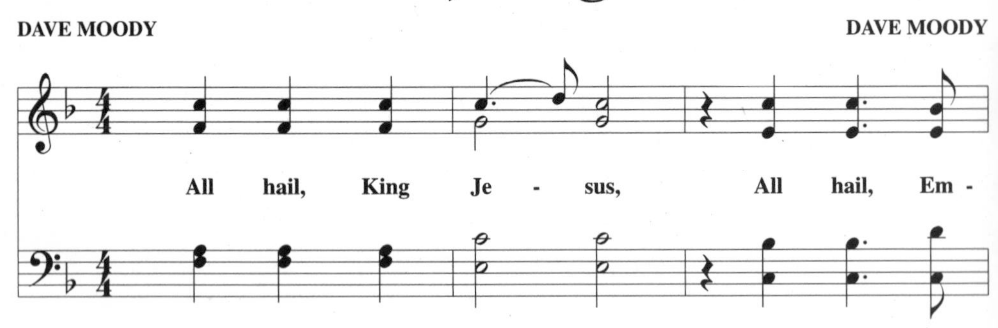

All hail, King Je - sus, All hail, Em -

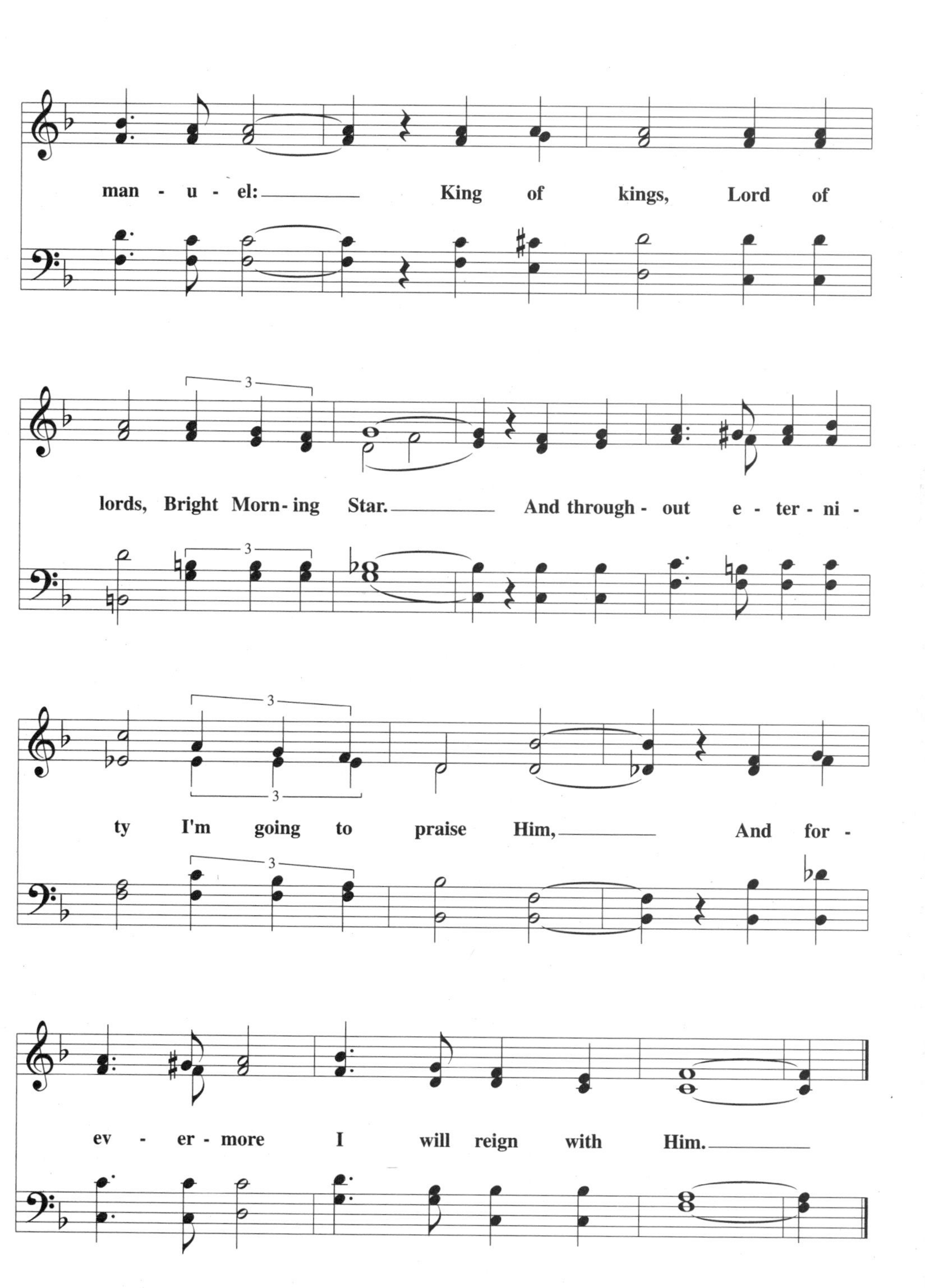

man - u - el:
King of kings, Lord of
lords, Bright Morn - ing Star.
And through - out e - ter - ni -
ty I'm going to praise Him,
And for -
ev - er - more I will reign with Him.
3

64 Our God Reigns

LEONARD E. SMITH, JR.   LEONARD E. SMITH, JR.

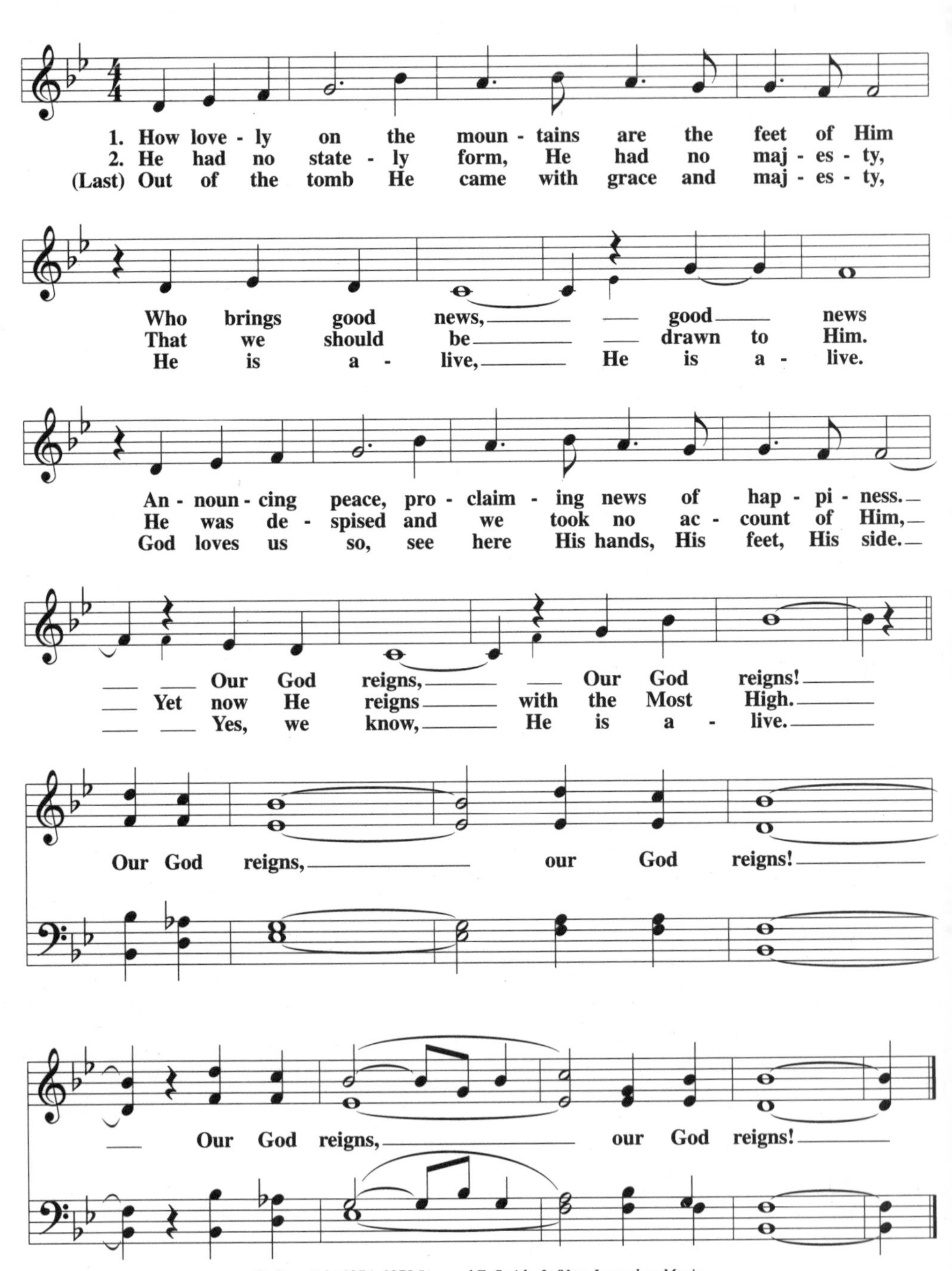

1. How love-ly on the moun-tains are the feet of Him
2. He had no state-ly form, He had no maj-es-ty,
(Last) Out of the tomb He came with grace and maj-es-ty,

Who brings good news, ____ ____ good ____ news
That we should be ____ ____ drawn to Him.
He is a-live, ____ He is a-live.

An-noun-cing peace, pro-claim-ing news of hap-pi-ness. ____
He was de-spised and we took no ac-count of Him,
God loves us so, see here His hands, His feet, His side.

____ Yet Our God reigns, ____ ____ Our God reigns! ____
____ Yet now He reigns ____ with the Most High. ____
____ ____ Yes, we know, ____ He is a-live.

Our God reigns, ____ our God reigns! ____

Our God reigns, ____ our God reigns! ____

OPTIONAL STANZAS TO *OUR GOD REIGNS:*

3. It was our sin and guilt that bruised
   and wounded Him.
   It was our sin that brought Him down.
   When we like sheep had gone astray,
   our Shepherd came
   And on His shoulders bore our shame.

4. Meek as a lamb that's led out to
   the slaughterhouse,
   Dumb as a sheep before its shearer,
   His life ran down upon the ground
   like pouring rain,
   That we might be born again.

We Bow Down

65

TWILA PARIS

TWILA PARIS

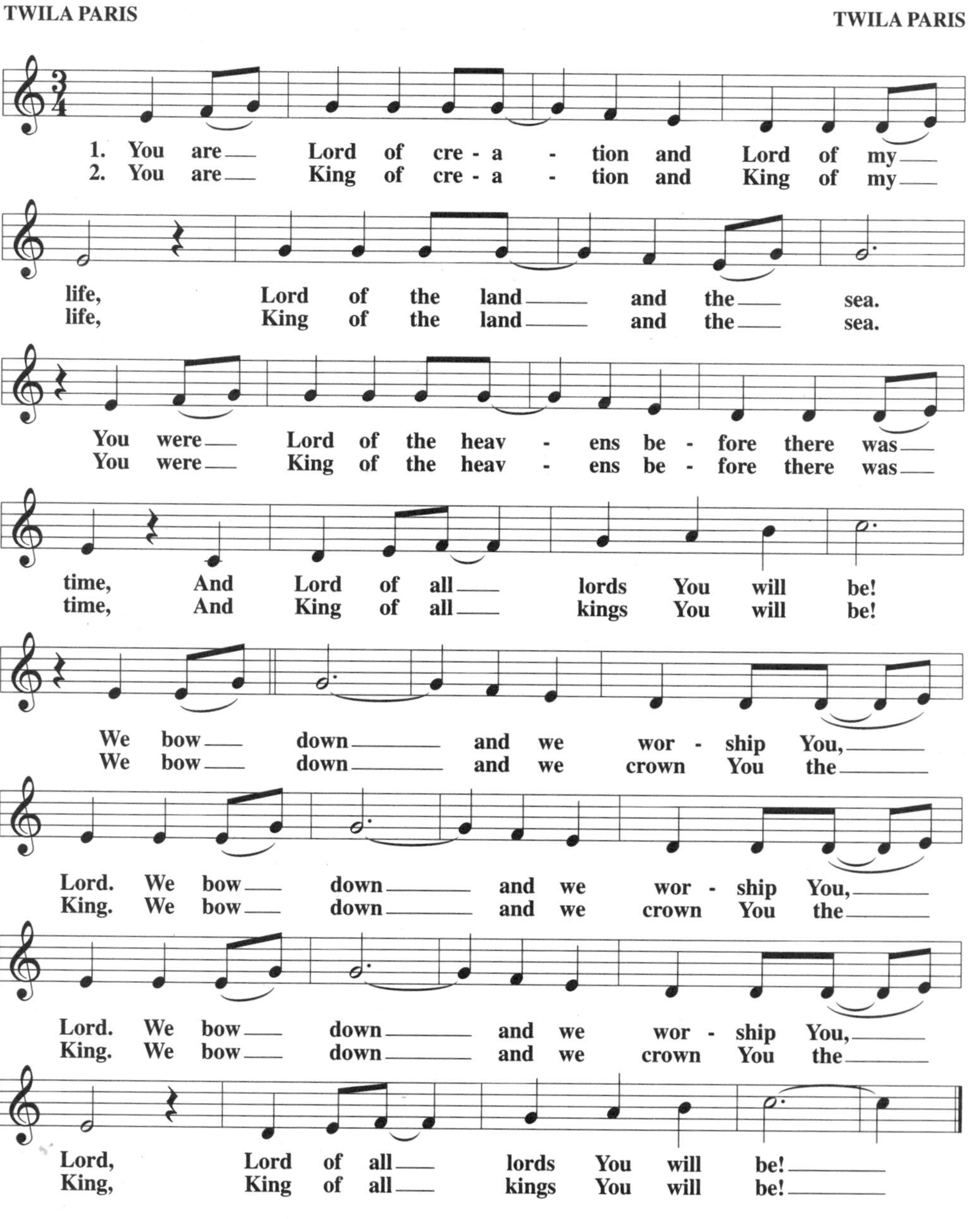

66 He Is Exalted

TWILA PARIS | TWILA PARIS

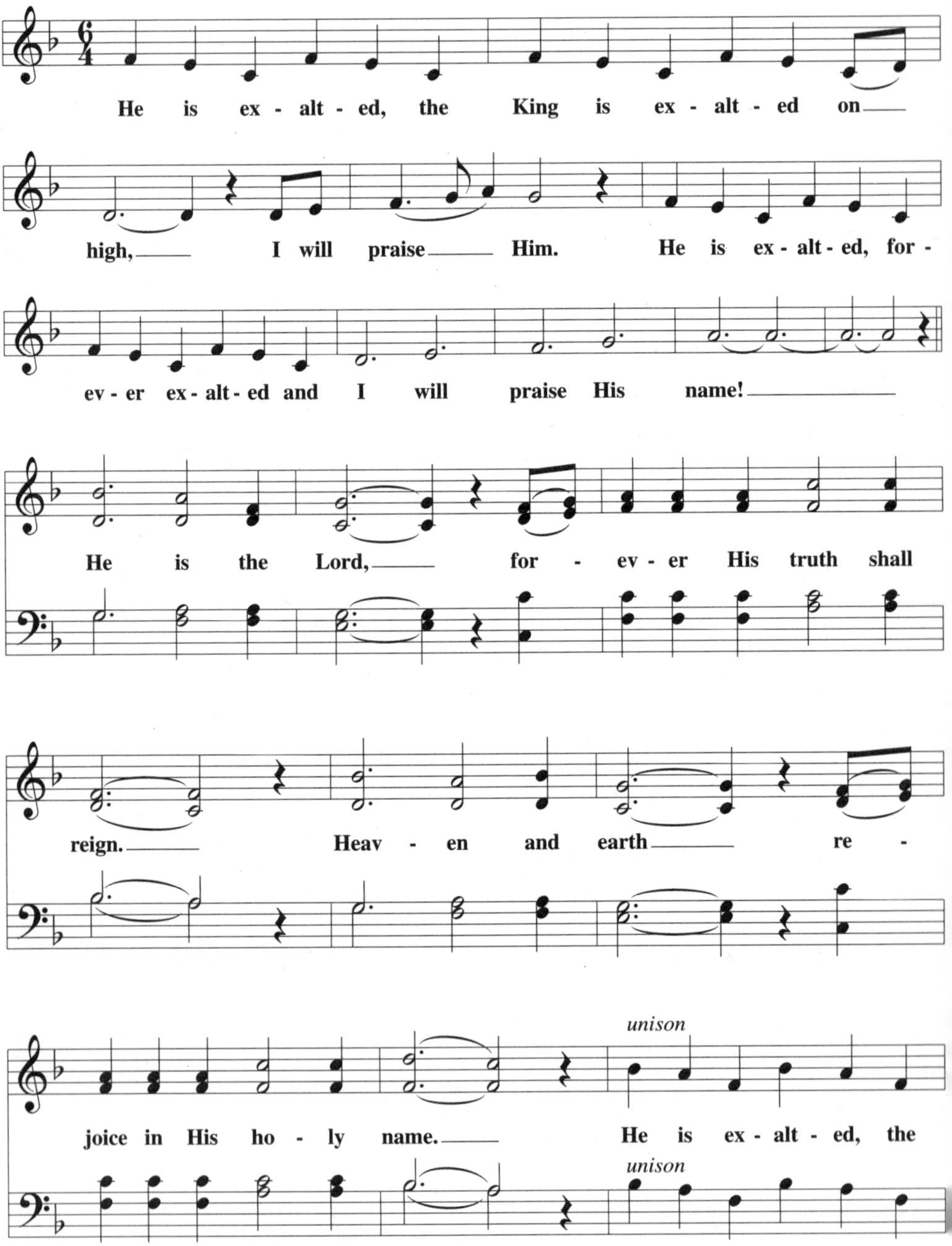
He is ex - alt - ed, the King is ex - alt - ed on
high, I will praise Him. He is ex - alt - ed, for -
ev - er ex - alt - ed and I will praise His name!
He is the Lord, for - ev - er His truth shall
reign. Heav - en and earth re -
joice in His ho - ly name. He is ex - alt - ed, the
unison
unison

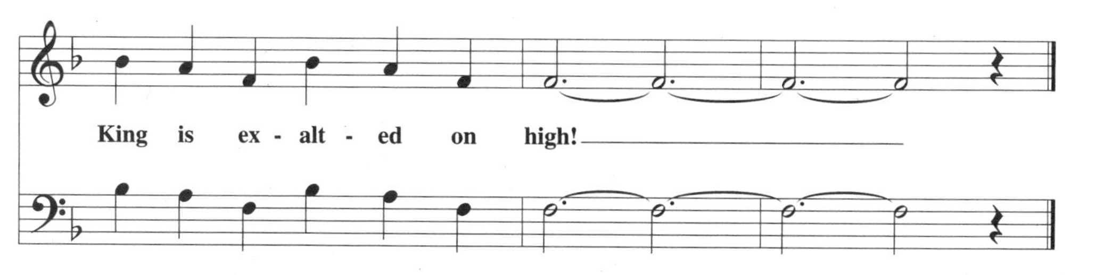

Lift High the Lord Our Banner

67

MACON DELAVAN

MACON DELAVAN

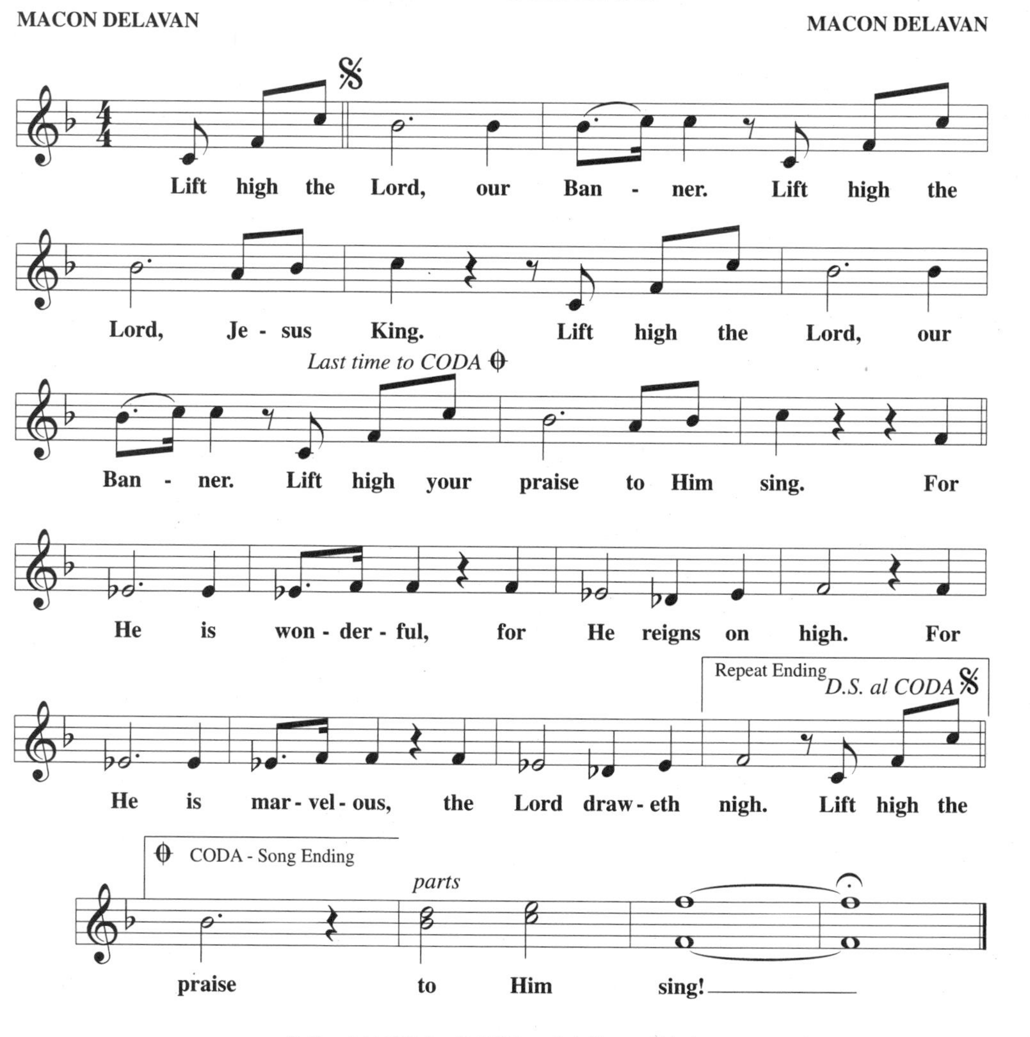

68 We Will Glorify

TWILA PARIS

TWILA PARIS

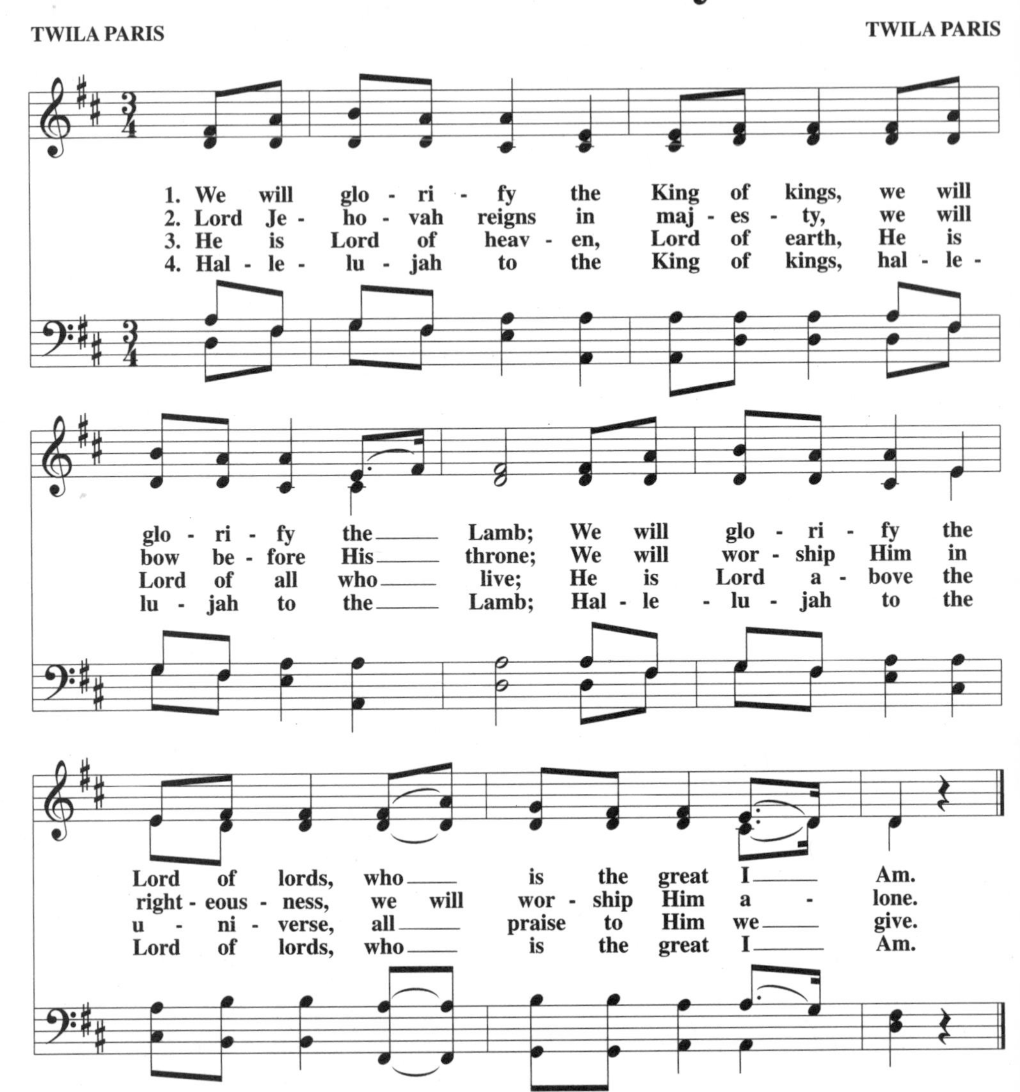

1. We will glo-ri-fy the King of kings, we will glo-ri-fy the Lamb; We will glo-ri-fy the Lord of lords, who is the great I Am.
2. Lord Je-ho-vah reigns in maj-es-ty, we will bow be-fore His throne; We will wor-ship Him in right-eous-ness, we will wor-ship Him a-lone.
3. He is Lord of heav-en, Lord of earth, He is Lord of all who live; He is Lord a-bove the u-ni-verse, all praise to Him we give.
4. Hal-le-lu-jah to the King of kings, hal-le-lu-jah to the Lamb; Hal-le-lu-jah to the Lord of lords, who is the great I Am.

69 A Perfect Heart

Words and Music by
DONY McGUIRE and REBA RAMBO

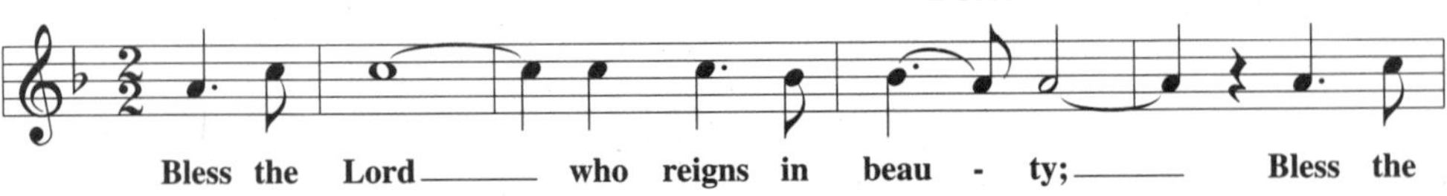

Bless the Lord who reigns in beau-ty; Bless the

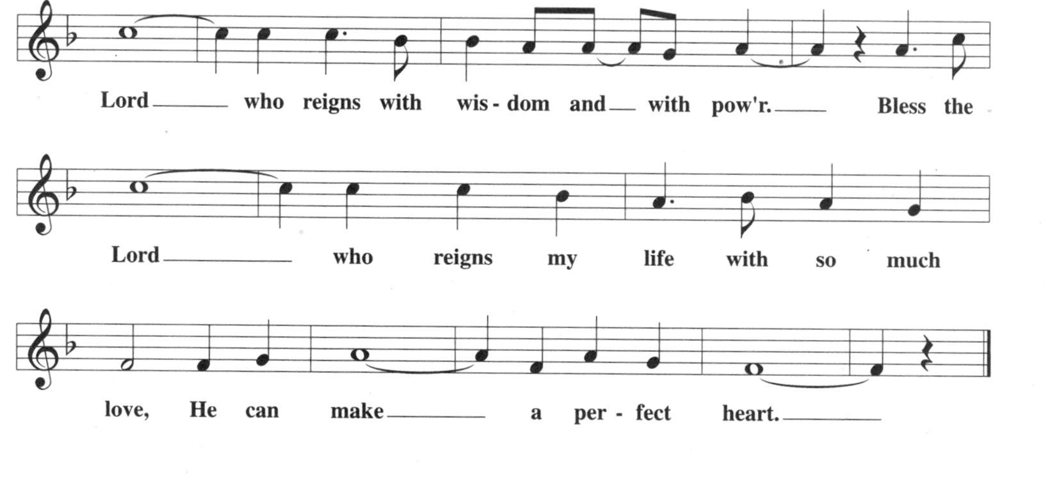

Lord ___ who reigns with wis-dom and ___ with pow'r. ___ Bless the

Lord ___ who reigns my life with so much

love, He can make ___ a per-fect heart. ___

Let There Be Glory and Honor and Praises

70

JAMES GREENELSH

ELIZABETH GREENELSH

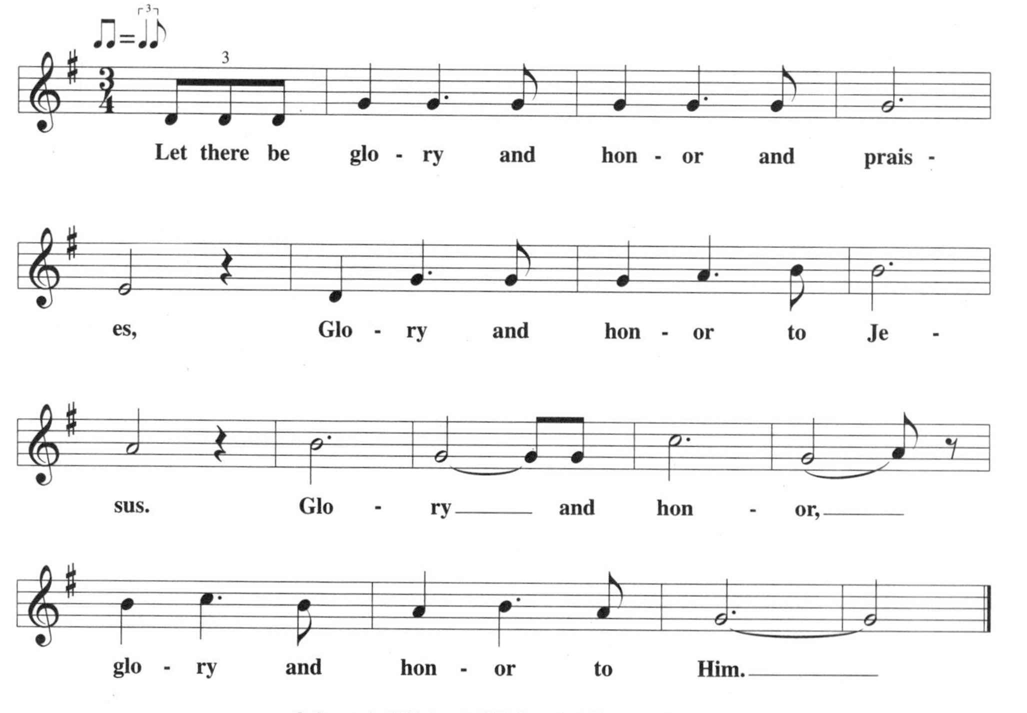

Let there be glo-ry and hon-or and prais-

es, Glo-ry and hon-or to Je-

sus. Glo-ry ___ and hon-or, ___

glo-ry and hon-or to Him. ___

71 When I Look into Your Holiness

Words and Music by
WAYNE and CATHY PERRIN

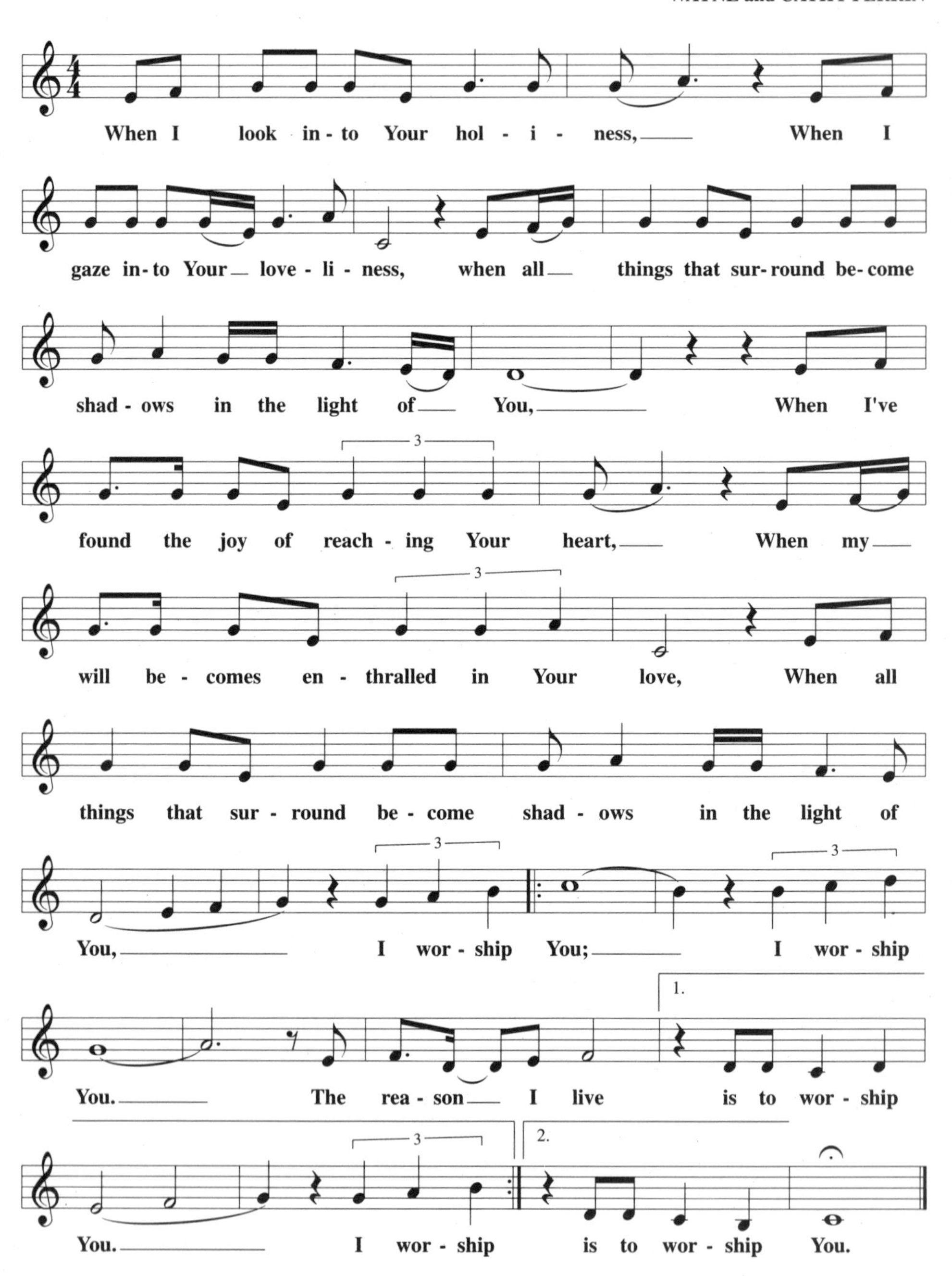

When I look in-to Your hol-i-ness, ____ When I gaze in-to Your ____ love-li-ness, when all ____ things that sur-round be-come shad-ows in the light of ____ You, ____ When I've found the joy of reach-ing Your heart, ____ When my ____ will be-comes en-thralled in Your love, When all things that sur-round be-come shad-ows in the light of You, ____ I wor-ship You; ____ I wor-ship You. ____

1. The rea-son ____ I live is to wor-ship You. ____

2. I wor-ship is to wor-ship You.

I Love You, Lord 72

LAURIE KLEIN   LAURIE KLEIN

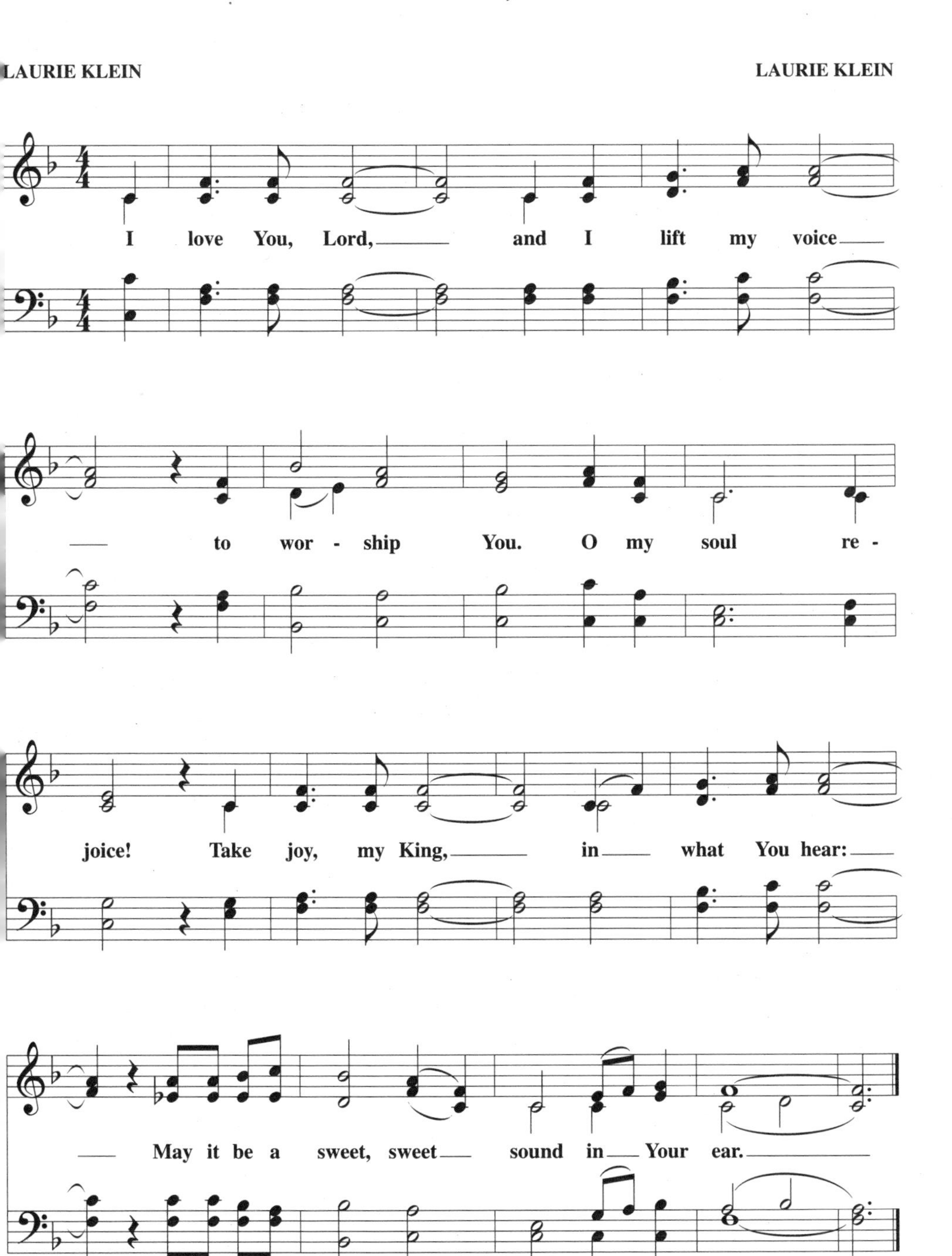

I love You, Lord, and I lift my voice to wor-ship You. O my soul re-joice! Take joy, my King, in what You hear: May it be a sweet, sweet sound in Your ear.

73 Majesty

JACK HAYFORD

JACK HAYFORD

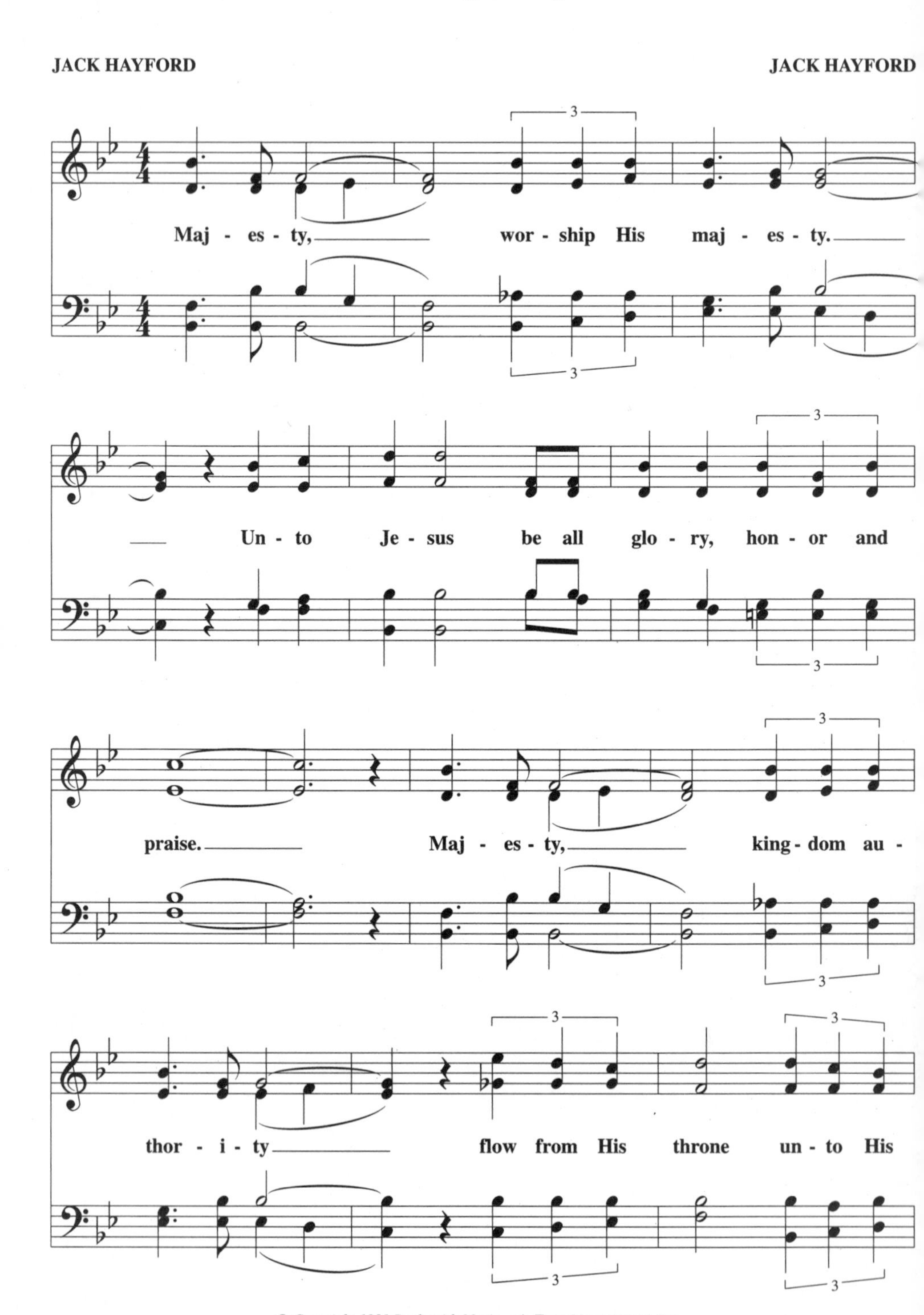

Maj - es - ty,_____ wor - ship His maj - es - ty._____

_____ Un - to Je - sus be all glo - ry, hon - or and

praise._____ Maj - es - ty,_____ king - dom au -

thor - i - ty_____ flow from His throne un - to His

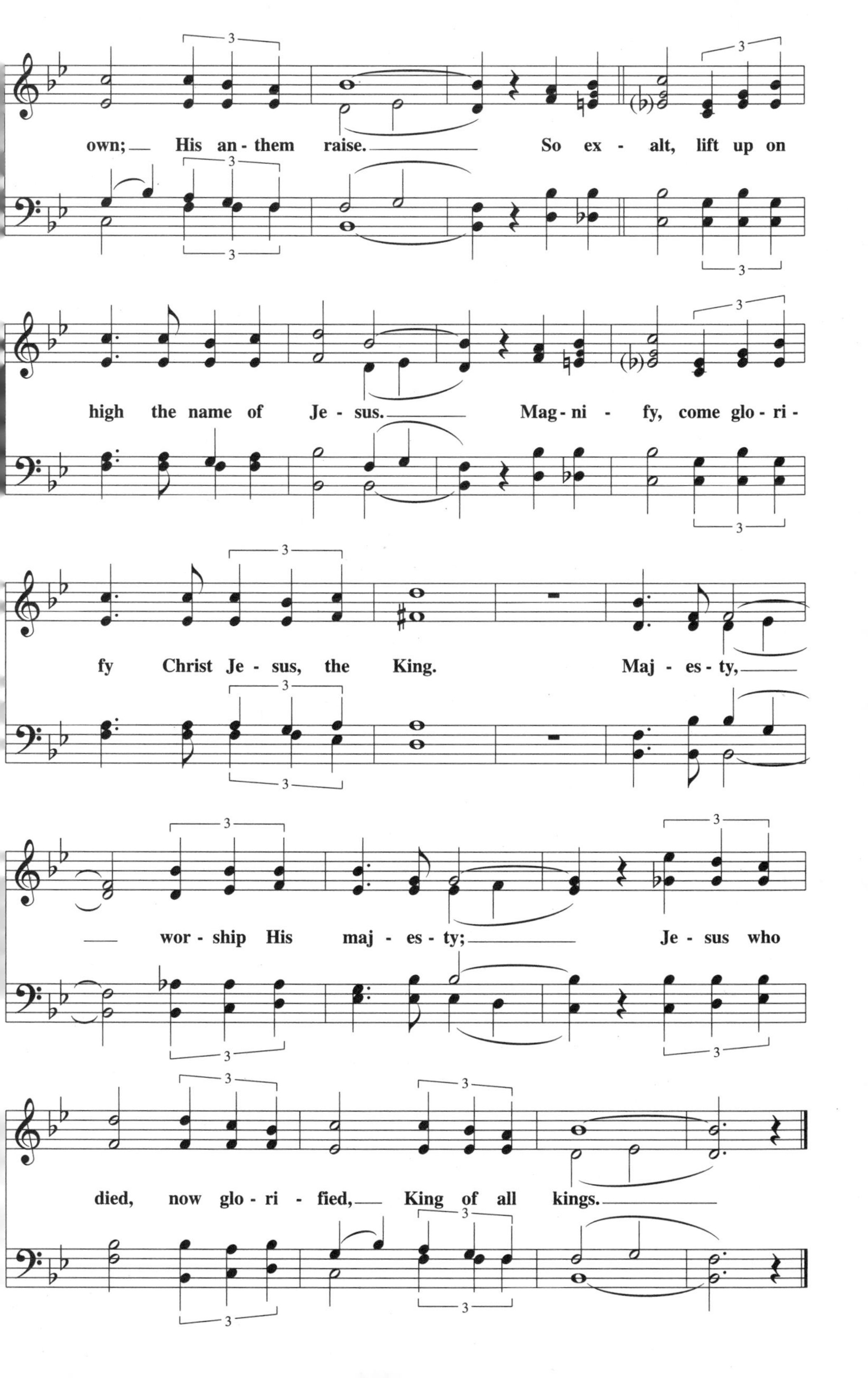
own; His an-them raise. So ex - alt, lift up on
high the name of Je - sus. Mag-ni - fy, come glo-ri -
fy Christ Je - sus, the King. Maj - es - ty,
wor - ship His maj - es - ty; Je - sus who
died, now glo - ri - fied, King of all kings.

74 Isn't He

JOHN WIMBER

JOHN WIMBER

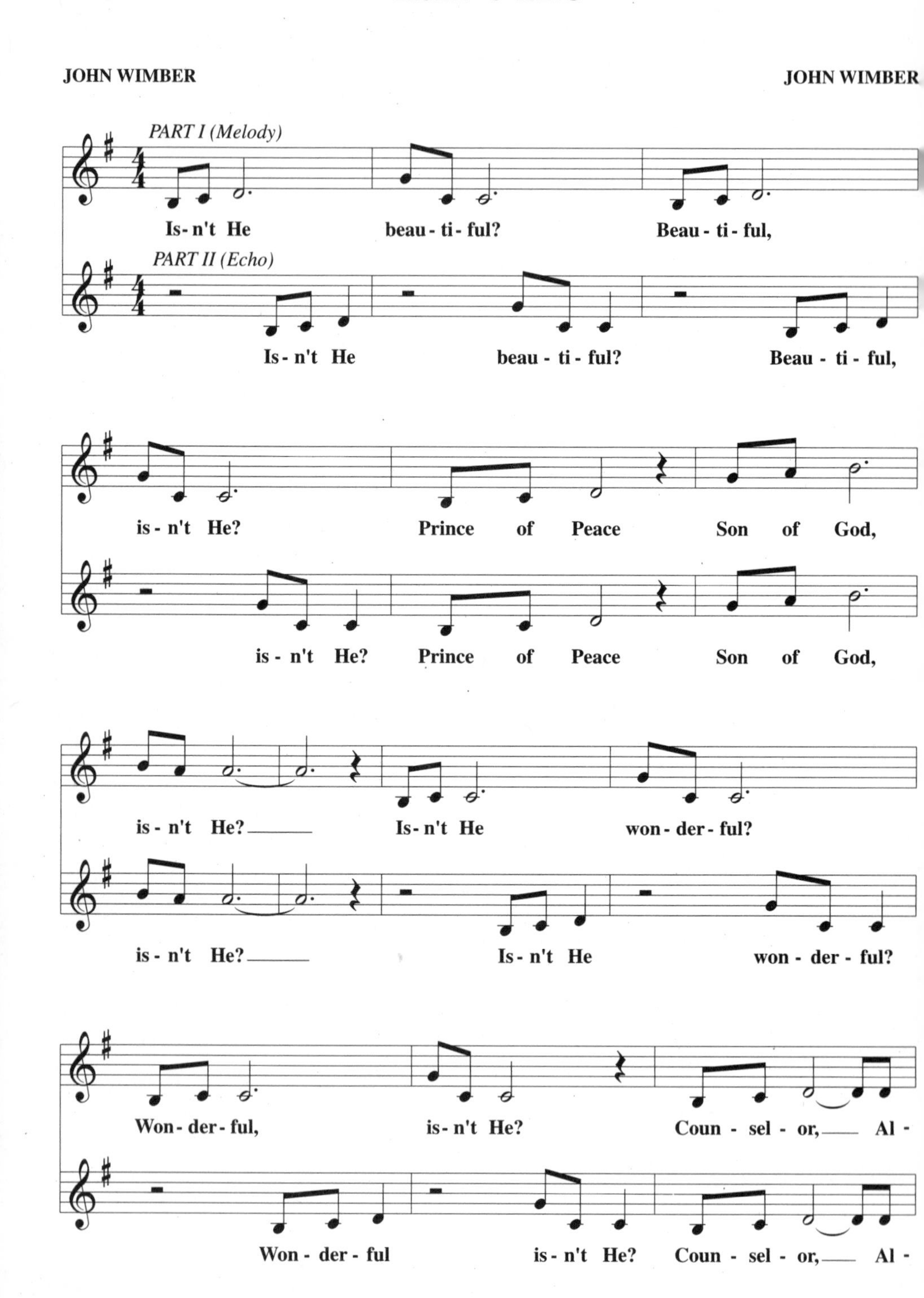

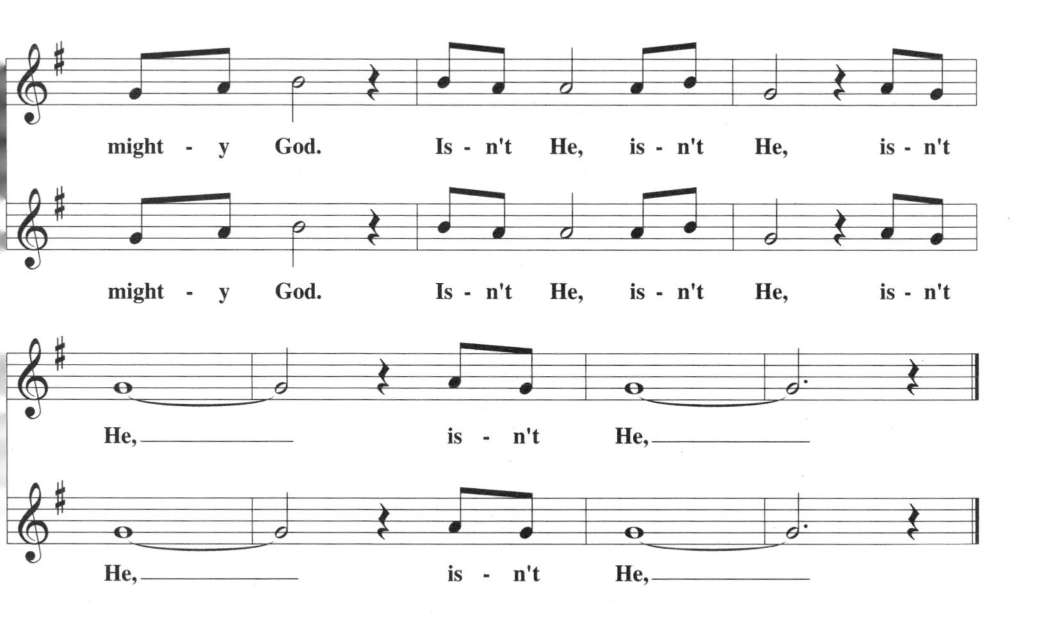

might - y God.   Is - n't He,   is - n't He,   is - n't

might - y God.   Is - n't He,   is - n't He,   is - n't

He, _____   is - n't   He, _____

He, _____   is - n't   He, _____

Emmanuel   75

BOB McGEE   **BOB McGEE**

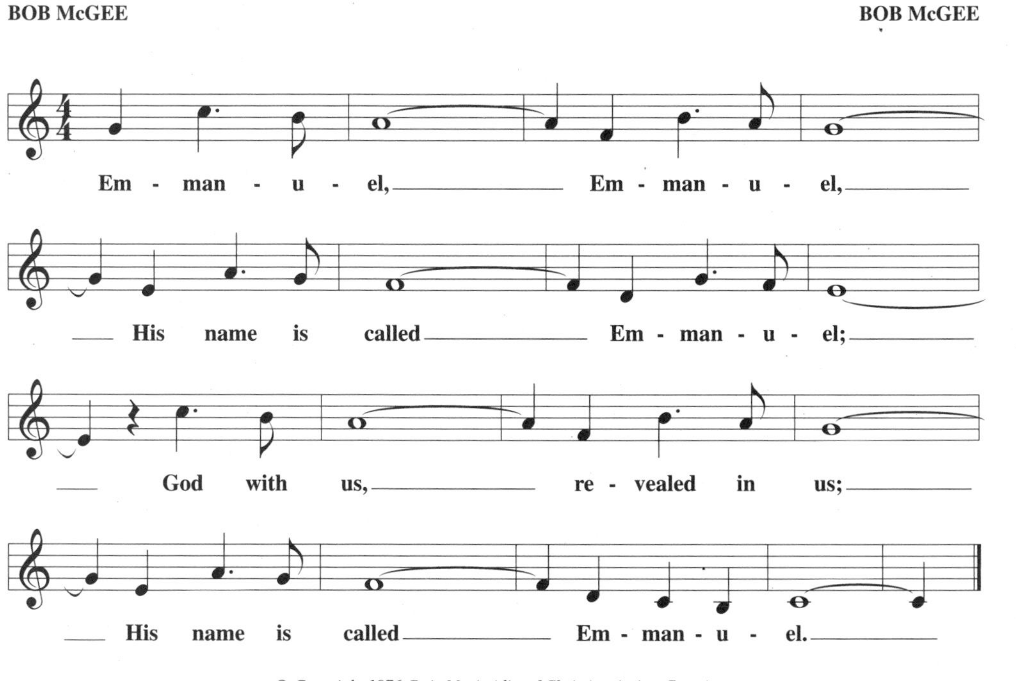

Em - man - u - el, _____ Em - man - u - el, _____

_____ His   name   is   called _____ Em - man - u - el; _____

_____ God   with   us, _____ re - vealed   in   us; _____

_____ His   name   is   called _____ Em - man - u - el.

76 Jesus, Name above All Names

NAIDA HEARN

NAIDA HEARN

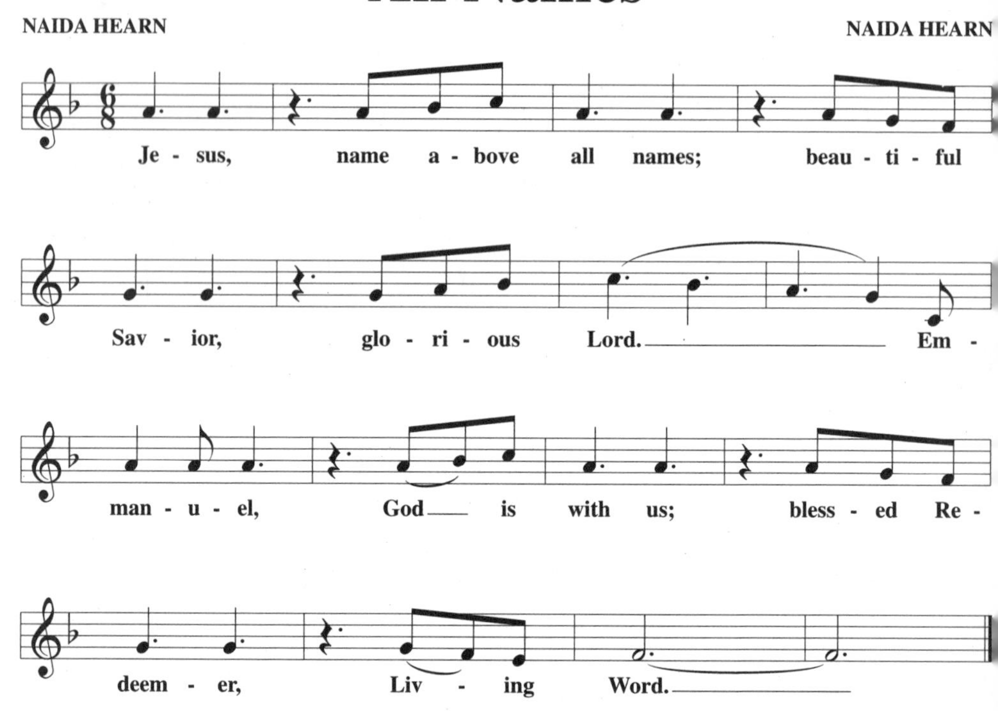

Je - sus, name a - bove all names; beau - ti - ful Sav - ior, glo - ri - ous Lord. Em - man - u - el, God is with us; bless - ed Re - deem - er, Liv - ing Word.

77 O Magnify the Lord

MICHAEL O'SHIELDS

MICHAEL O'SHIELDS

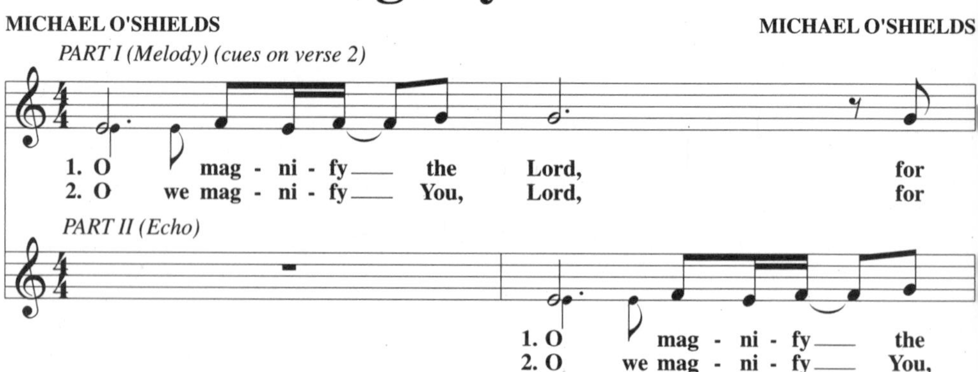

PART I (Melody) (cues on verse 2)

1. O mag - ni - fy the Lord, for
2. O we mag - ni - fy You, Lord, for

PART II (Echo)

1. O mag - ni - fy the
2. O we mag - ni - fy You,

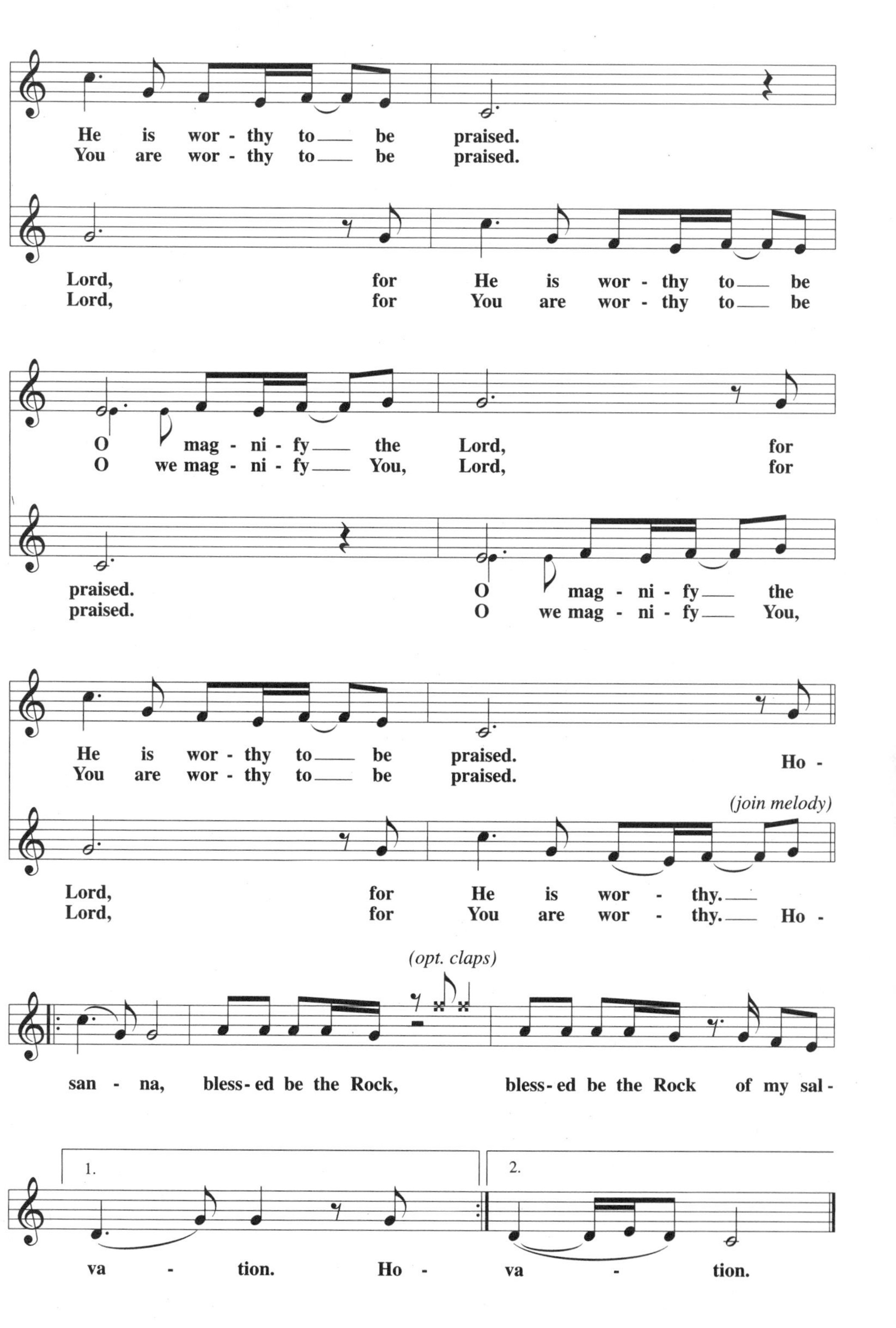

He is wor - thy to be praised.
You are wor - thy to be praised.
Lord, for He is wor - thy to be
Lord, for You are wor - thy to be
O mag - ni - fy the Lord, for
O we mag - ni - fy You, Lord, for
praised. O mag - ni - fy the
praised. O we mag - ni - fy You,
He is wor - thy to be praised. Ho -
You are wor - thy to be praised.
(join melody)
Lord, for He is wor - thy.
Lord, for You are wor - thy. Ho -
(opt. claps)
san - na, bless - ed be the Rock, bless - ed be the Rock of my sal -
1.
2.
va - tion. Ho - va - tion.

78   I Extol You

JENNIFER RANDOLPH   JENNIFER RANDOLPH

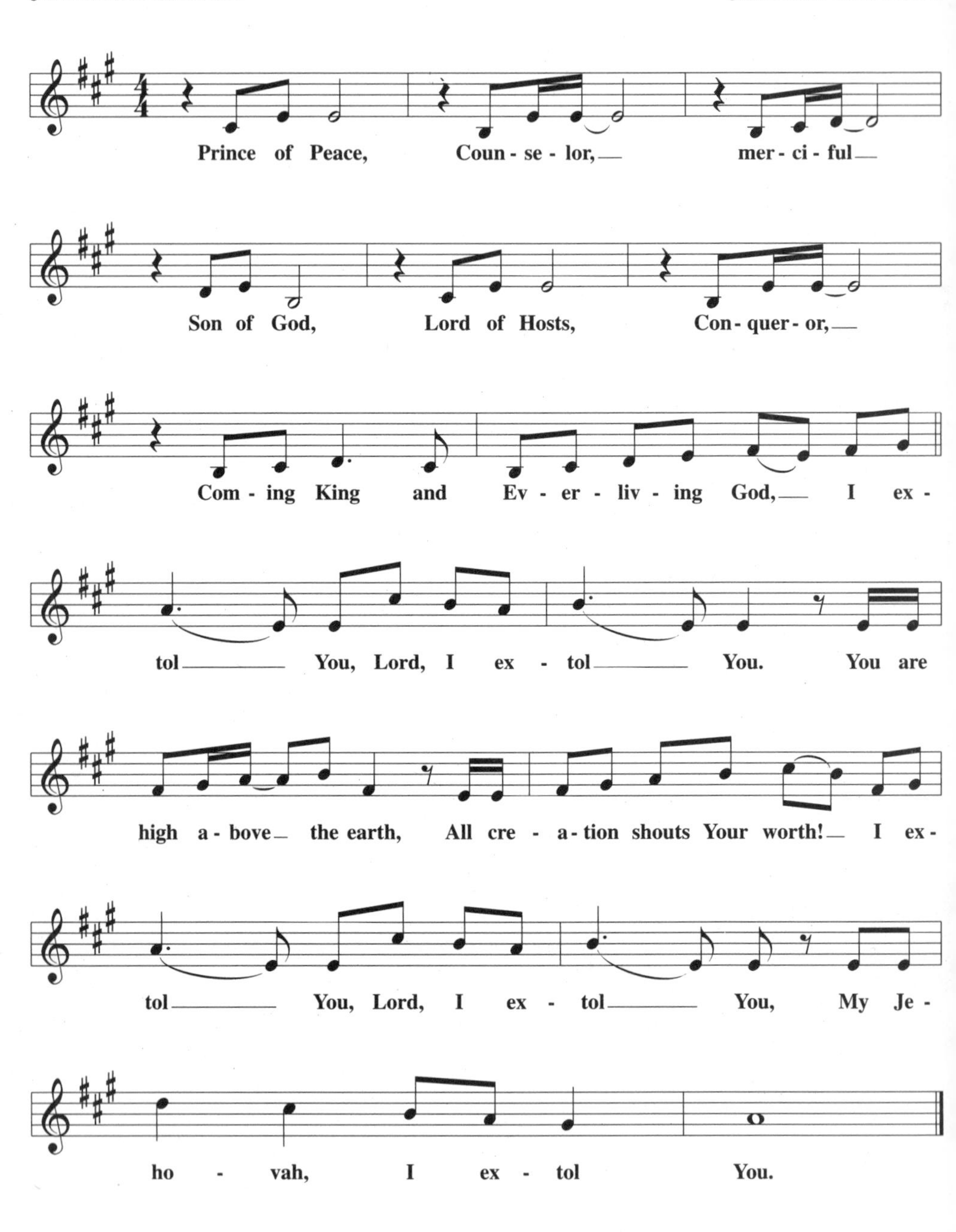

Prince of Peace, Coun-se-lor,— mer-ci-ful— Son of God, Lord of Hosts, Con-quer-or,— Com-ing King and Ev-er-liv-ing God,— I ex-tol——— You, Lord, I ex-tol——— You. You are high a-bove— the earth, All cre-a-tion shouts Your worth!— I ex-tol——— You, Lord, I ex-tol——— You, My Je-ho-vah, I ex-tol You.

No Other Name

79

ROBERT GAY

ROBERT GAY

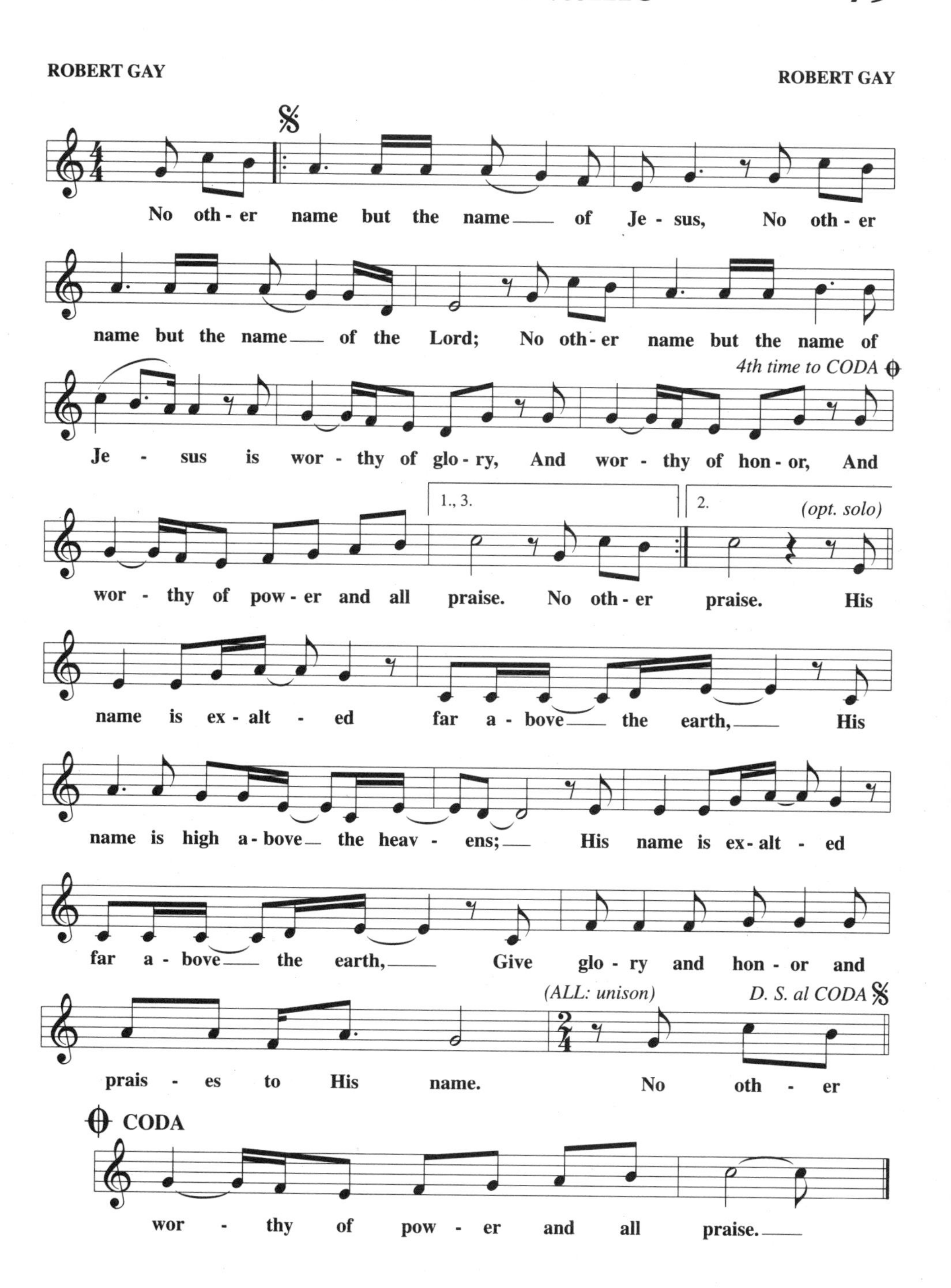

No oth-er name but the name of Je-sus, No oth-er name but the name of the Lord; No oth-er name but the name of

4th time to CODA

Je-sus is wor-thy of glo-ry, And wor-thy of hon-or, And

1., 3. wor-thy of pow-er and all praise. No oth-er

2. *(opt. solo)* praise. His

name is ex-alt-ed far a-bove the earth, His

name is high a-bove the heav-ens; His name is ex-alt-ed

far a-bove the earth, Give glo-ry and hon-or and

(ALL: unison) *D. S. al CODA* prais-es to His name. No oth-er

CODA wor-thy of pow-er and all praise.

80 Blessed Be the Name of the Lord

DON MOEN

DON MOEN

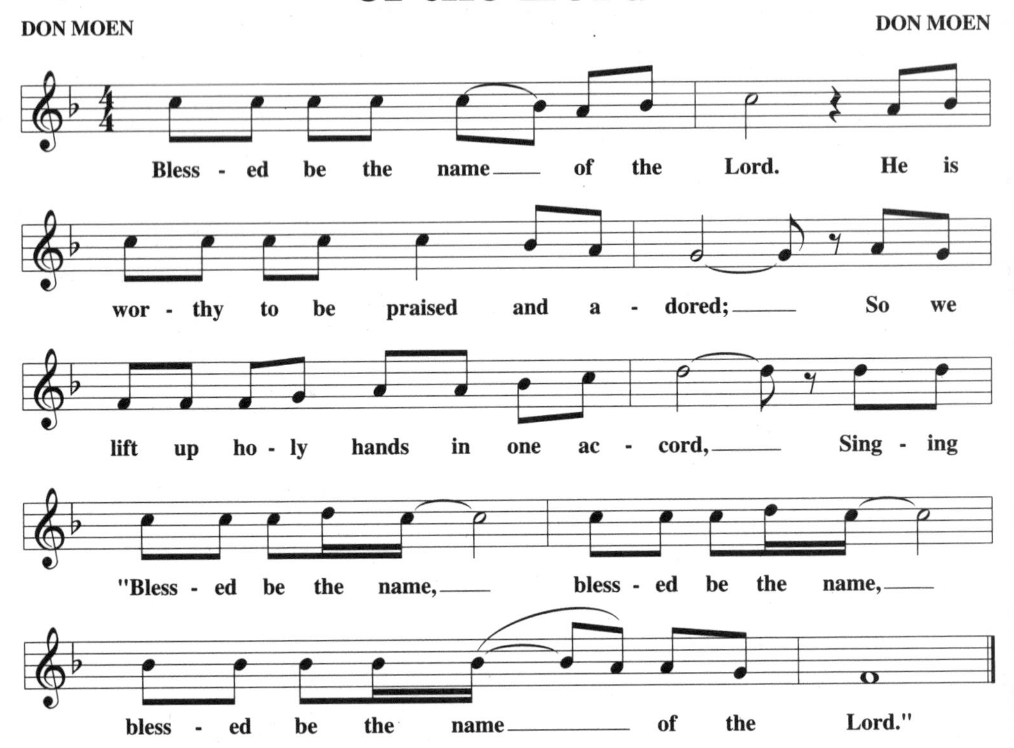

Bless - ed be the name of the Lord. He is wor - thy to be praised and a - dored;___ So we lift up ho - ly hands in one ac - cord,___ Sing - ing "Bless - ed be the name,___ bless - ed be the name,___ bless - ed be the name___ of the Lord."

81 Worthy, You Are Worthy

DON MOEN

DON MOEN

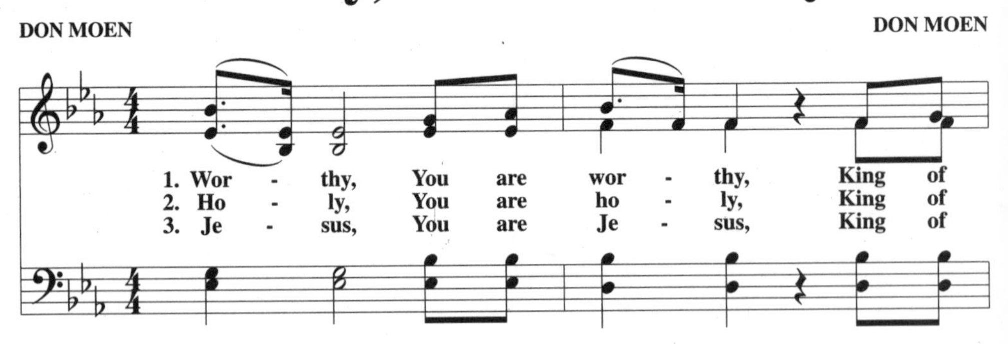

1. Wor - thy, You are wor - thy, King of
2. Ho - ly, You are ho - ly, King of
3. Je - sus, You are Je - sus, King of

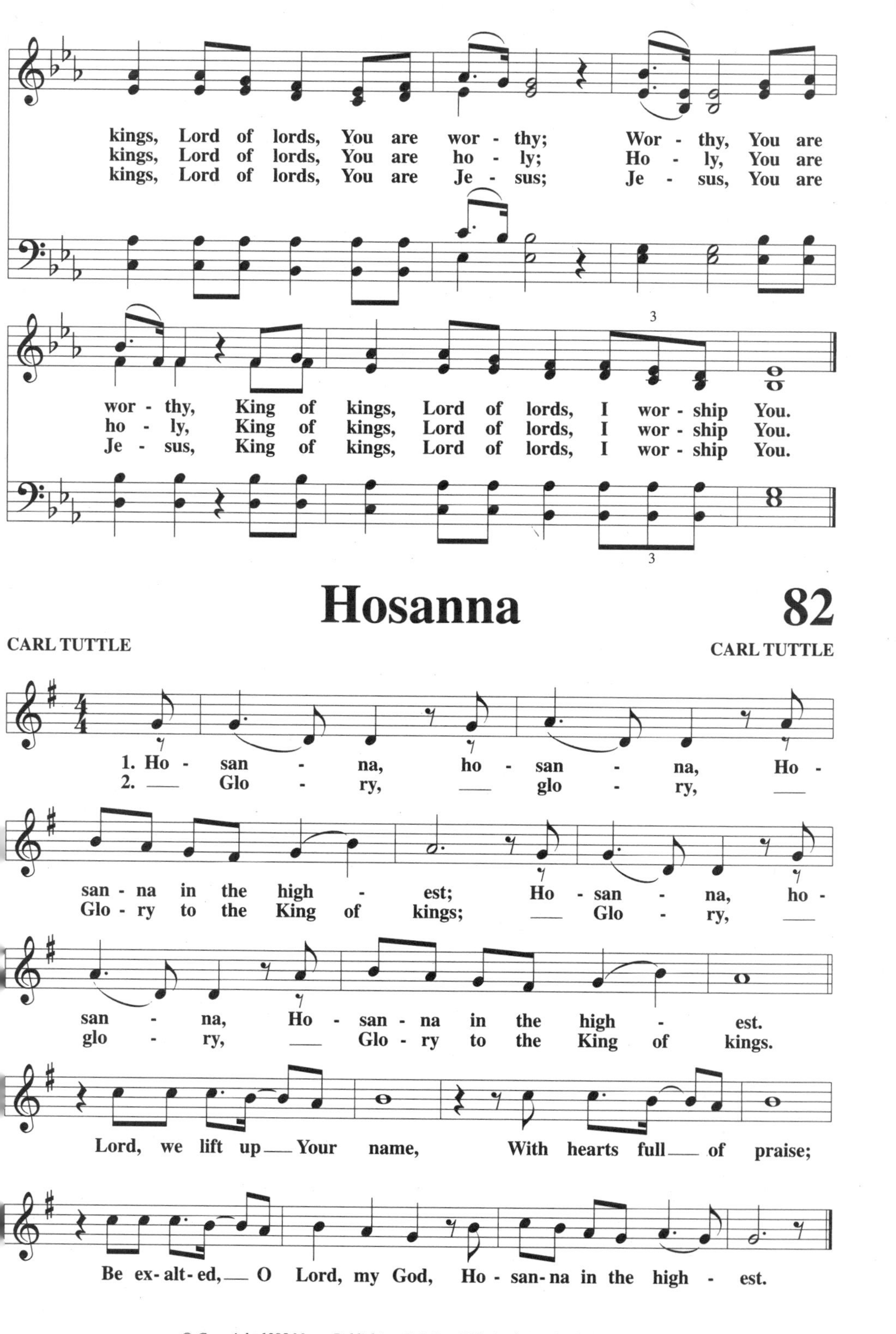

kings, Lord of lords, You are wor - thy; Wor - thy, You are
kings, Lord of lords, You are ho - ly; Ho - ly, You are
kings, Lord of lords, You are Je - sus; Je - sus, You are

wor - thy, King of kings, Lord of lords, I wor - ship You.
ho - ly, King of kings, Lord of lords, I wor - ship You.
Je - sus, King of kings, Lord of lords, I wor - ship You.

Hosanna 82

CARL TUTTLE
CARL TUTTLE

1. Ho - san - na, ho - san - na, Ho -
2. Glo - ry, glo - ry,

san - na in the high - est; Ho - san - na, ho -
Glo - ry to the King of kings; Glo - ry,

san - na, Ho - san - na in the high - est.
glo - ry, Glo - ry to the King of kings.

Lord, we lift up Your name, With hearts full of praise;

Be ex - alt - ed, O Lord, my God, Ho - san - na in the high - est.

83 Glory to the King

TOM McLAIN   TOM McLAIN

Glo - ry! Glo - ry! Glo - ry to the King!

Glo - ry! Glo - ry! Glo - ry to the King!

Who is the King of Glo - ry? King

Je - sus is His name. He is high and lift - ed up a -

bove the earth, And His name I will pro -

1. claim!   D.C. 2. claim!

Glo - ry! Glo - ry! Glo - ry to the King!

Glo - ry! Glo - ry! Glo - ry to the King!

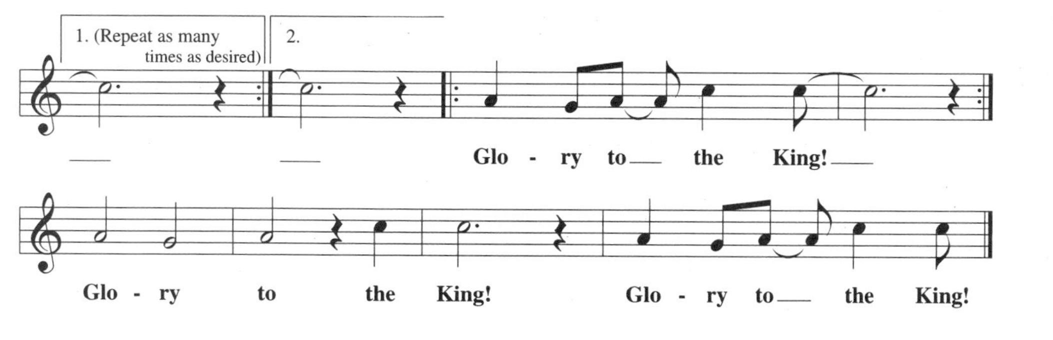

I Love to Praise Him

84

JENNIFER RANDOLPH

JENNIFER RANDOLPH

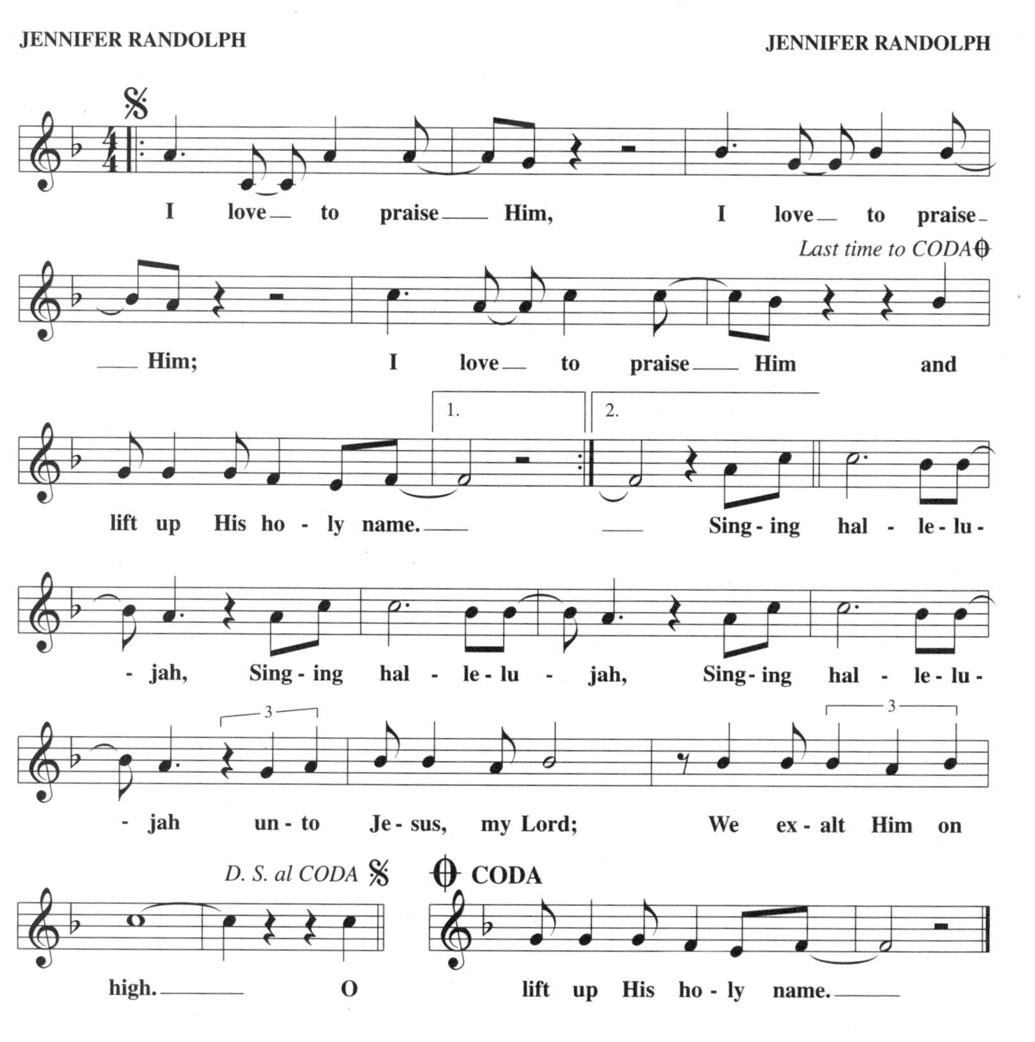

85 Holy Ground

CHRISTOPHER BEATTY

CHRISTOPHER BEATTY

1. This is ho - ly ground,_____ we're stand - ing on
2. These are ho - ly hands,_____ He's giv - en us

ho - ly ground,_____ For the Lord is pre - sent and
ho - ly hands,_____ He works through these hands,_____ and

where He is is ho - ly._____ This is
so these hands are ho - ly._____ These are

ho - ly ground,_____ we're stand - ing on ho - ly ground,_____
ho - ly hands,_____ He's giv - en us ho - ly hands,_____

For the Lord is pre - sent and
He works through these hands,_____ and

where He is is ho - ly._____
so these hands are ho - ly._____

86 Holy Ground

GERON DAVIS

GERON DAVIS

We__ are__ stand - ing_____ on ho - ly

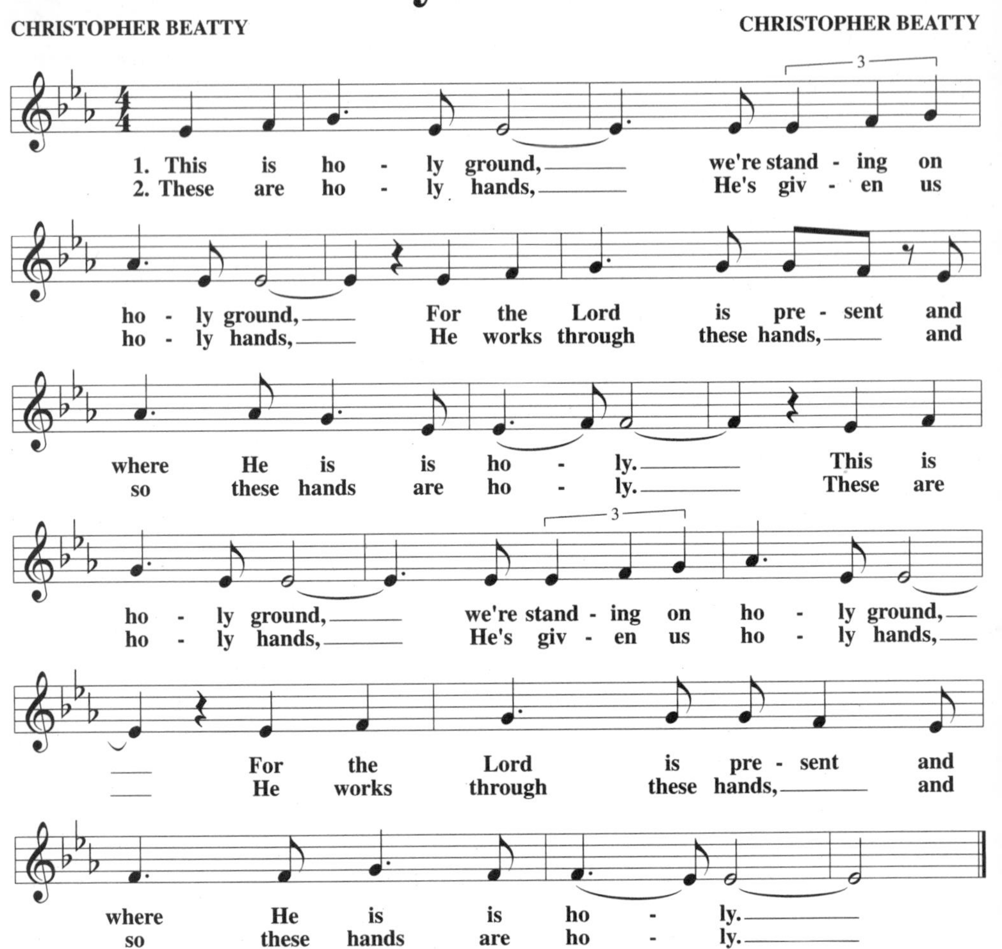

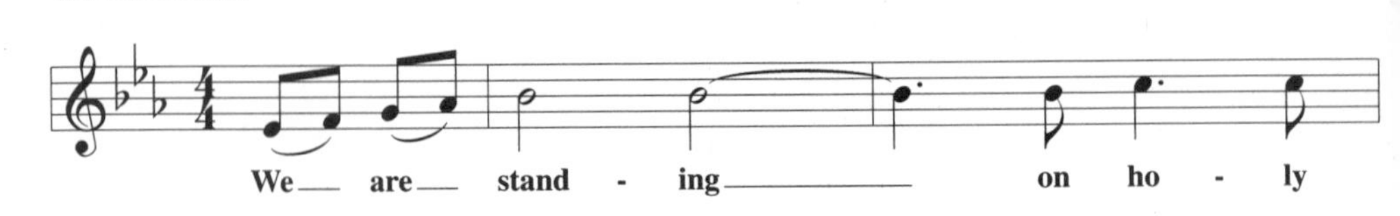

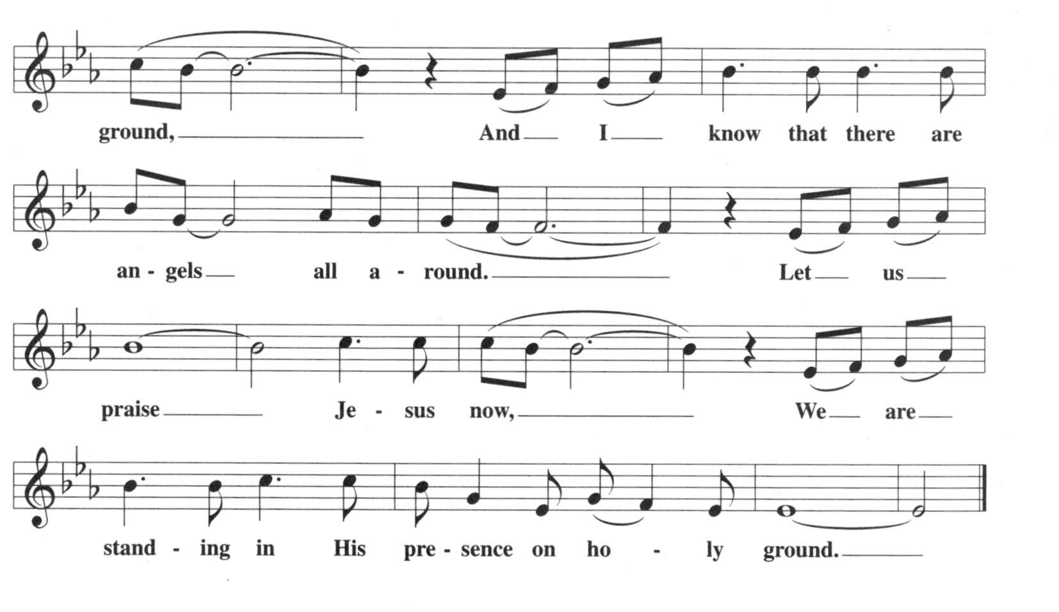

ground, _____ And _ I _ know that there are

an-gels _ all a-round. _____ Let us _

praise _____ Je-sus now, _____ We _ are _

stand-ing in His pre-sence on ho-ly ground. _

Praise the Name of Jesus 87

ROY HICKS, JR.   ROY HICKS, JR.

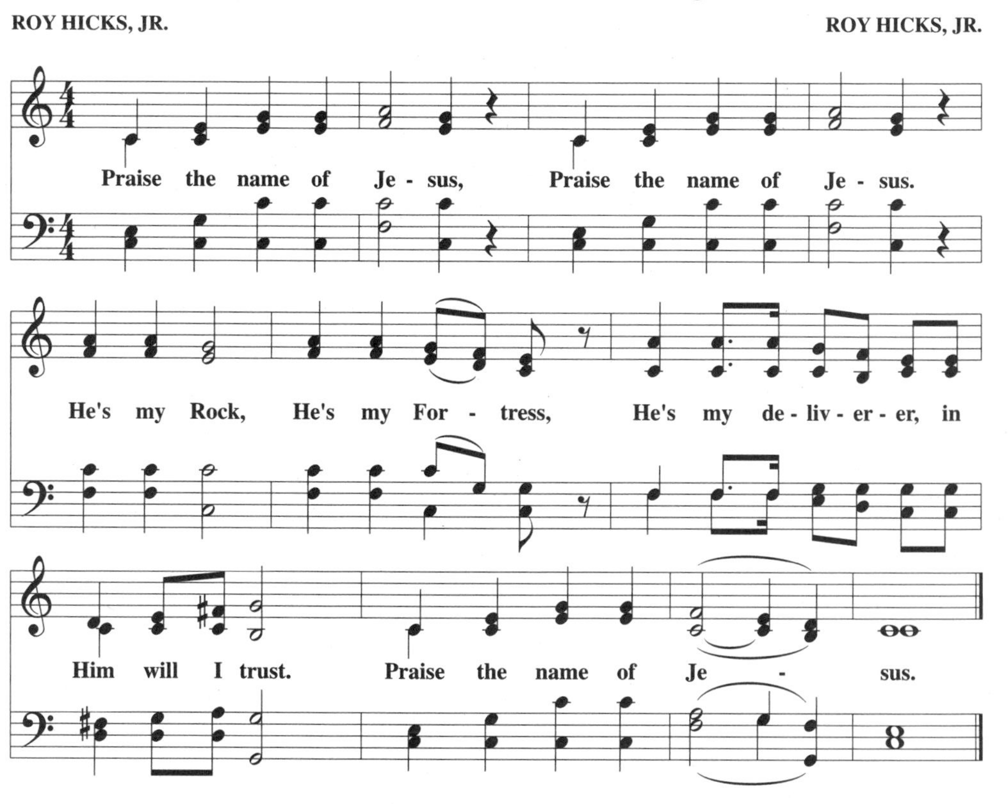

Praise the name of Je-sus, Praise the name of Je-sus.

He's my Rock, He's my For-tress, He's my de-liv-er-er, in

Him will I trust. Praise the name of Je - sus.

88 His Name Is Life

Words and Music by
CARMAN LICCIARDELLO and WILLIAM J. GAITHER

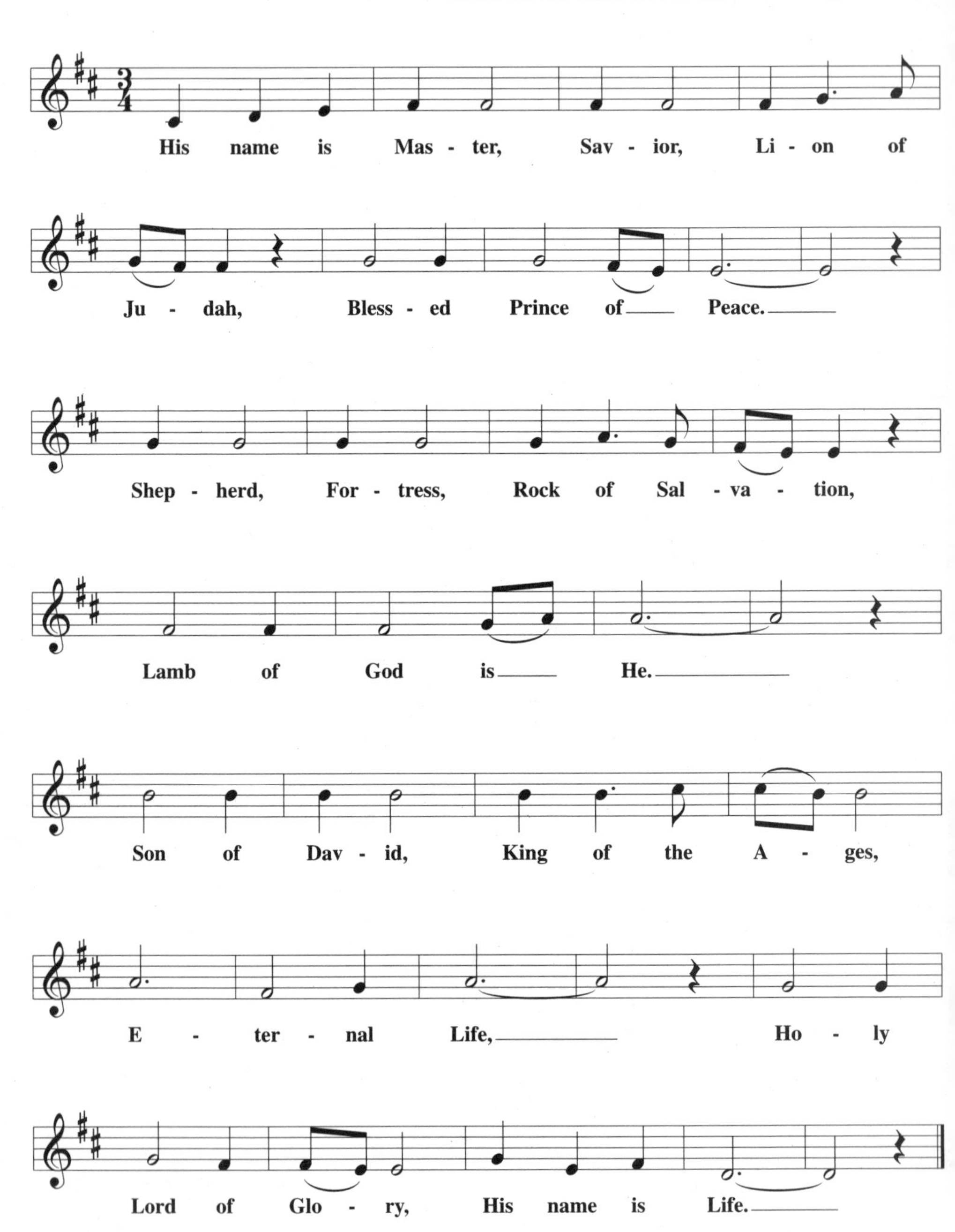

His name is Mas - ter, Sav - ior, Li - on of

Ju - dah, Bless - ed Prince of Peace.

Shep - herd, For - tress, Rock of Sal - va - tion,

Lamb of God is He.

Son of Dav - id, King of the A - ges,

E - ter - nal Life, Ho - ly

Lord of Glo - ry, His name is Life.

There's Something about That Name

89

Words and Music by
WILLIAM J. and GLORIA GAITHER

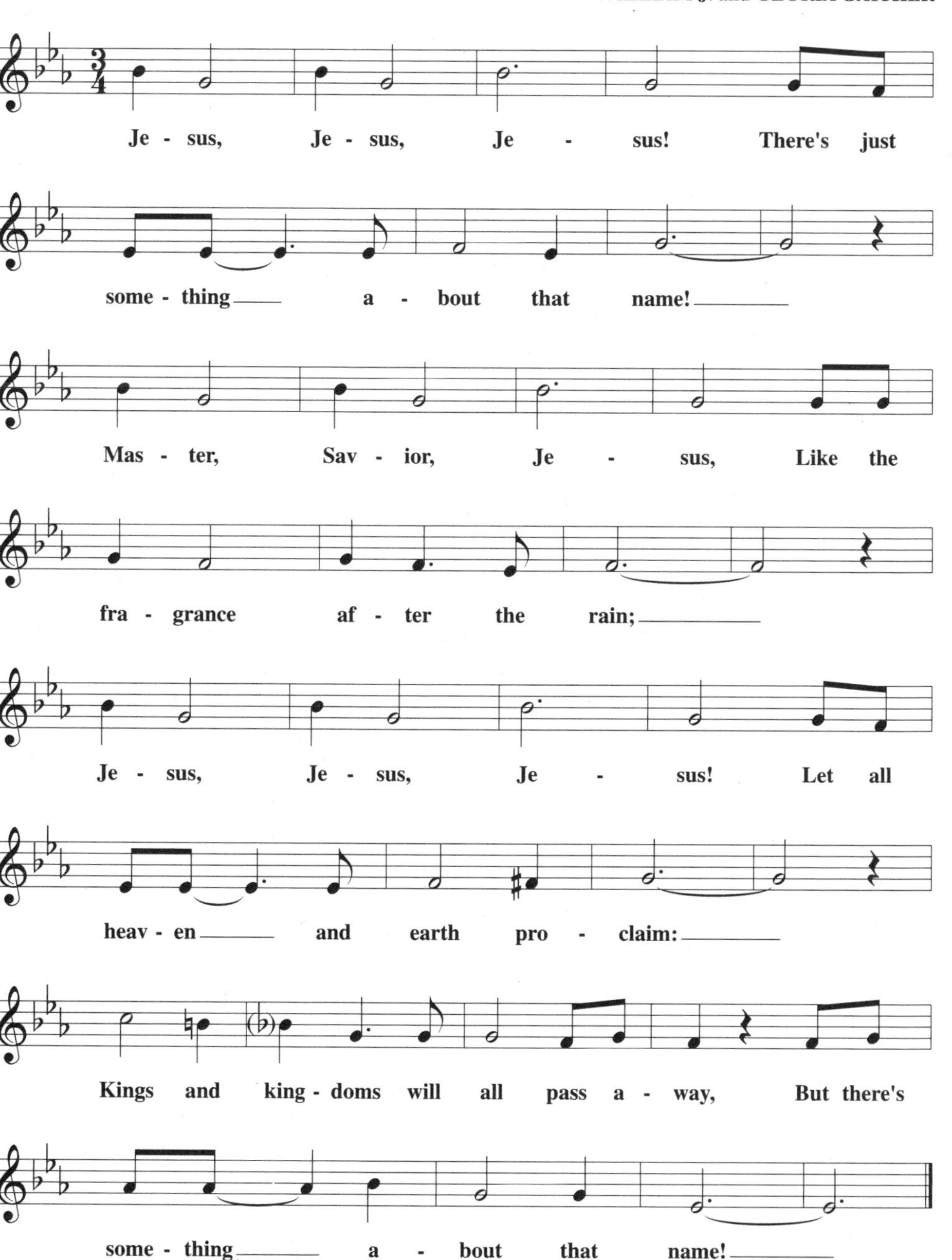

90 His Name Is Wonderful

AUDREY MIEIR   AUDREY MIEIR

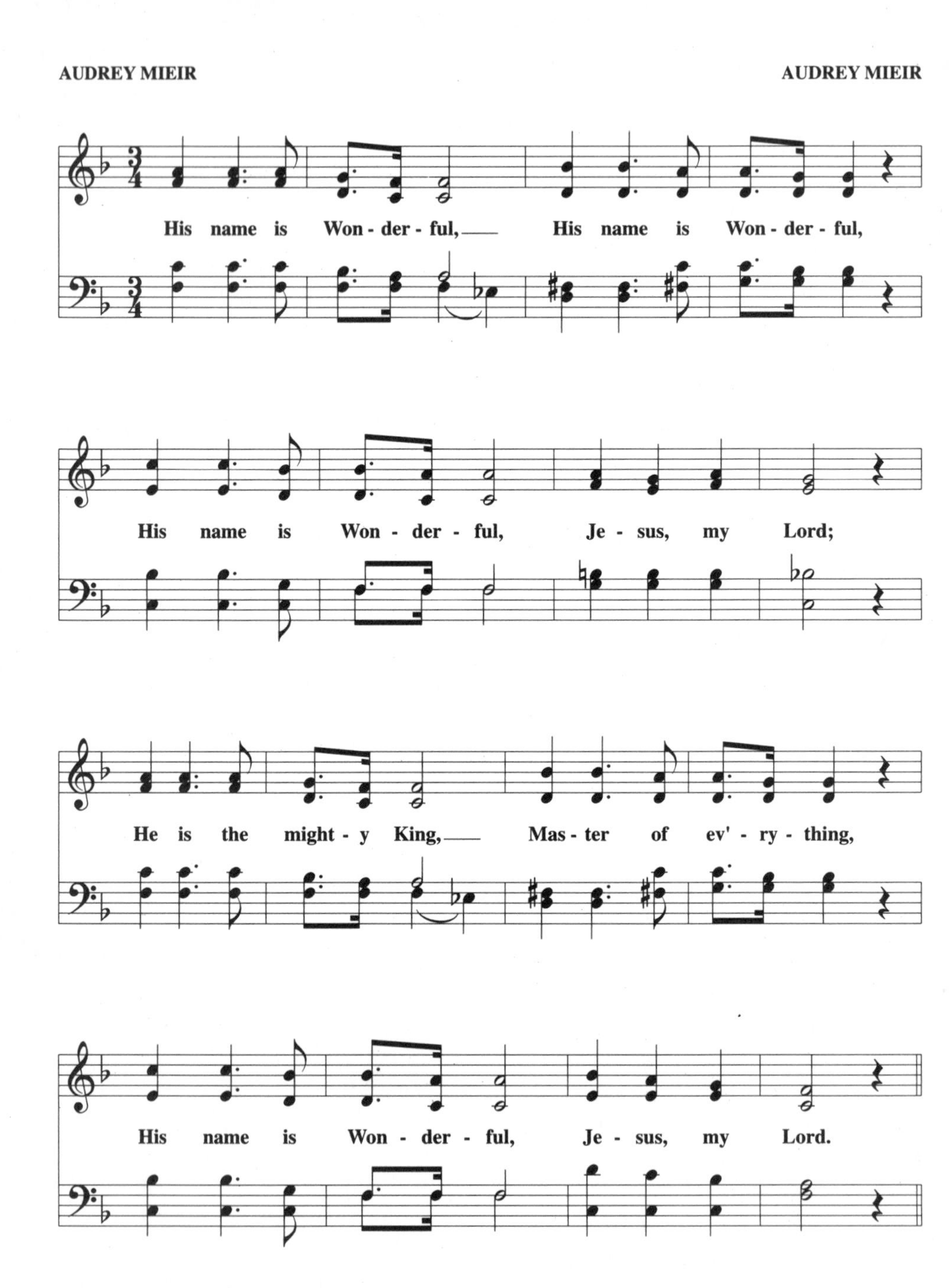

His name is Won-der-ful,— His name is Won-der-ful,

His name is Won-der-ful, Je-sus, my Lord;

He is the might-y King,— Mas-ter of ev'-ry-thing,

His name is Won-der-ful, Je-sus, my Lord.

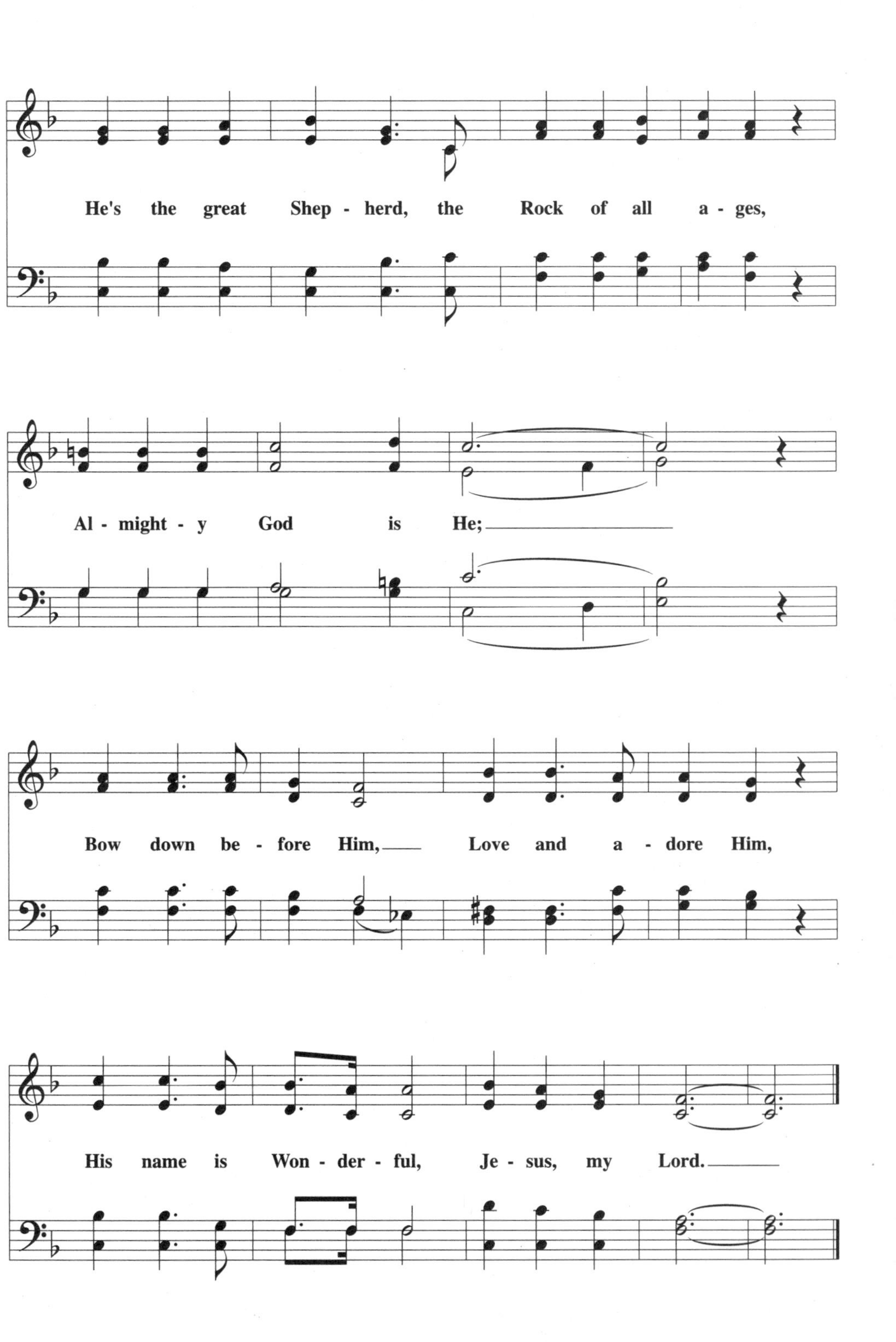
He's the great Shep - herd, the Rock of all a - ges,
Al - might - y God is He;
Bow down be - fore Him, Love and a - dore Him,
His name is Won - der - ful, Je - sus, my Lord.

91 Holy Is the Lord

Words and Music by
STEVE HOLCOMB
Arranged by Tom Fettke

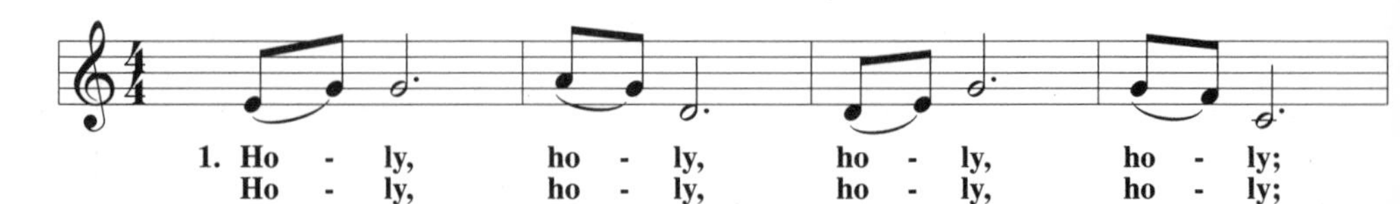

1. Ho - ly, ho - ly, ho - ly, ho - ly;
Ho - ly, ho - ly, ho - ly, ho - ly;

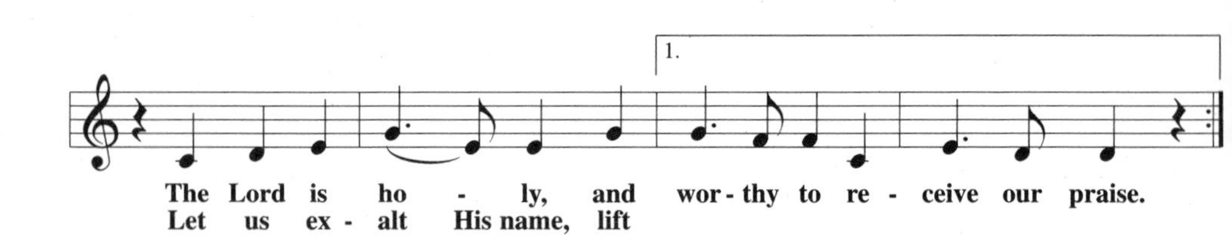

The Lord is ho - ly, and wor - thy to re - ceive our praise.
Let us ex - alt His name, lift

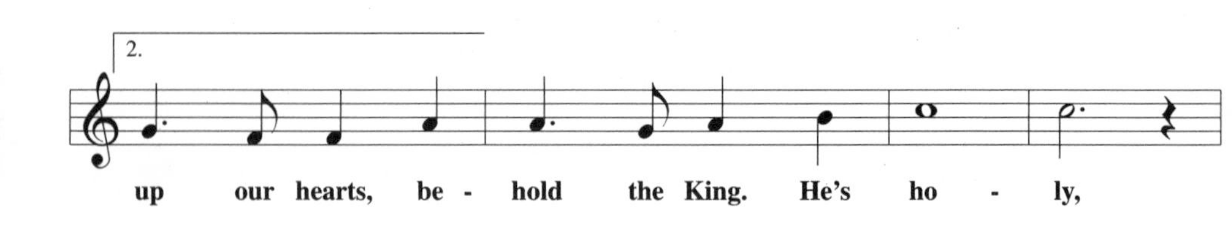

up our hearts, be - hold the King. He's ho - ly,

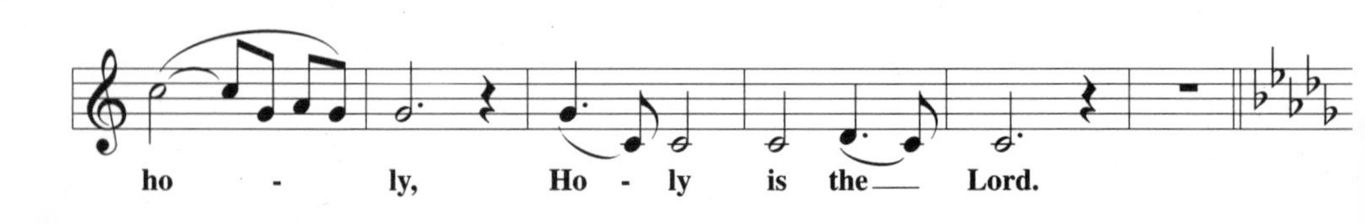

ho - ly, Ho - ly is the___ Lord.

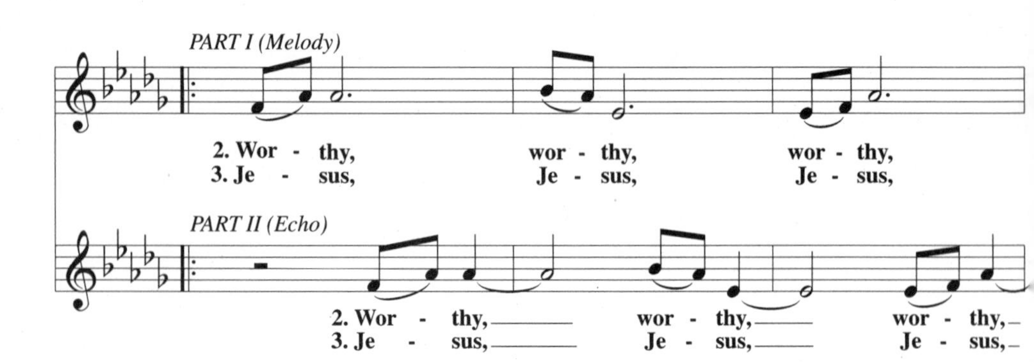

PART I (Melody)

2. Wor - thy, wor - thy, wor - thy,
3. Je - sus, Je - sus, Je - sus,

PART II (Echo)

2. Wor - thy,___ wor - thy,___ wor - thy,
3. Je - sus,___ Je - sus,___ Je - sus,

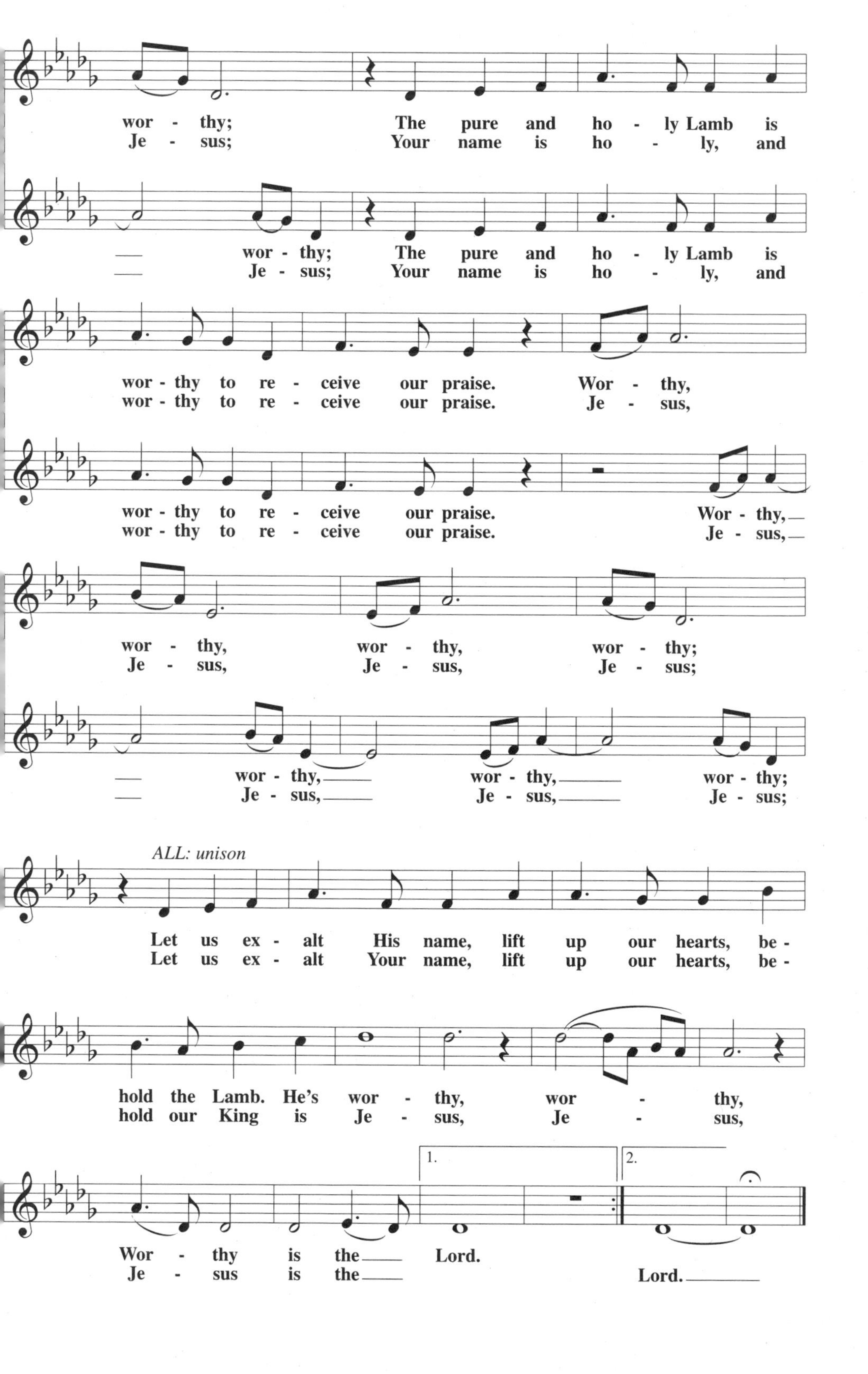

wor - thy; The pure and ho - ly Lamb is
Je - sus; Your name is ho - ly, and

— wor - thy; The pure and ho - ly Lamb is
— Je - sus; Your name is ho - ly, and

wor - thy to re - ceive our praise. Wor - thy,
wor - thy to re - ceive our praise. Je - sus,

wor - thy to re - ceive our praise. Wor - thy,—
wor - thy to re - ceive our praise. Je - sus,—

wor - thy, wor - thy, wor - thy;
Je - sus, Je - sus, Je - sus;

— wor - thy,—— wor - thy,—— wor - thy;
— Je - sus,—— Je - sus,—— Je - sus;

ALL: unison

Let us ex - alt His name, lift up our hearts, be -
Let us ex - alt Your name, lift up our hearts, be -

hold the Lamb. He's wor - thy, wor - thy,
hold our King is Je - sus, Je - sus,

1.
Wor - thy is the—— Lord.
Je - sus is the—— Lord.

2.
Lord.——

92 There Is No Other Name

DAVE BELL

DAVE BELL

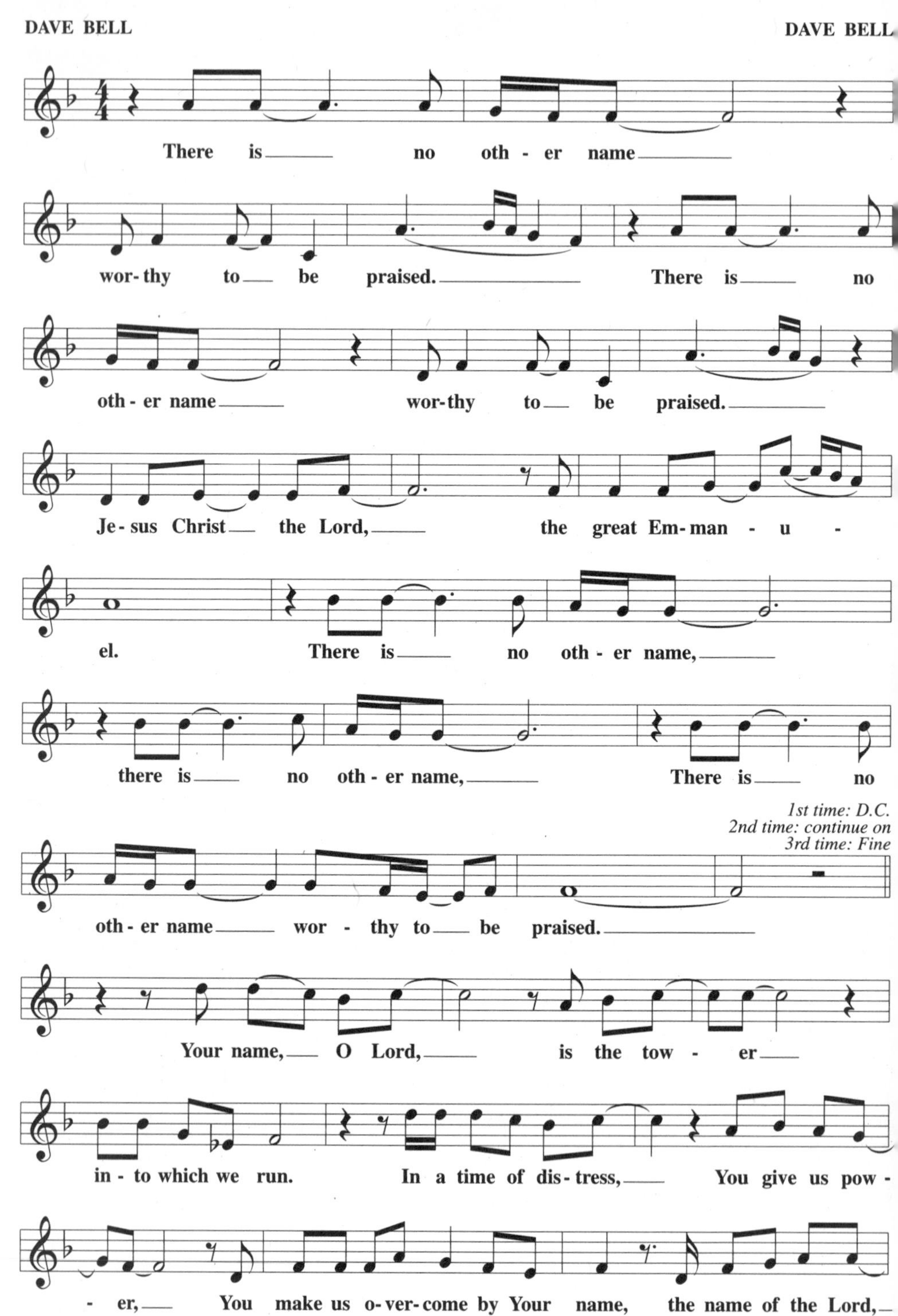

1st time: D.C.
2nd time: continue on
3rd time: Fine

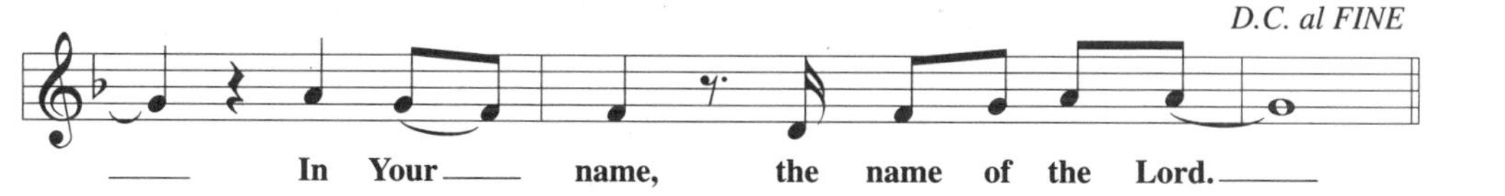

D.C. al FINE

In Your name, the name of the Lord.

Sing Hallelujah

93

LINDA STASSEN

LINDA STASSEN

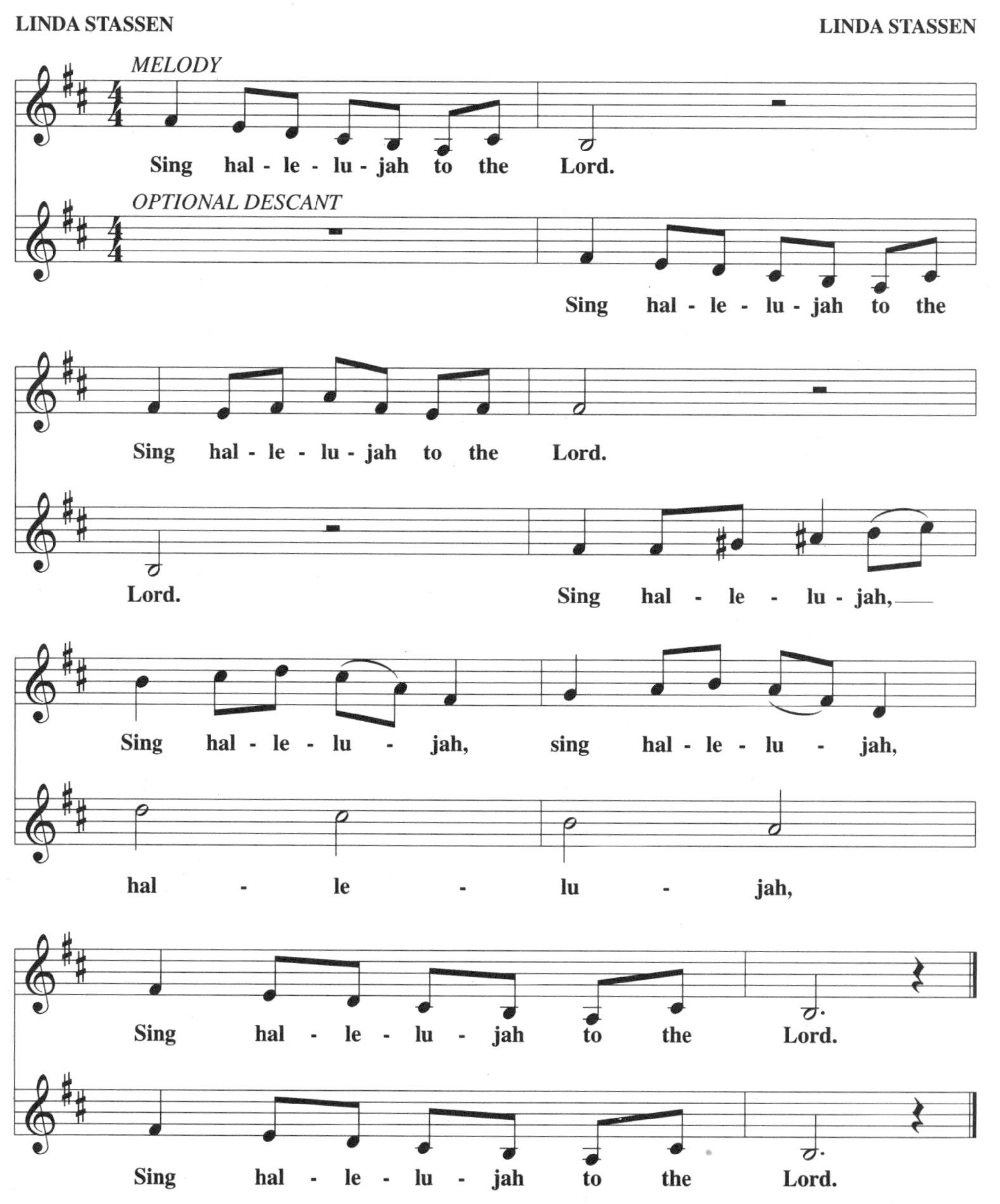

MELODY

Sing hal - le - lu - jah to the Lord.

OPTIONAL DESCANT

Sing hal - le - lu - jah to the

Sing hal - le - lu - jah to the Lord.

Lord. Sing hal - le - lu - jah,—

Sing hal - le - lu - jah, sing hal - le - lu - jah,

hal - le - lu - jah,

Sing hal - le - lu - jah to the Lord.

Sing hal - le - lu - jah to the Lord.

94 King of Kings

SOPHIE CONTY and NAOMI BATYA

ANCIENT HEBREW FOLKSONG

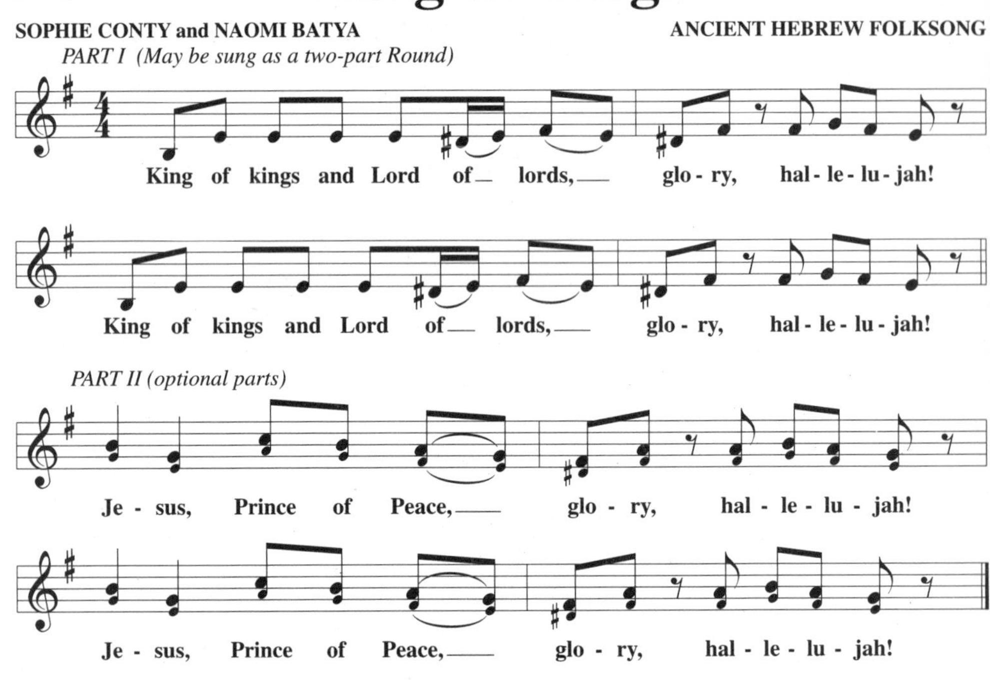

PART I (May be sung as a two-part Round)

King of kings and Lord of lords, glo - ry, hal - le - lu - jah!

King of kings and Lord of lords, glo - ry, hal - le - lu - jah!

PART II (optional parts)

Je - sus, Prince of Peace, glo - ry, hal - le - lu - jah!

Je - sus, Prince of Peace, glo - ry, hal - le - lu - jah!

95 Holy Is He

CLAIRE CLONINGER

DAVID T. CLYDESDALE

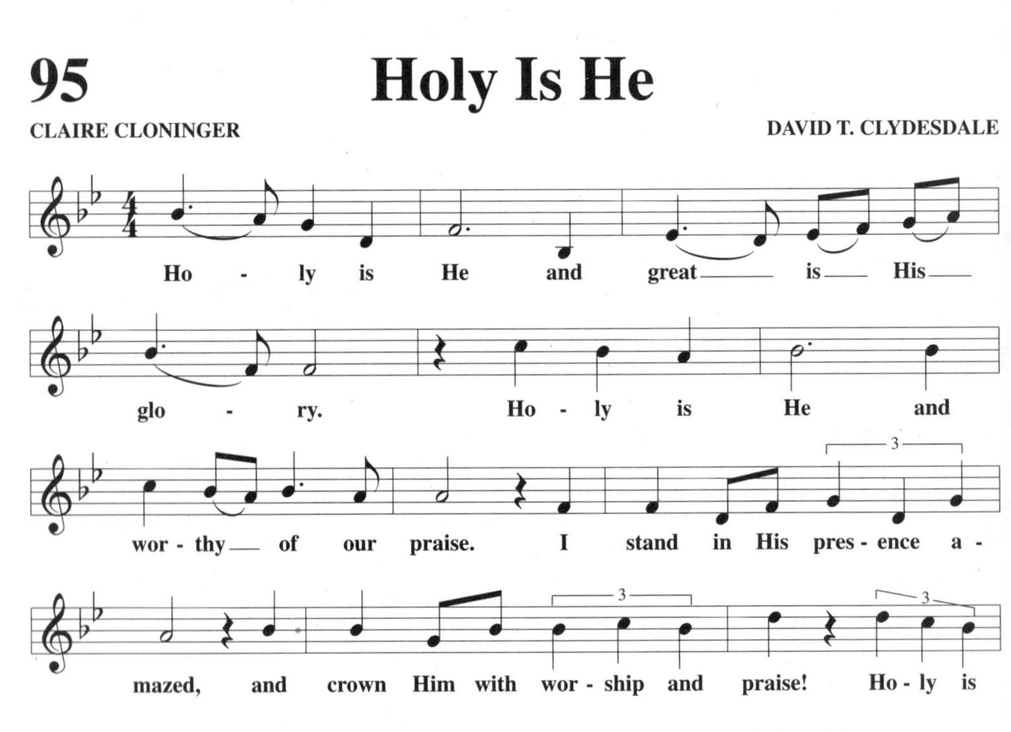

Ho - ly is He and great is His glo - ry. Ho - ly is He and wor - thy of our praise. I stand in His pres - ence a - mazed, and crown Him with wor - ship and praise! Ho - ly is

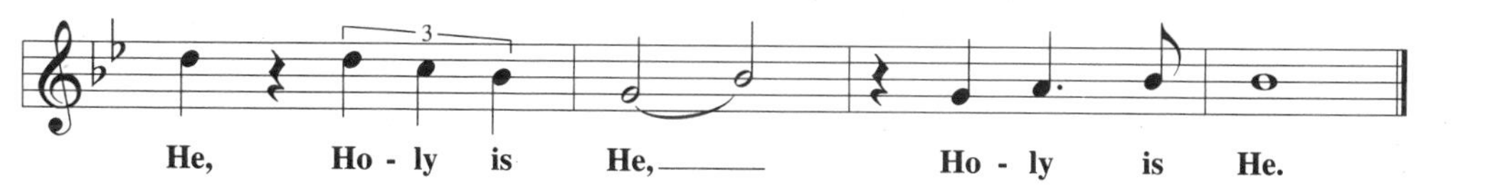

He, Ho - ly is He, _____ Ho - ly is He.

Holy Is Your Name   96

Words and Music by
MIKE DAY and DAVE BELL

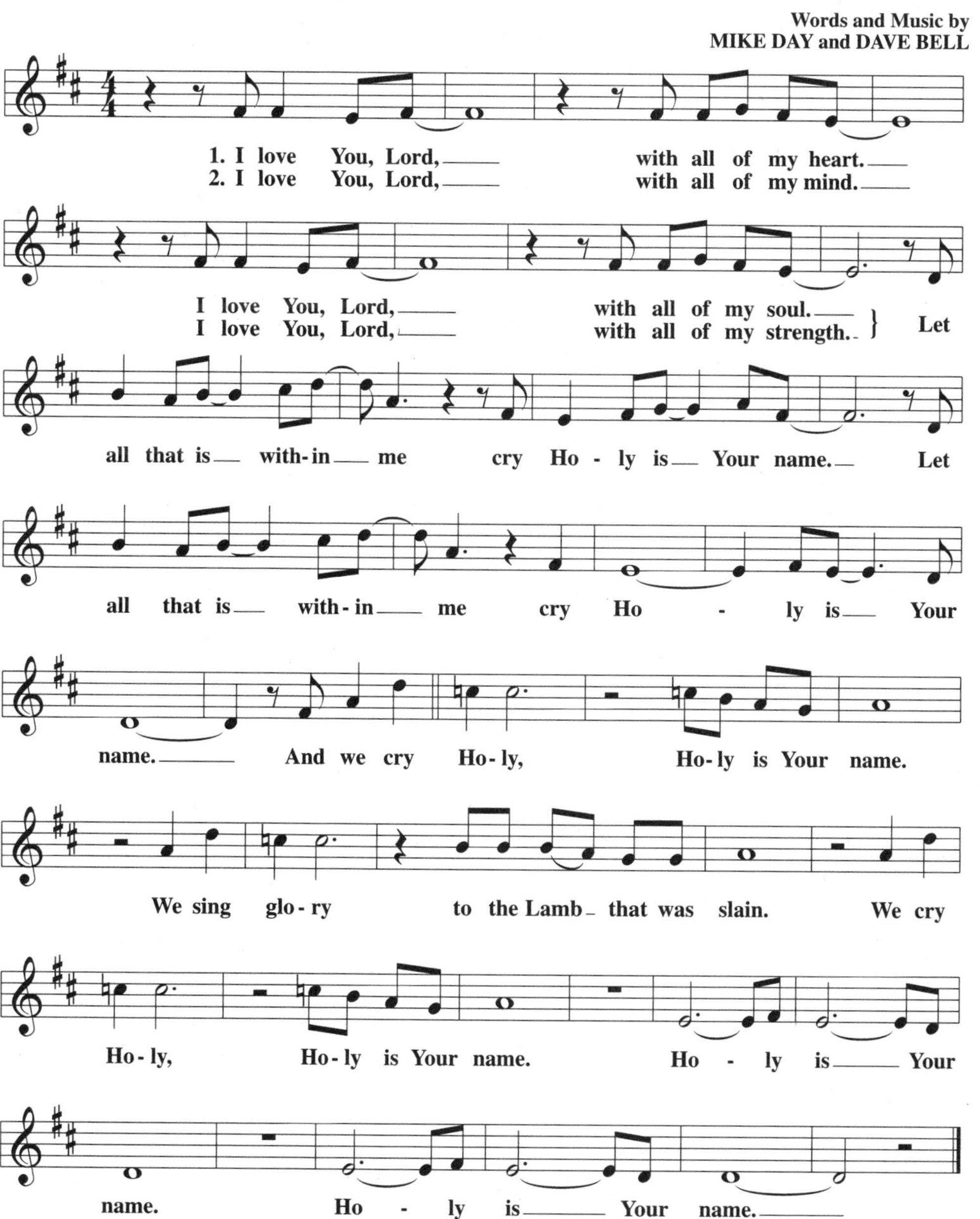

1. I love You, Lord, _____ with all of my heart. _____
2. I love You, Lord, _____ with all of my mind. _____

I love You, Lord, _____ with all of my soul. _____ } Let
I love You, Lord, _____ with all of my strength. } Let

all that is _ with-in _ me cry Ho - ly is _ Your name. _ Let

all that is _ with-in _ me cry Ho - ly is _ Your

name. _____ And we cry Ho - ly, Ho - ly is Your name.

We sing glo - ry to the Lamb _ that was slain. We cry

Ho - ly, Ho - ly is Your name. Ho - ly is _____ Your

name. Ho - ly is _____ Your name. _____

97 In Moments Like These

DAVID GRAHAM   DAVID GRAHAM

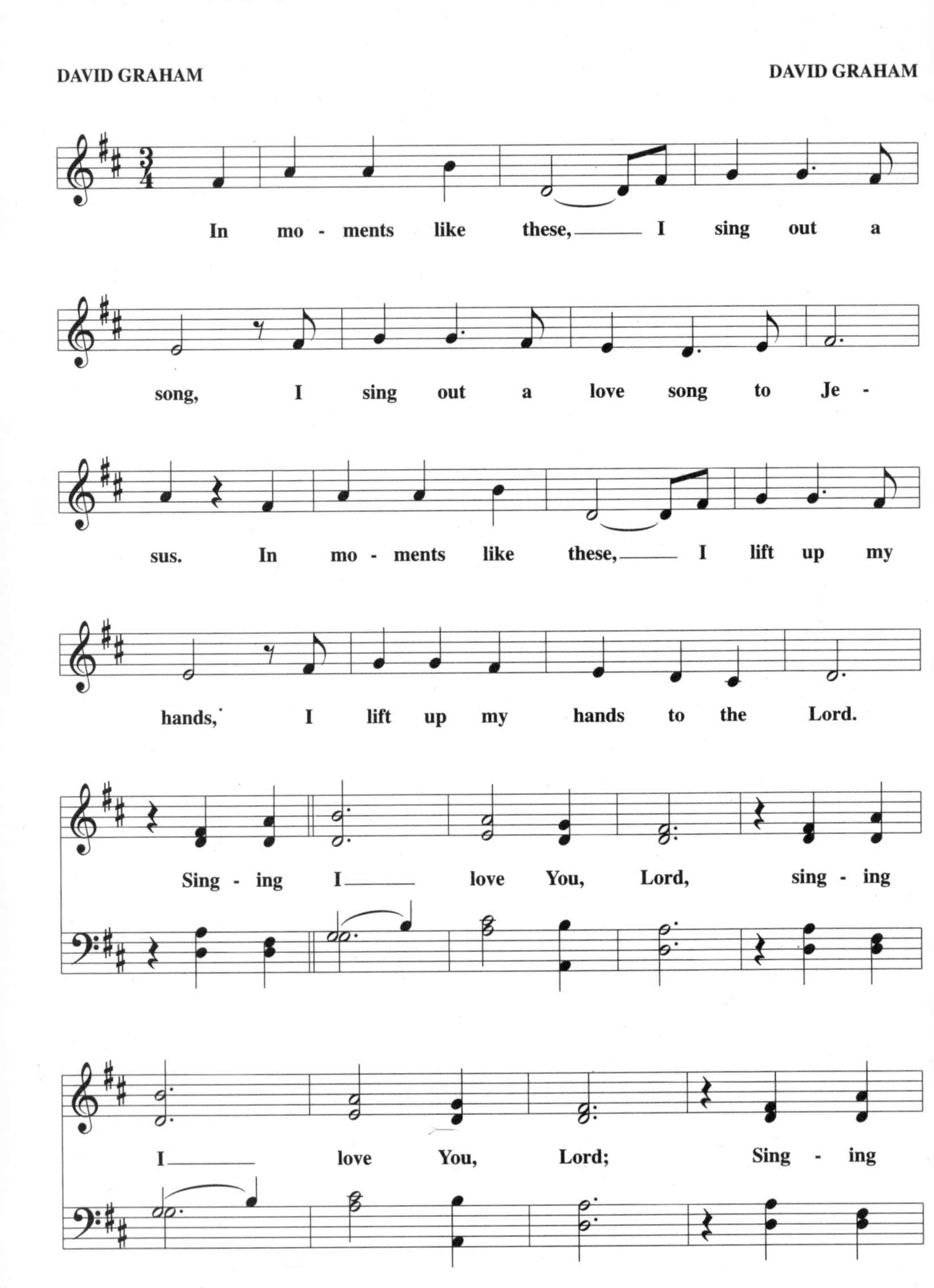

In mo - ments like these, —— I sing out a song, I sing out a love song to Je - sus. In mo - ments like these, —— I lift up my hands, I lift up my hands to the Lord. Sing - ing I —— love You, Lord, sing - ing I —— love You, Lord; Sing - ing

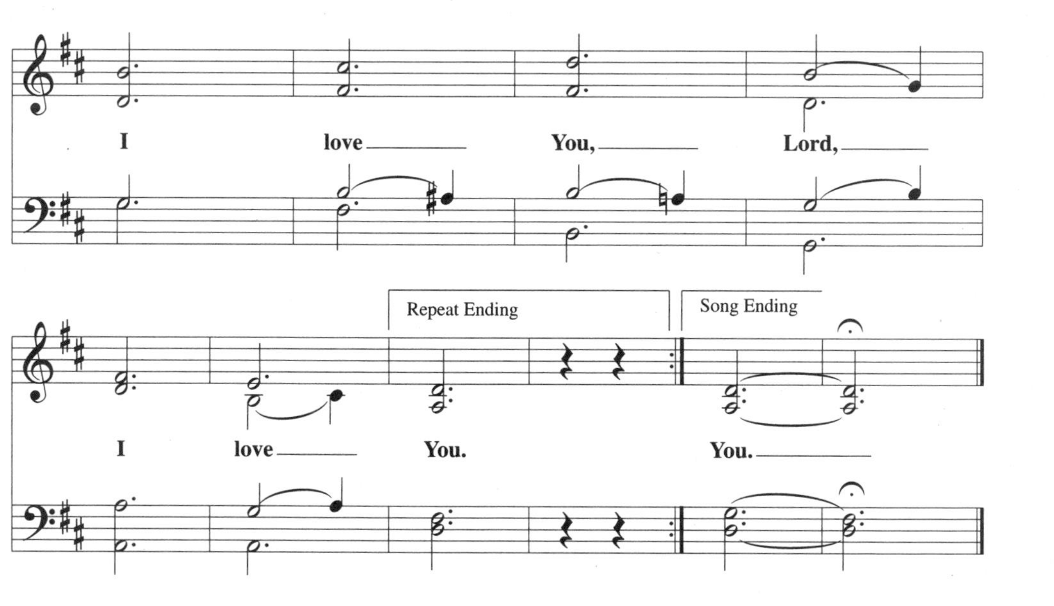

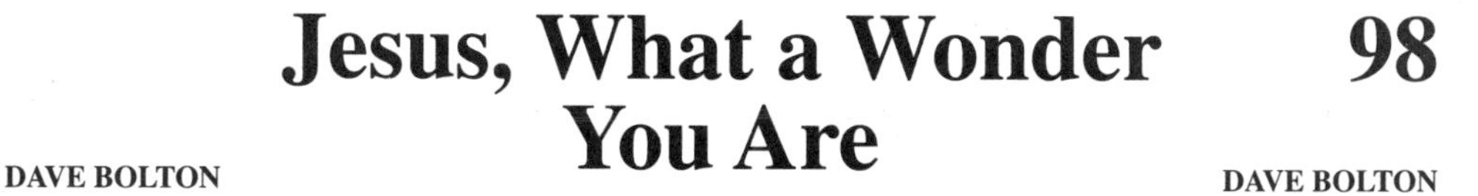

I love You, Lord,

Repeat Ending | Song Ending

I love You. You.

Jesus, What a Wonder You Are 98

DAVE BOLTON   **DAVE BOLTON**

Je - sus, _____ what a won - der You are.

_____ You are so gen - tle, _____ so pure, and so kind. _____

_____ You _____ shine _____ like the morn - ing star. _____

_____ Je - sus, _____ what a won - der You are. _____

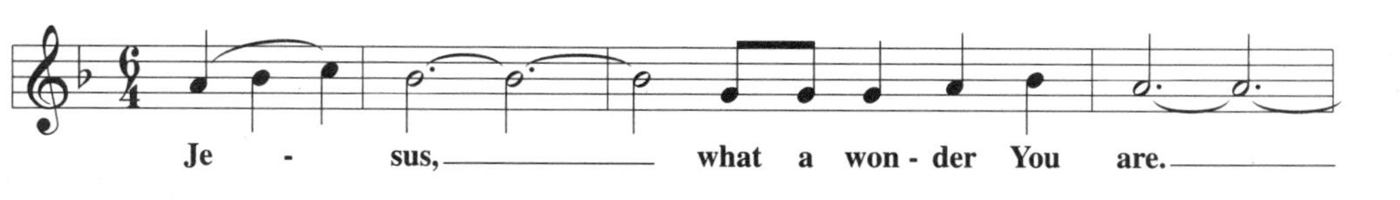

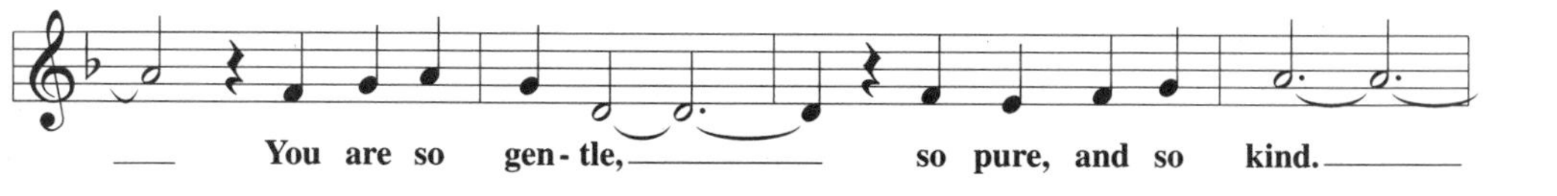

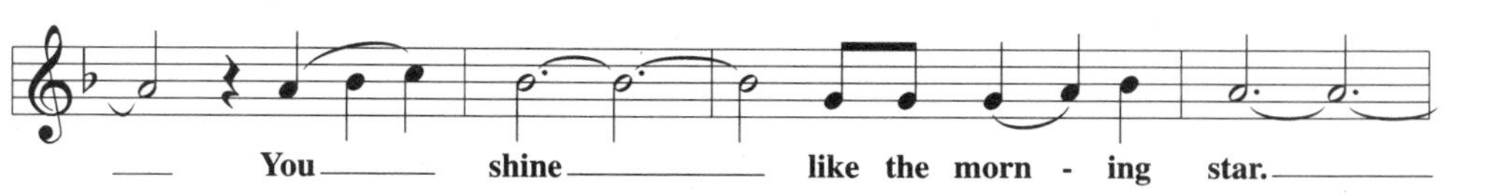

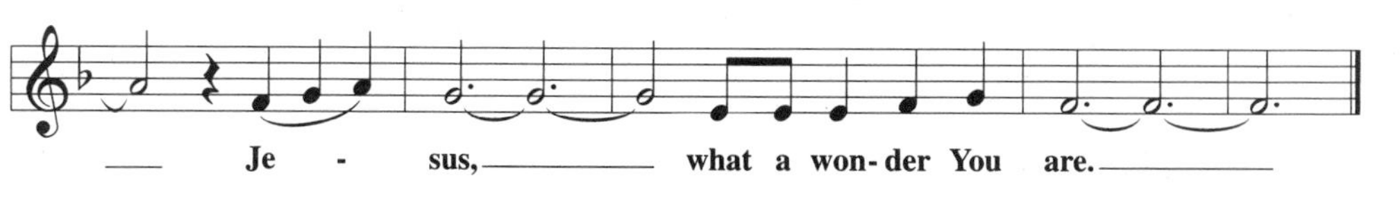

99 More Precious than Silver

LYNN DeSHAZO
Based on Proverbs 3:13-15

LYNN DeSHAZO

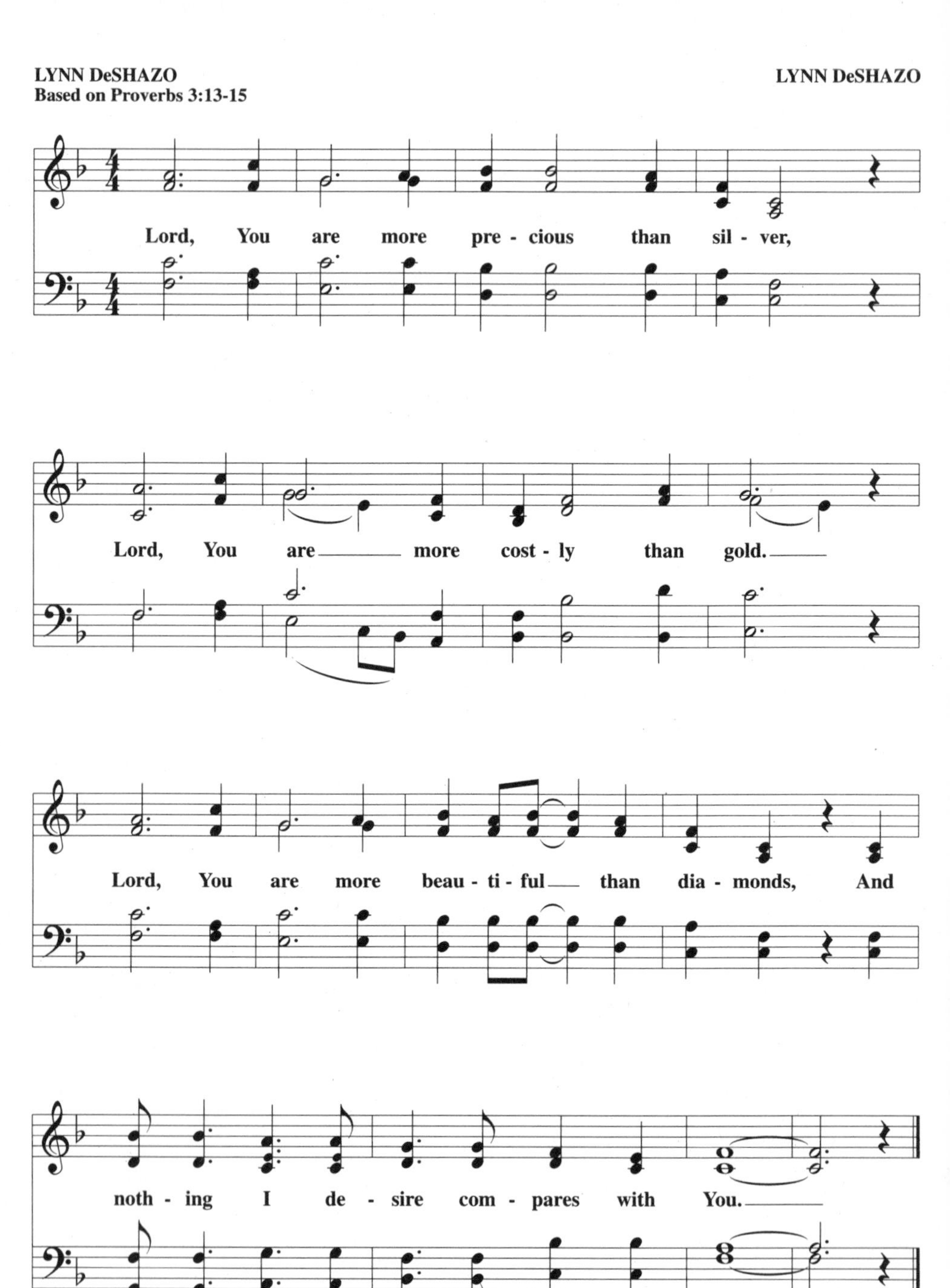

Lord, You are more pre-cious than sil-ver,

Lord, You are more cost-ly than gold.

Lord, You are more beau-ti-ful than dia-monds, And

noth-ing I de-sire com-pares with You.

Bless the Name of Jesus 100

CARMAN LICCIARDELLO

CARMAN LICCIARDELLO

Bless the name — of Je - sus, Praise the name — of Je - sus,

Sing un - to the King —— of Is - ra - el. ——

Bless the name — of Je - sus, Praise the name — of Je - sus,

Sing un - to the King —— of Is - ra - el. And I sing

glo - ry, glo - ry, Glo - ry

to His name for - ev - er. Glo - ry,

glo - ry, Glo - ry to His name. ——

101 Worthy of Worship

TERRY YORK

MARK BLANKENSHIP

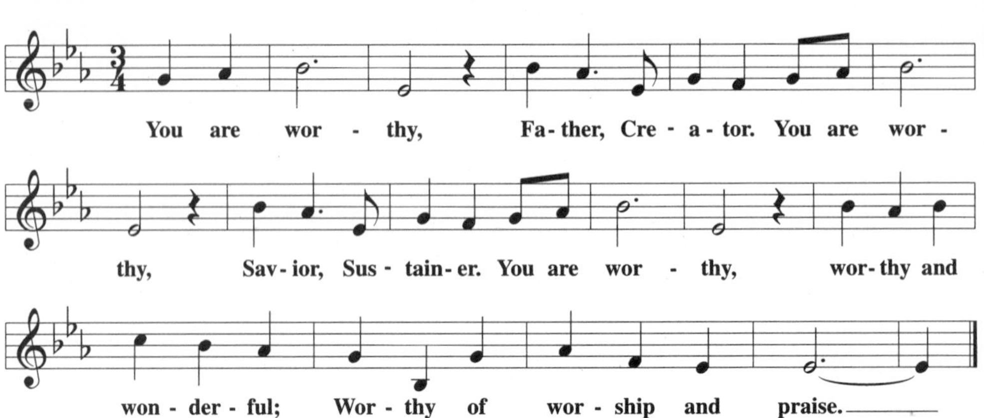

You are wor - thy, Fa-ther, Cre - a - tor. You are wor -
thy, Sav-ior, Sus - tain-er. You are wor - thy, wor-thy and
won - der - ful; Wor - thy of wor - ship and praise.

102 Great Are You, Lord

Words and Music by
STEVE and VIKKI COOK

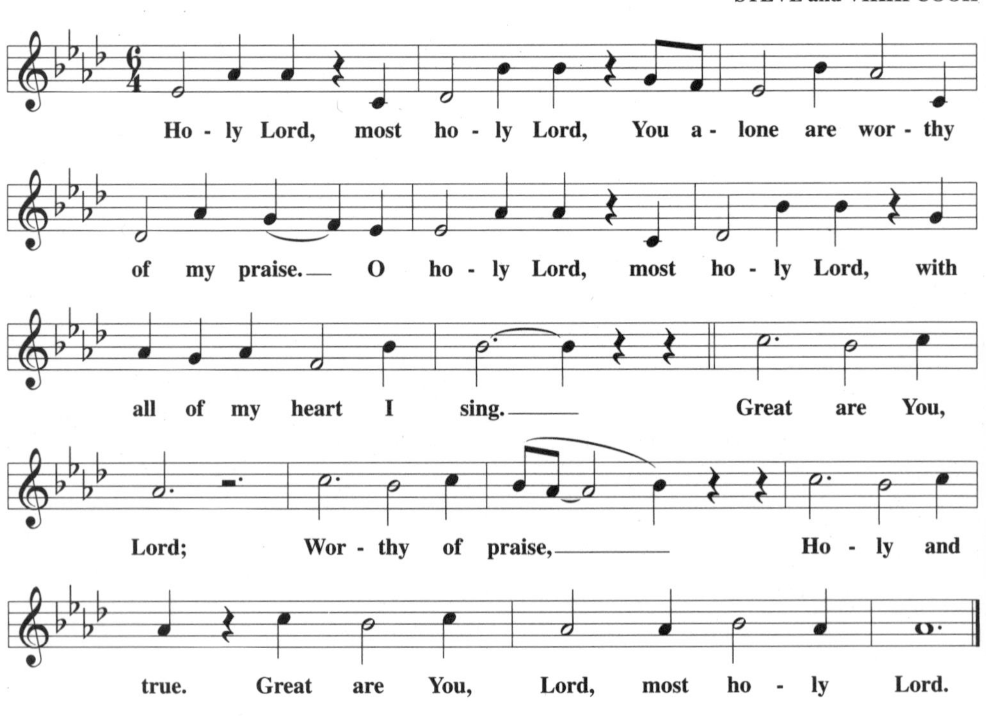

Ho - ly Lord, most ho - ly Lord, You a - lone are wor - thy
of my praise. O ho - ly Lord, most ho - ly Lord, with
all of my heart I sing. Great are You,
Lord; Wor - thy of praise, Ho - ly and
true. Great are You, Lord, most ho - ly Lord.

We Worship and Adore You

103

TRADITIONAL

TRADITIONAL

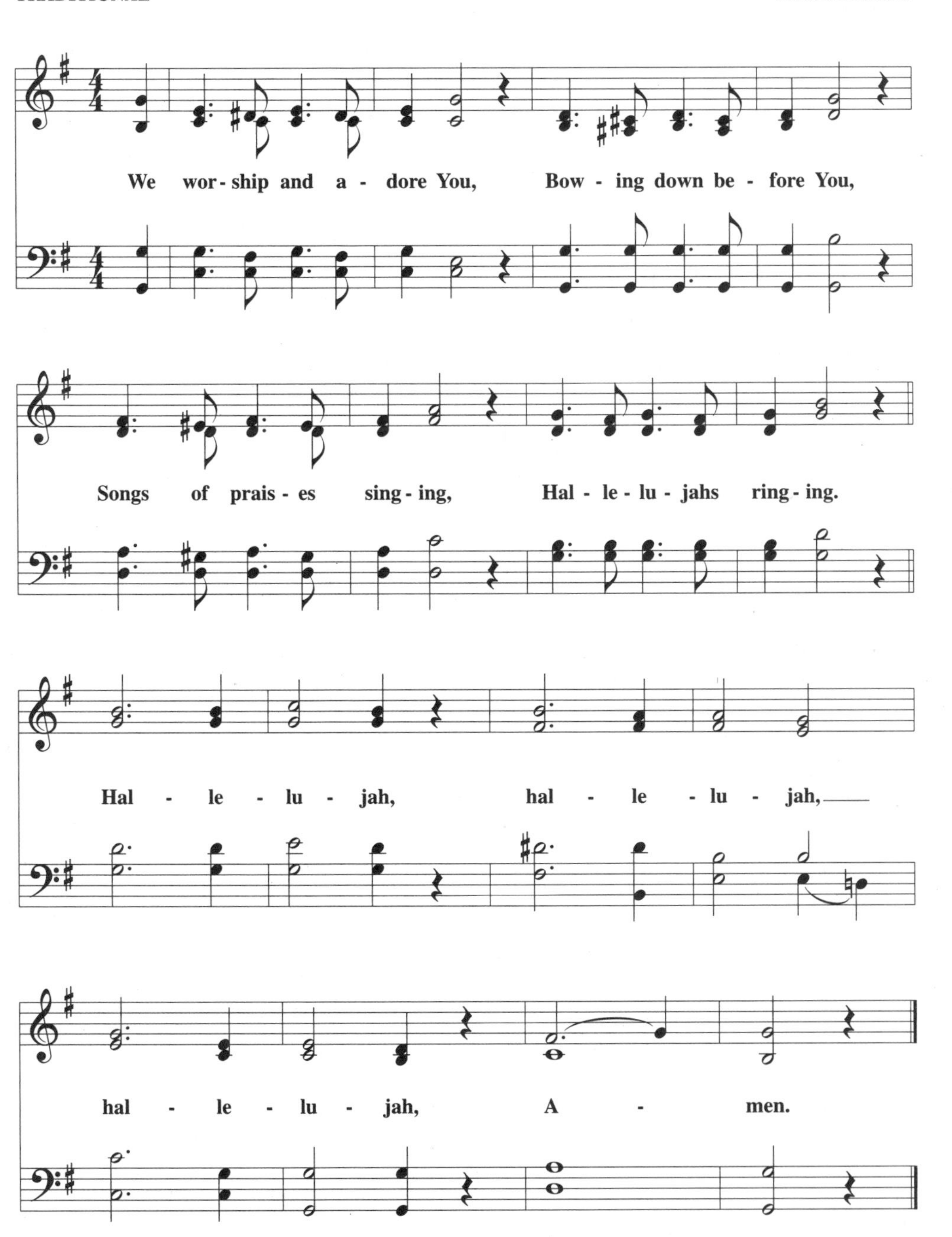

We wor-ship and a - dore You, Bow - ing down be - fore You,

Songs of prais - es sing - ing, Hal - le - lu - jahs ring - ing.

Hal - le - lu - jah, hal - le - lu - jah,___

hal - le - lu - jah, A - men.

104 Praise Him

TWILA PARIS

TWILA PARIS

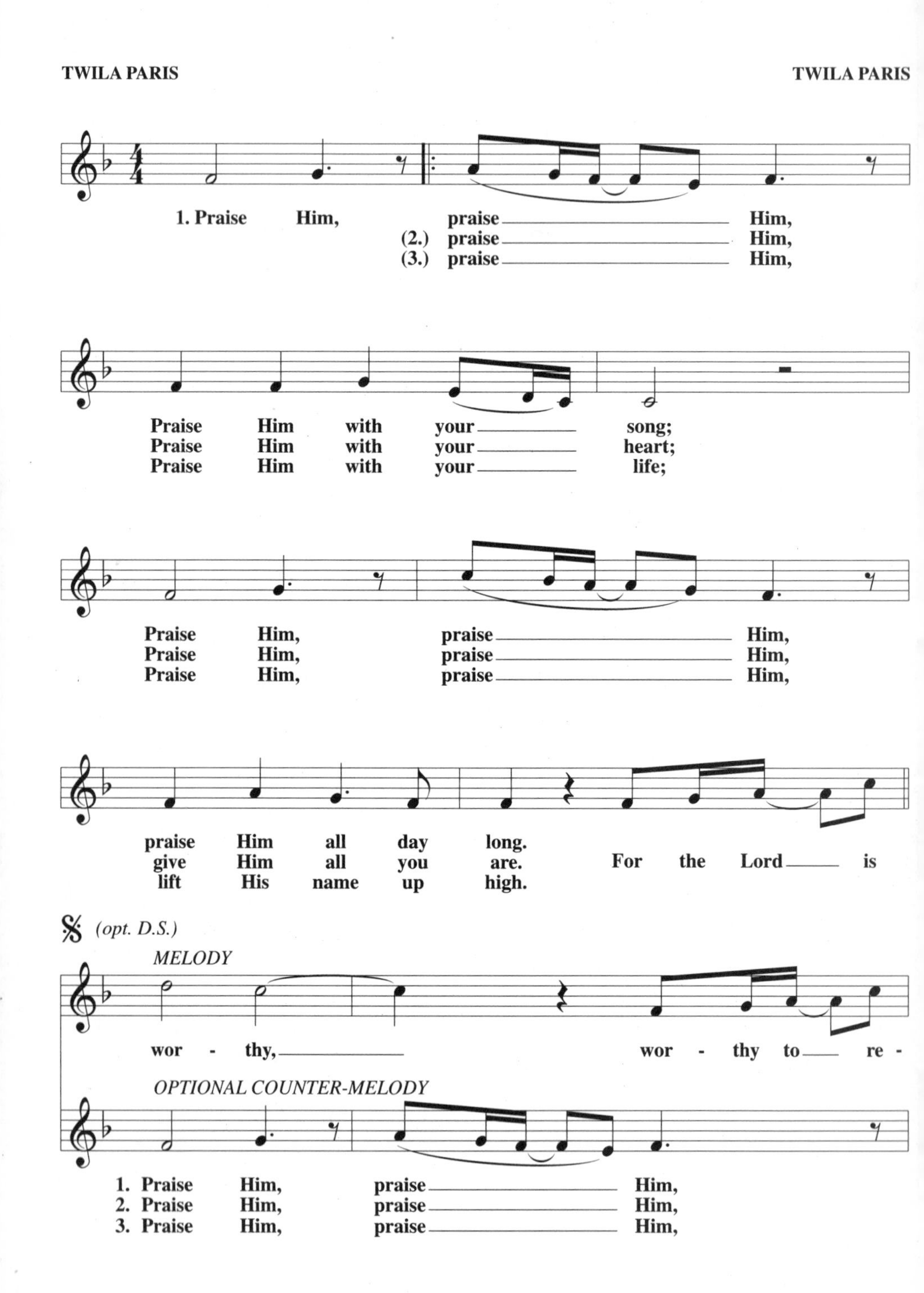

1. Praise Him, praise Him,
(2.) praise Him,
(3.) praise Him,

Praise Him with your song;
Praise Him with your heart;
Praise Him with your life;

Praise Him, praise Him,
Praise Him, praise Him,
Praise Him, praise Him,

praise Him all day long.
give Him all you are.
lift His name up high.

For the Lord is

(opt. D.S.)

MELODY

wor - thy, wor - thy to re -

OPTIONAL COUNTER-MELODY

1. Praise Him, praise Him,
2. Praise Him, praise Him,
3. Praise Him, praise Him,

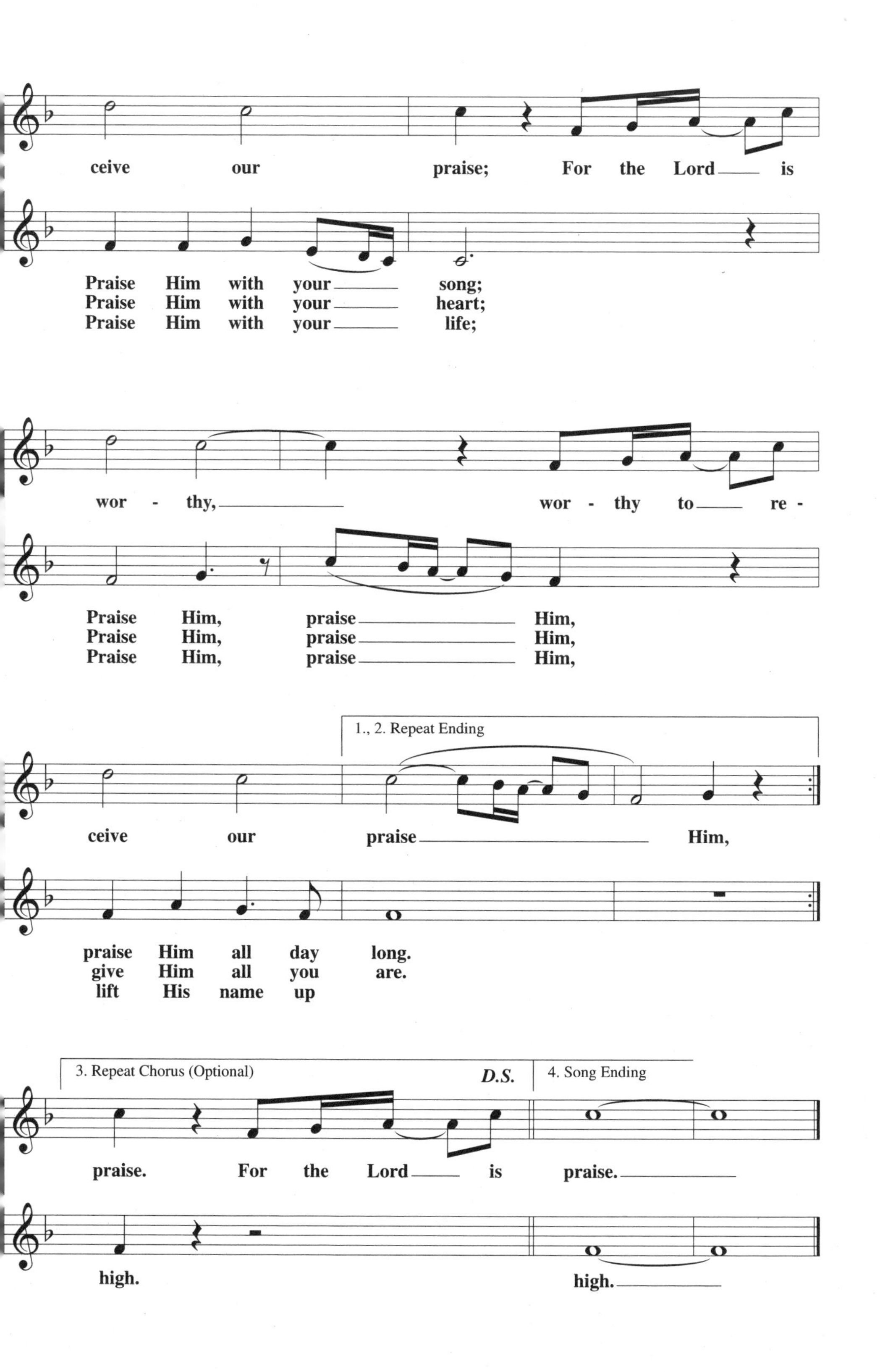
ceive our praise; For the Lord is
Praise Him with your song;
Praise Him with your heart;
Praise Him with your life;
wor - thy,
wor - thy to re -
Praise Him, praise Him,
Praise Him, praise Him,
Praise Him, praise Him,
1., 2. Repeat Ending
ceive our praise Him,
praise Him all day long.
give Him all you are.
lift His name up
3. Repeat Chorus (Optional)
D.S.
4. Song Ending
praise. For the Lord is praise.
high. high.

105   We Give You Praise

MORRIS CHAPMAN

MORRIS CHAPMAN

We give You praise, we give You praise; Lord, now and

al - ways, we give You praise. we give You

praise. We give You praise, praise, praise, we give You

praise; ____ With our hands lift - ed high ____ and our

voic - es to the sky, ____ we give You praise. ____

We give You praise, we give You praise;

Lord, now and al - ways, we give You praise.

© Copyright 1982 Word Music (a div. of WORD, INC.)/M.U.D.A.S.A. (admin. by Word Music)
All Rights Reserved. International Copyright Secured. Used by Permission.

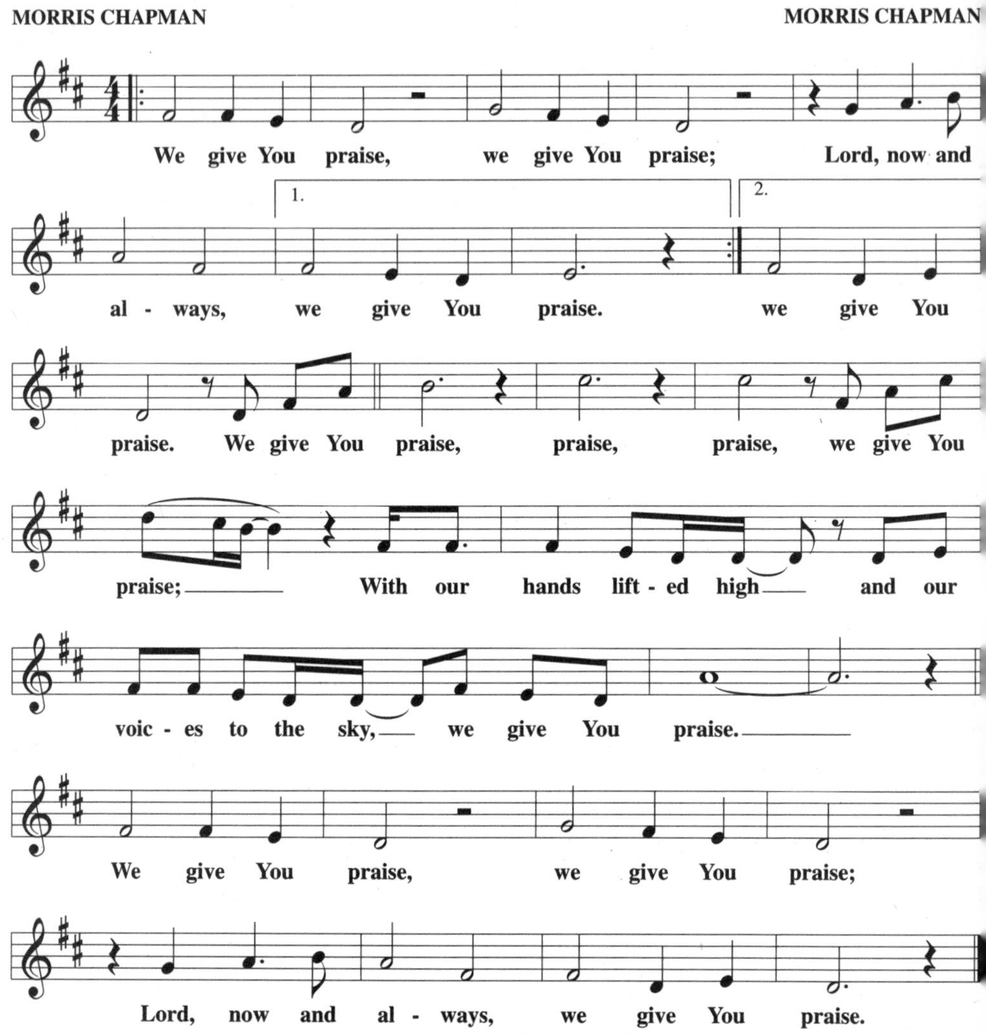

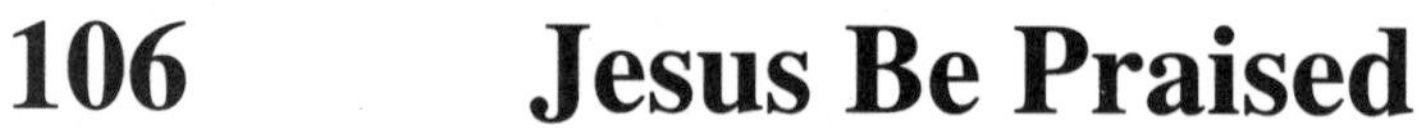

106   Jesus Be Praised

CAROL CYMBALA

CAROL CYMBALA

Je - sus be praised, ____ Je - sus be praised. ____

© Copyright 1991, Arr. © 1992 Word Music (a div. of WORD, INC.)/Carol Joy Music (ASCAP).
Used by Permission of Integrated Copyright Group, Inc.
All Rights Reserved. International Copyright Secured.

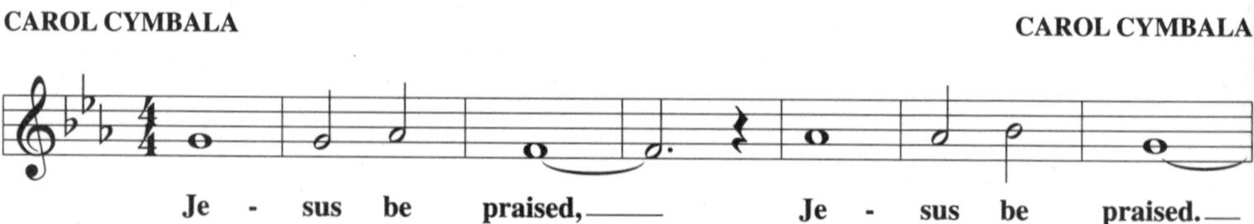

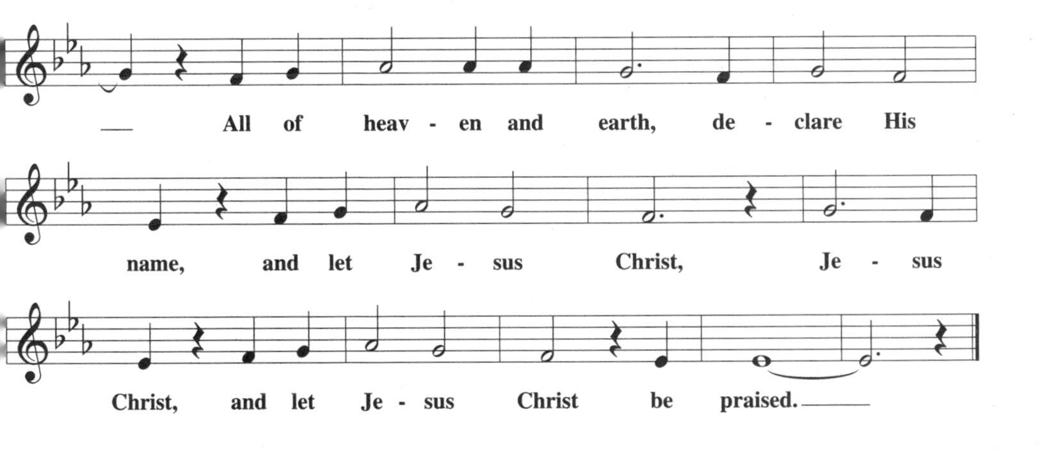

All of heav - en and earth, de - clare His name, and let Je - sus Christ, Je - sus Christ, and let Je - sus Christ be praised.

We Give You Praise 107

LANNY WOLFE

LANNY WOLFE

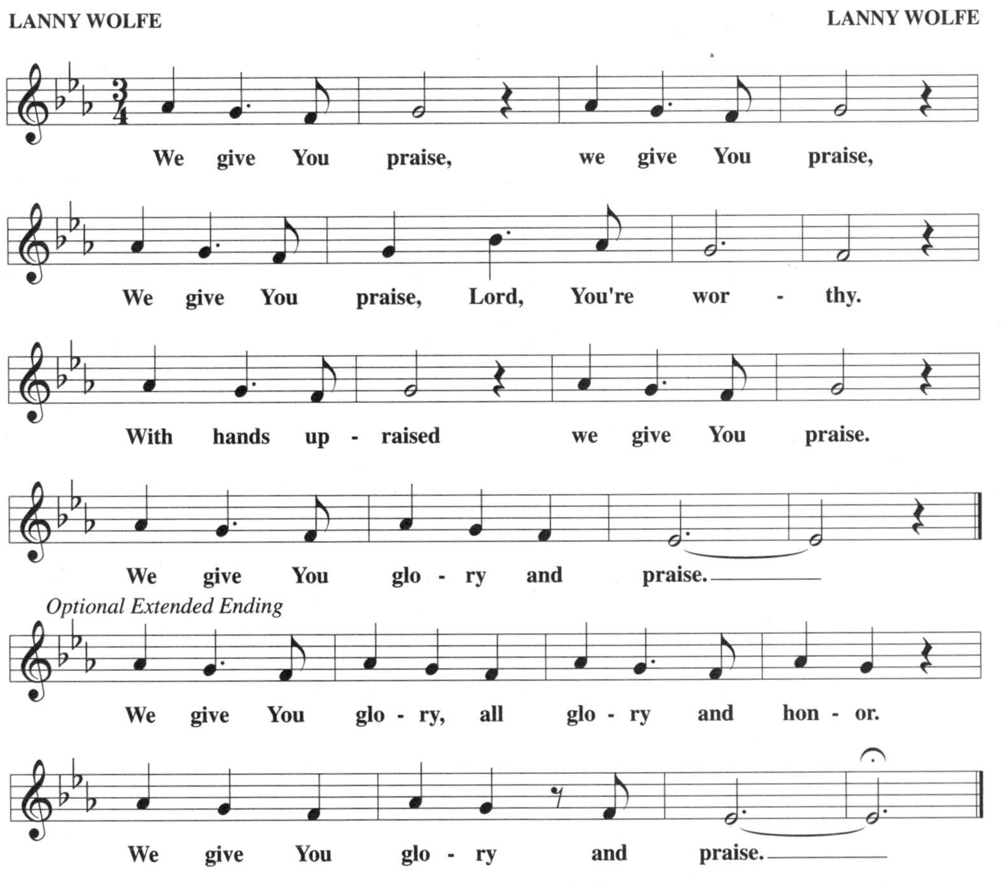

We give You praise, we give You praise,

We give You praise, Lord, You're wor - thy.

With hands up - raised we give You praise.

We give You glo - ry and praise.

Optional Extended Ending

We give You glo - ry, all glo - ry and hon - or.

We give You glo - ry and praise.

108 Alleluia

JERRY SINCLAIR

JERRY SINCLAIR

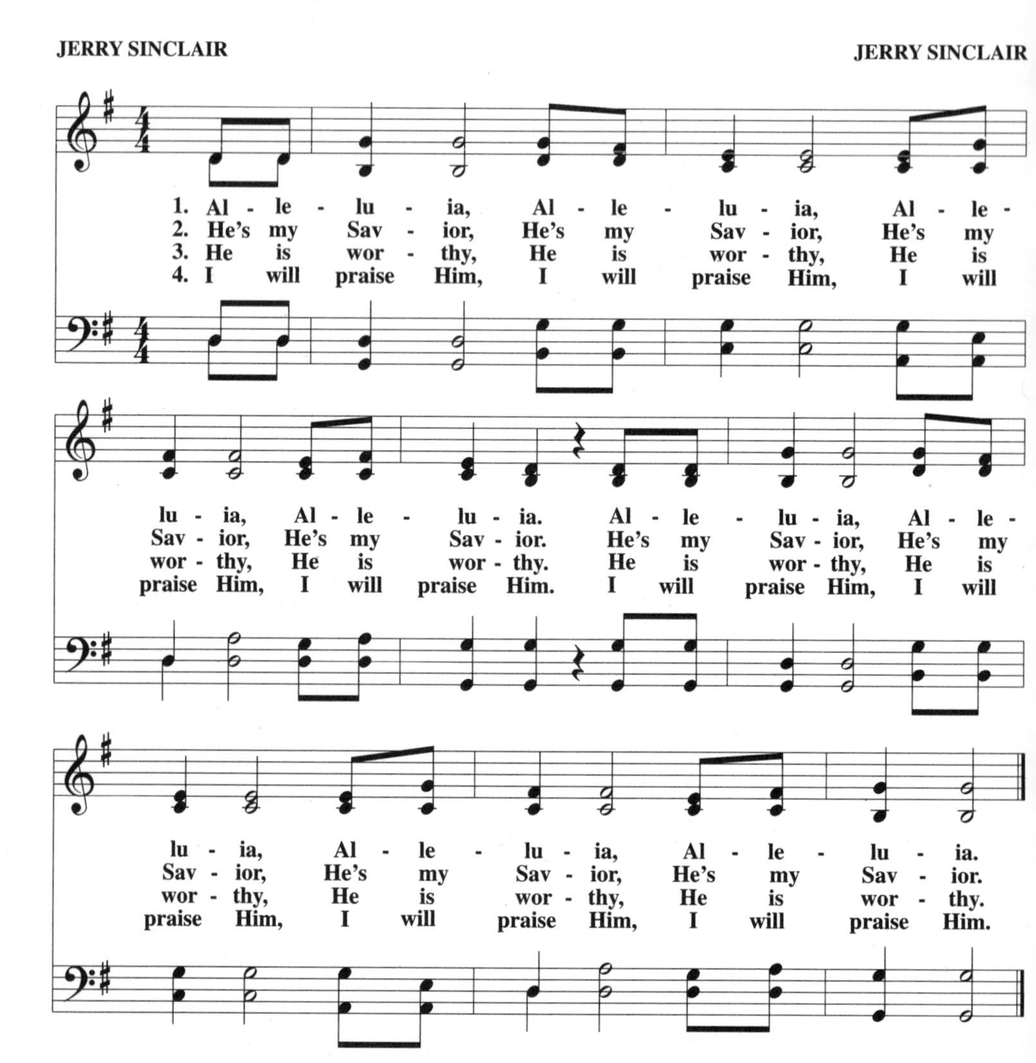

1. Al - le - lu - ia, Al - le - lu - ia, Al - le -
2. He's my Sav - ior, He's my Sav - ior, He's my
3. He is wor - thy, He is wor - thy, He is
4. I will praise Him, I will praise Him, I will

lu - ia, Al - le - lu - ia. Al - le - lu - ia, Al - le -
Sav - ior, He's my Sav - ior. He's my Sav - ior, He's my
wor - thy, He is wor - thy. He is wor - thy, He is
praise Him, I will praise Him. I will praise Him, I will

lu - ia, Al - le - lu - ia, Al - le - lu - ia.
Sav - ior, He's my Sav - ior, He's my Sav - ior.
wor - thy, He is wor - thy, He is wor - thy.
praise Him, I will praise Him, I will praise Him.

109 Oh for a Thousand Tongues

DAVID BINION

DAVID BINION

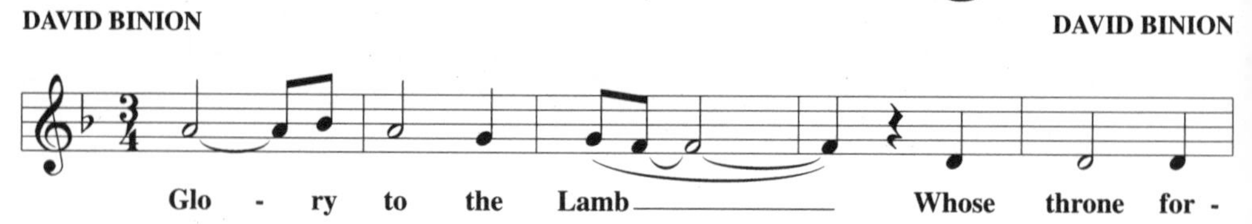

Glo - ry to the Lamb_____ Whose throne for -

ev - er reigns;_____ God in the high - est,_____

_____ Wor - thy to mer - it our praise._____

Oh for a thou - sand tongues to sing prais - es

un - to Thee;_____ Oh for a thou - sand

hands to raise in hon - or to the King._____

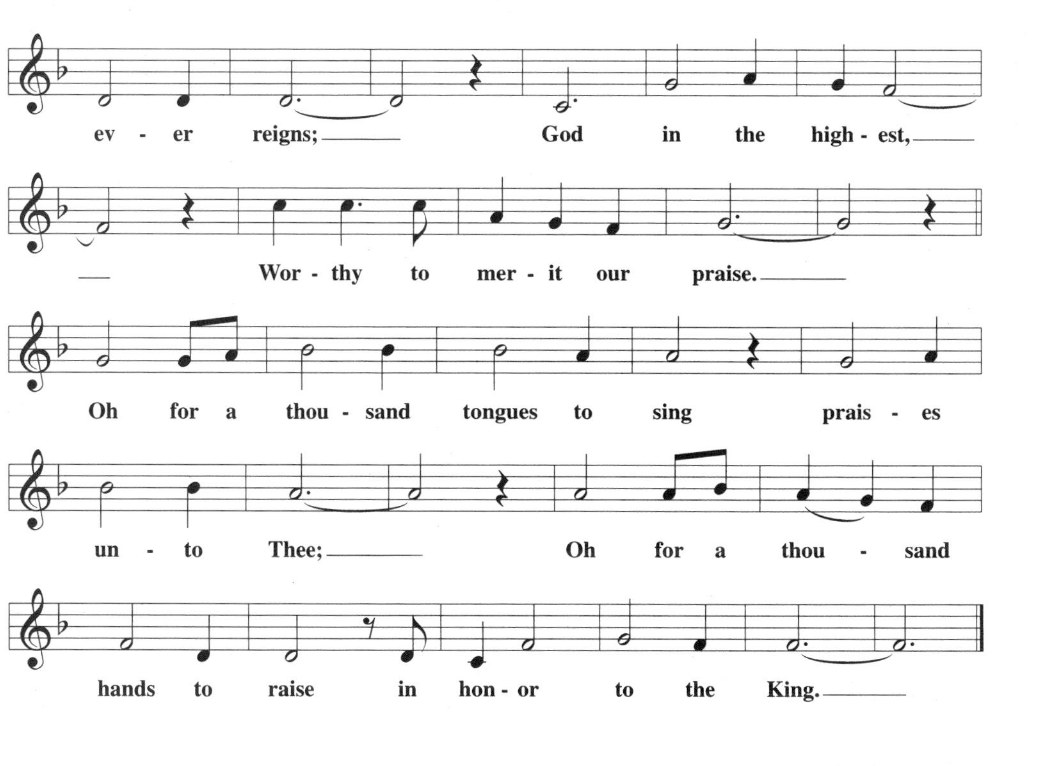

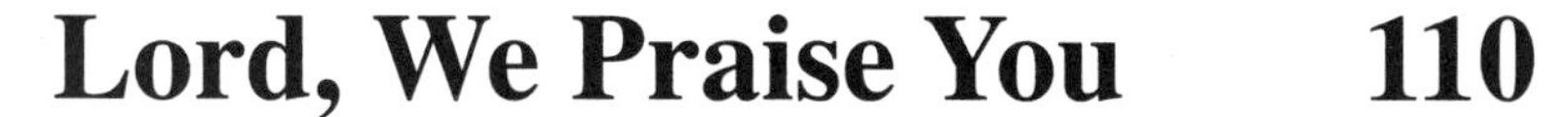

Lord, We Praise You   110

OTIS SKILLINGS   OTIS SKILLINGS

1. Lord, we praise You. Lord, we praise You.
2. Lord, we love You. Lord, we love You.
3. Al - le - lu - ia! Al - le - lu - ia!

Lord, we praise You. We praise You, Lord.
Lord, we love You. We love You, Lord.
Al - le - lu - ia! We give You praise.

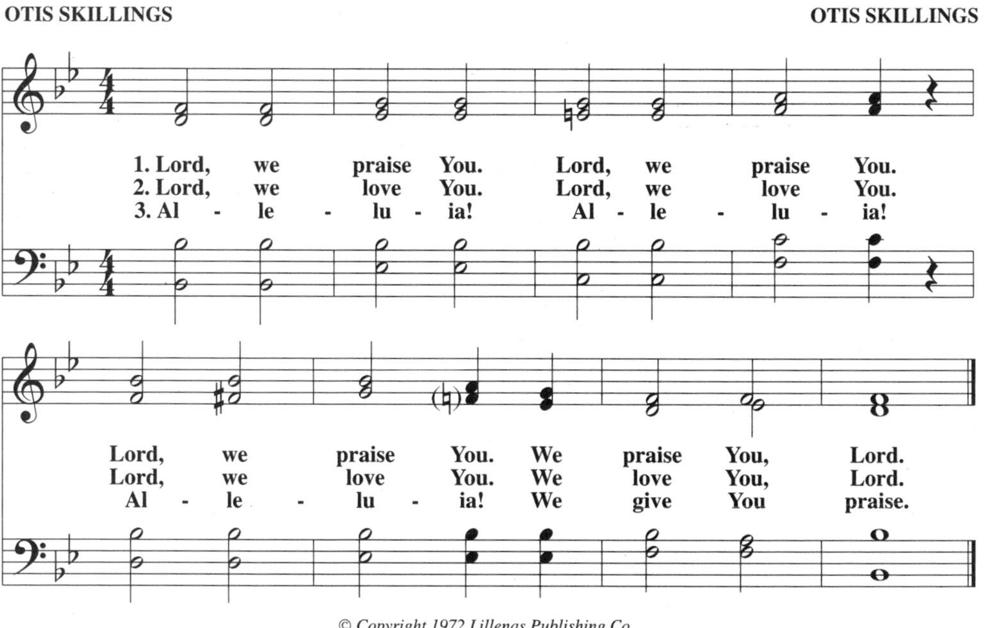

111 There Is a Redeemer

MELODY GREEN   MELODY GREEN

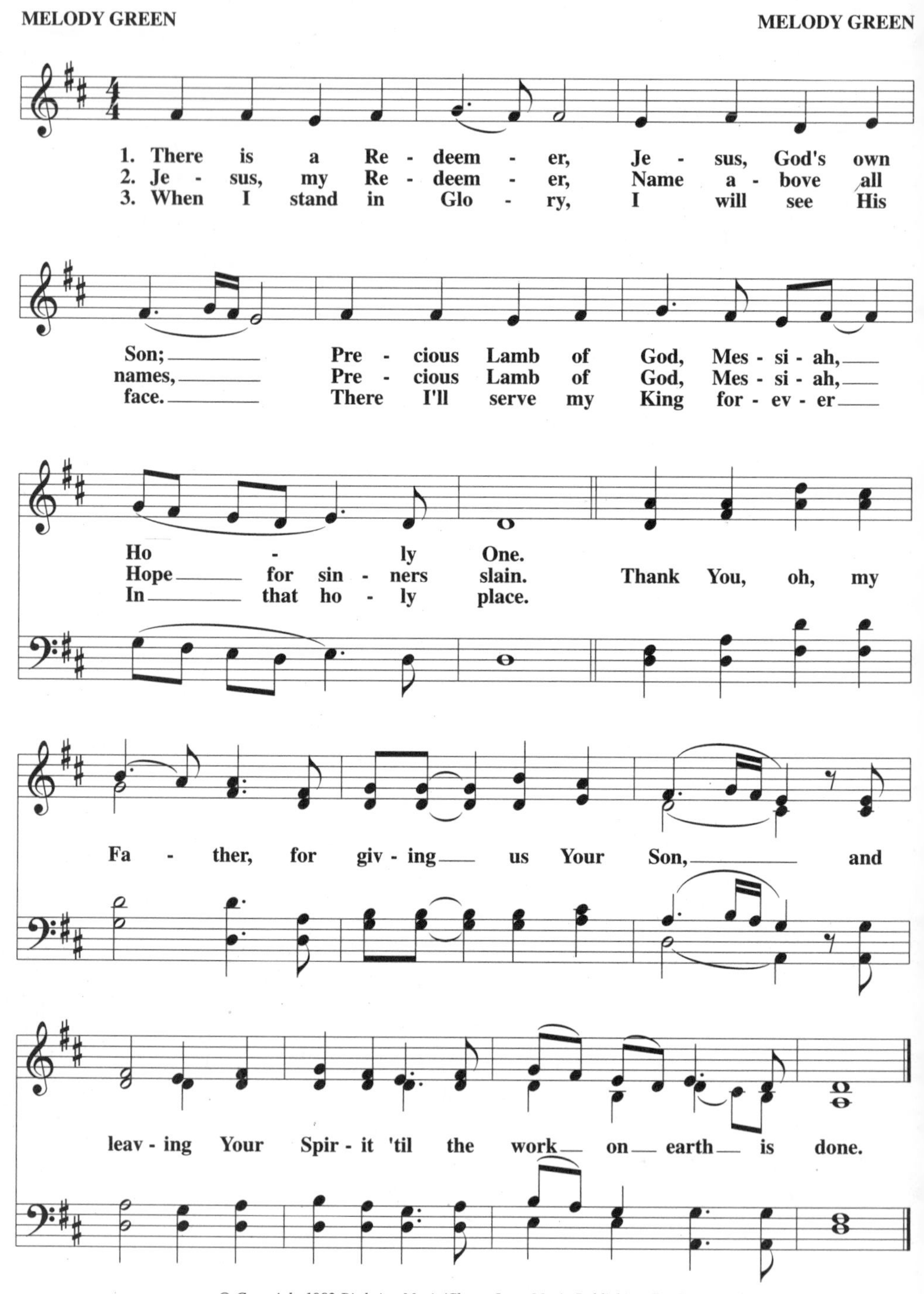

1. There is a Re - deem - er, Je - sus, God's own Son; _____ Pre - cious Lamb of God, Mes - si - ah, _____ Ho - ly One.
2. Je - sus, my Re - deem - er, Name a - bove all names, _____ Pre - cious Lamb of God, Mes - si - ah, _____ Hope _____ for sin - ners slain.
3. When I stand in Glo - ry, I will see His face. _____ There I'll serve my King for - ev - er _____ In _____ that ho - ly place.

Thank You, oh, my Fa - ther, for giv - ing _____ us Your Son, _____ and leav - ing Your Spir - it 'til the work _____ on _____ earth _____ is done.

Lamb of God

112

TWILA PARIS   TWILA PARIS

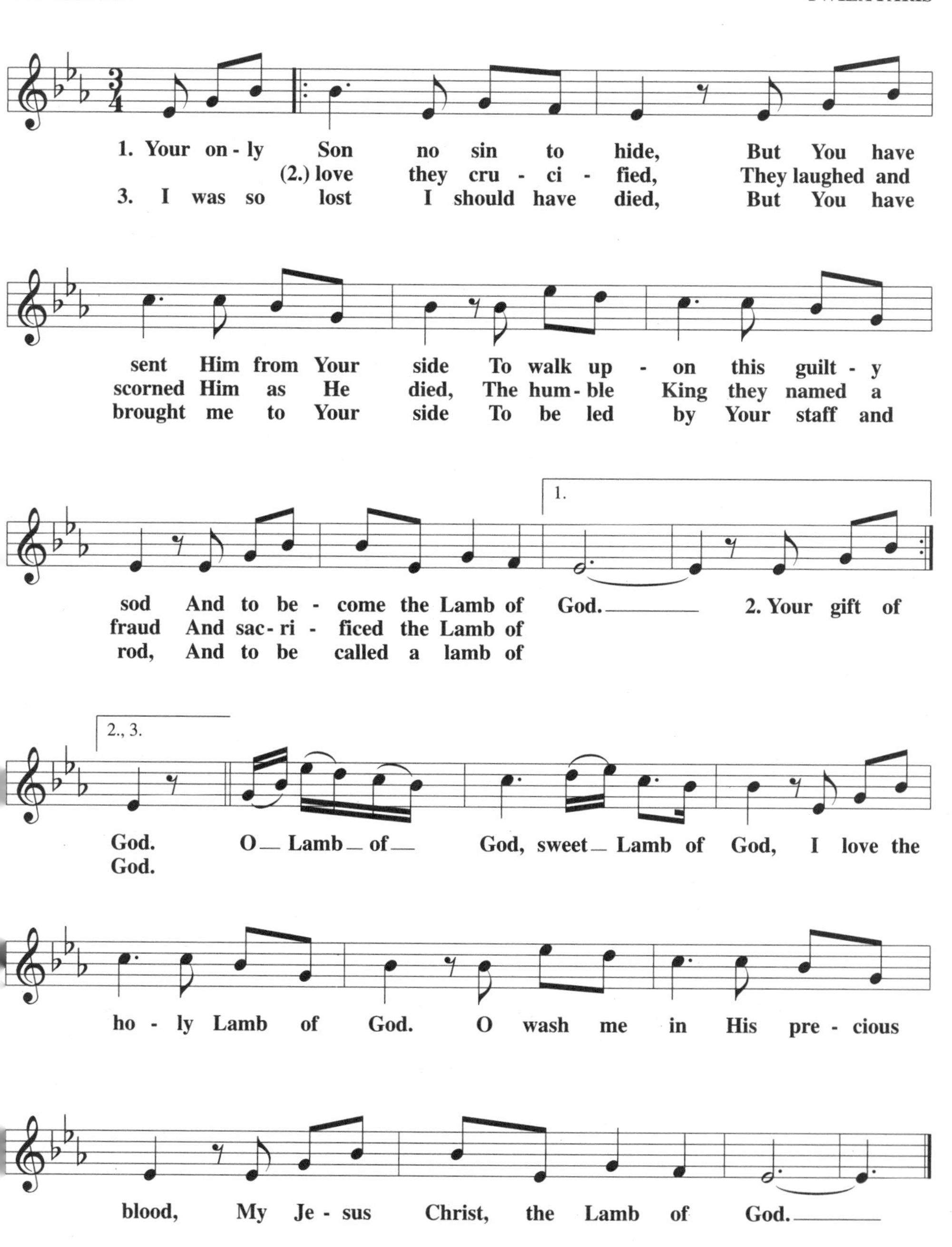

1. Your on-ly Son no sin to hide, But You have
   (2.) love they cru-ci-fied, They laughed and
3. I was so lost I should have died, But You have

sent Him from Your side To walk up-on this guilt-y
scorned Him as He died, The hum-ble King they named a
brought me to Your side To be led by Your staff and

1.
sod And to be-come the Lamb of God._____ 2. Your gift of
fraud And sac-ri-ficed the Lamb of
rod, And to be called a lamb of

2., 3.
God. O—Lamb—of—God, sweet—Lamb of God, I love the
God.

ho-ly Lamb of God. O wash me in His pre-cious

blood, My Je-sus Christ, the Lamb of God._____

113 Oh, How He Loves You and Me

KURT KAISER   KURT KAISER

1. Oh, how He loves you and me,
   Oh, how He loves you and me.
   He gave His life, what more could He give?
   Oh, how He loves you; Oh, how He loves me;
   Oh, how He loves you and me!

2. Je - sus to Cal - v'ry did go,
   His love for sin - ners to show.
   What He did there brought hope from de - spair.

I'm Forever Grateful 114

MARK ALTROGGE

MARK ALTROGGE

You did not wait for me to draw near to You, But You

clothed Your-self with frail hu-man-i-ty. You

did not wait for me to cry out to You, But You

let me hear Your voice call-ing me. And I'm for-ev-er

grate-ful to You, I'm for-ev-er grate-ful for the

cross. I'm for-ev-er grate-ful to You that You

came to seek and save the lost.

115 He Is Lovely

BOB FITTS

BOB FITTS

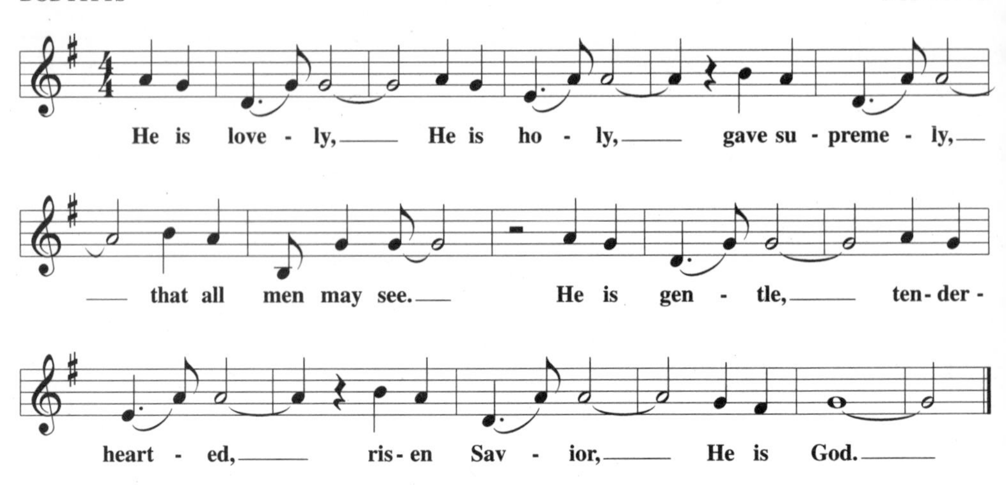

He is love - ly, ___ He is ho - ly, ___ gave su - preme - ly, ___ that all men may see. ___ He is gen - tle, ___ tender - heart - ed, ___ ris - en Sav - ior, ___ He is God. ___

116 Jesus Is Lord of All

Words and Music by
ERNIE RETTINO and DEBBY KERNER RETTINO

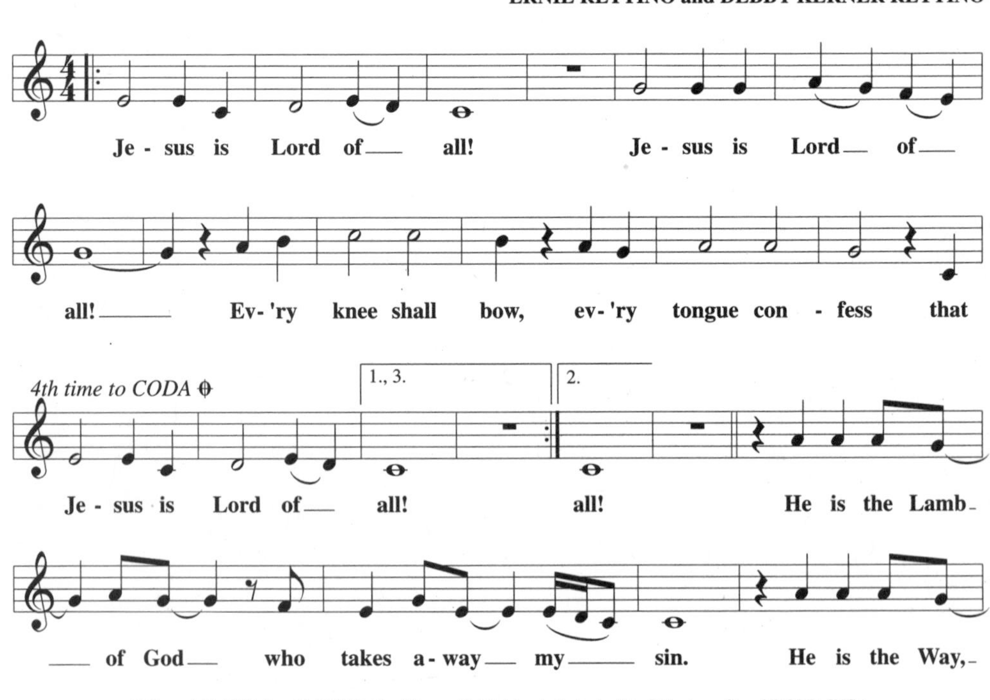

Je - sus is Lord of ___ all! Je - sus is Lord ___ of ___ all! ___ Ev - 'ry knee shall bow, ev - 'ry tongue con - fess that

4th time to CODA ⊕

1., 3.

2.

Je - sus is Lord of ___ all! all! He is the Lamb ___ of God ___ who takes a - way ___ my ___ sin. He is the Way, ___

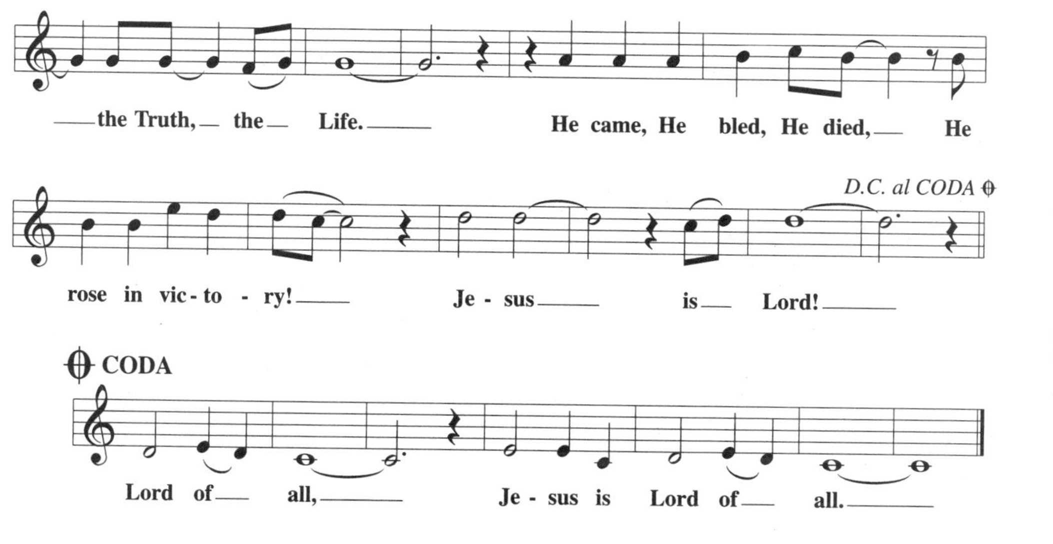

the Truth, — the — Life. _____ He came, He bled, He died, — He

D.C. al CODA ⊕

rose in vic - to - ry! _____ Je - sus _____ is — Lord! _____

⊕ **CODA**

Lord of — all, _____ Je - sus is Lord of — all. _____

O the Blood of Jesus 117

UNKNOWN

UNKNOWN
Arranged by Ken Barker

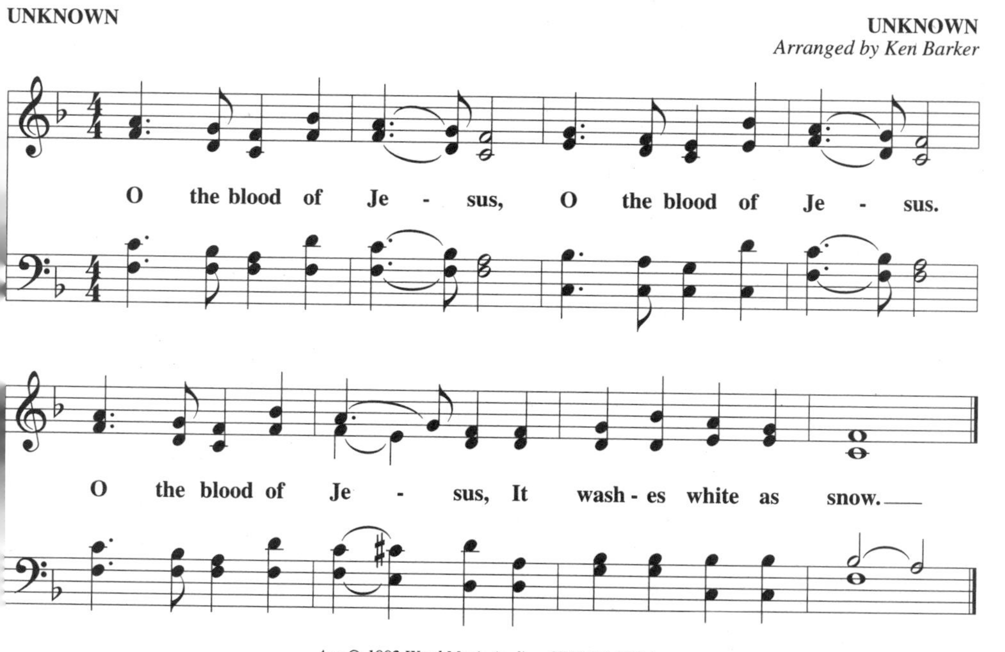

O the blood of Je - sus, O the blood of Je - sus.

O the blood of Je - sus, It wash - es white as snow. _____

118

My Tribute
(To God Be the Glory)

ANDRAÉ CROUCH   ANDRAÉ CROUCH

To God ___ be the glo - ry, To

God ___ be the glo - ry; To God ___ be the

glo - ry for the things He has done. ___ With His

blood ___ He has saved me; With His pow'r ___ He has

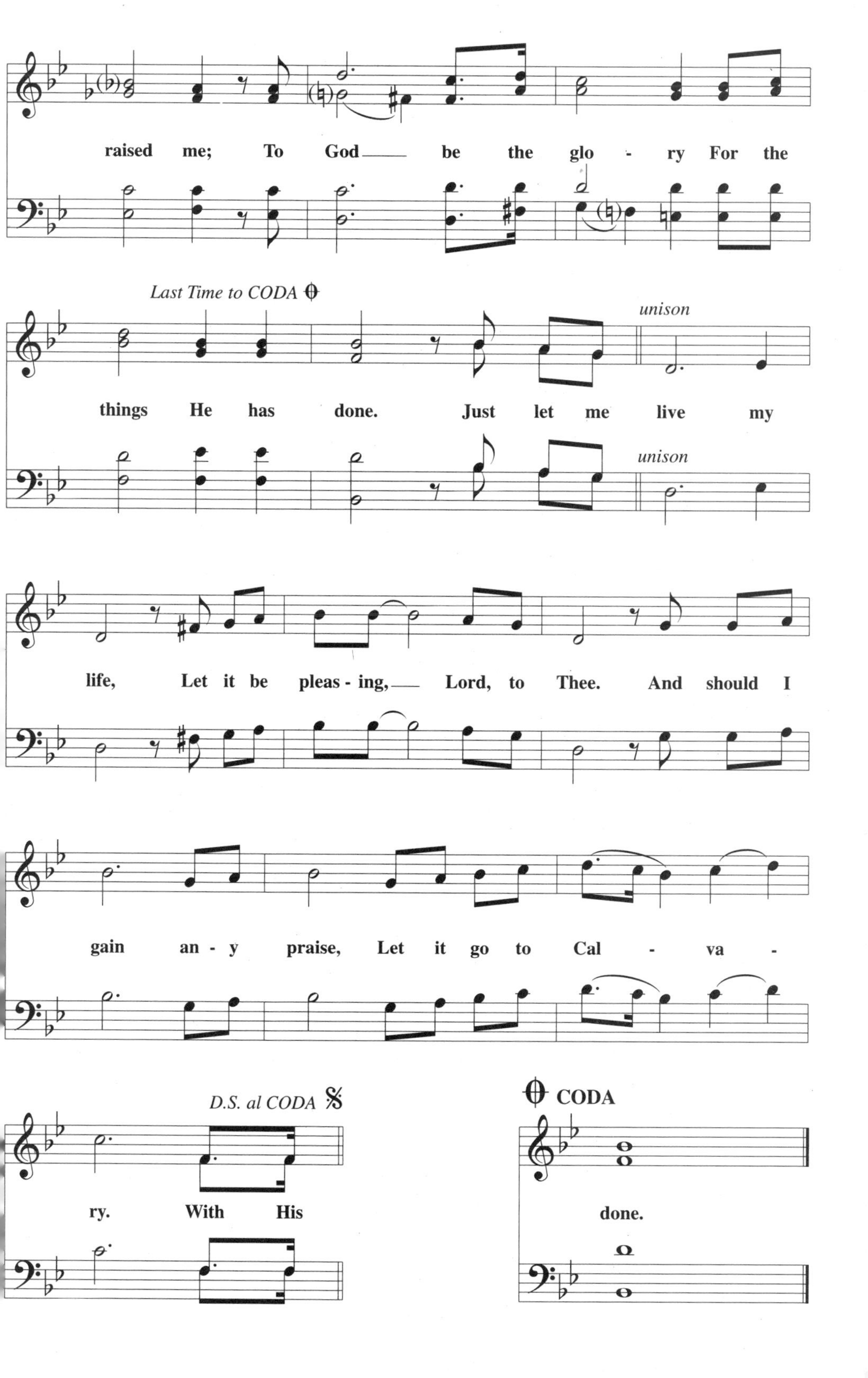
raised me; To God be the glo - ry For the
Last Time to CODA
unison
things He has done. Just let me live my
unison
life, Let it be pleas - ing, Lord, to Thee. And should I
gain an - y praise, Let it go to Cal - va -
D.S. al CODA
ry. With His
CODA
done.

119 Worthy Is the Lamb

Adapted by DON WYRTZEN
Based on Rev. 5:12

DON WYRTZEN

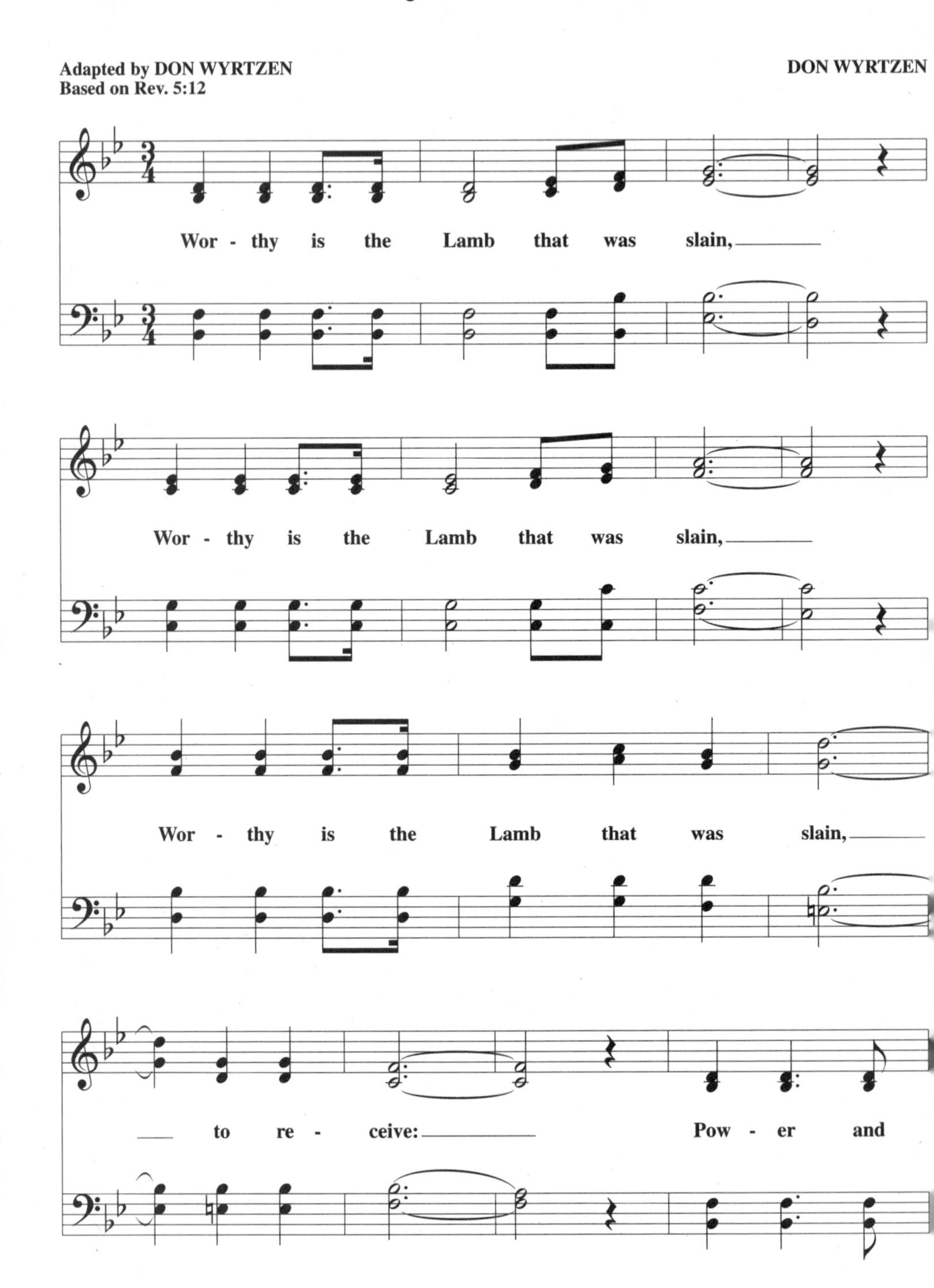

Wor - thy is the Lamb that was slain,_____

Wor - thy is the Lamb that was slain,_____

Wor - thy is the Lamb that was slain,_____

_____ to re - ceive:_____ Pow - er and

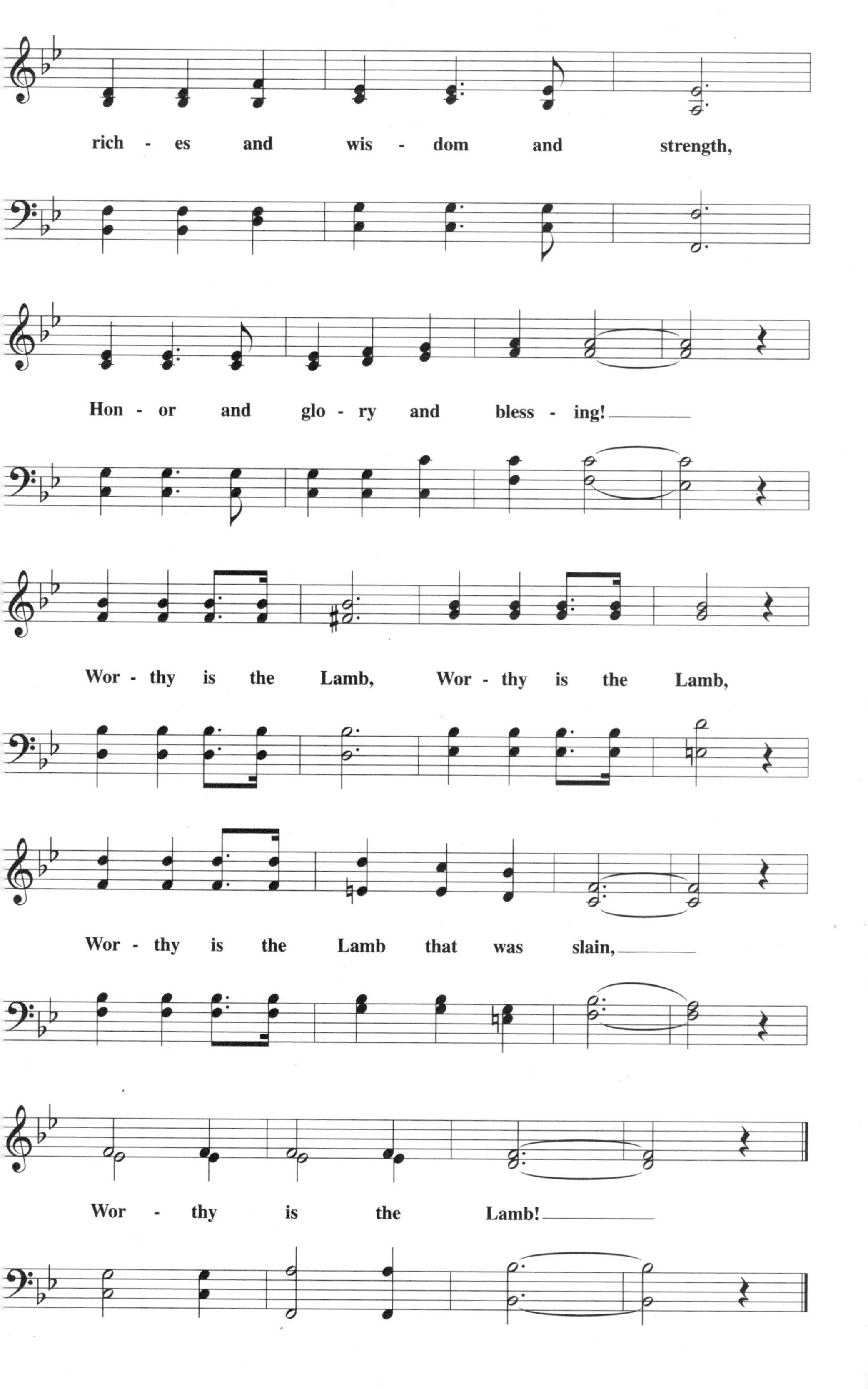
rich - es and wis - dom and strength,
Hon - or and glo - ry and bless - ing!
Wor - thy is the Lamb, Wor - thy is the Lamb,
Wor - thy is the Lamb that was slain,
Wor - thy is the Lamb!

120 The Strong Name of Jesus

CLAIRE CLONINGER

MORRIS CHAPMAN

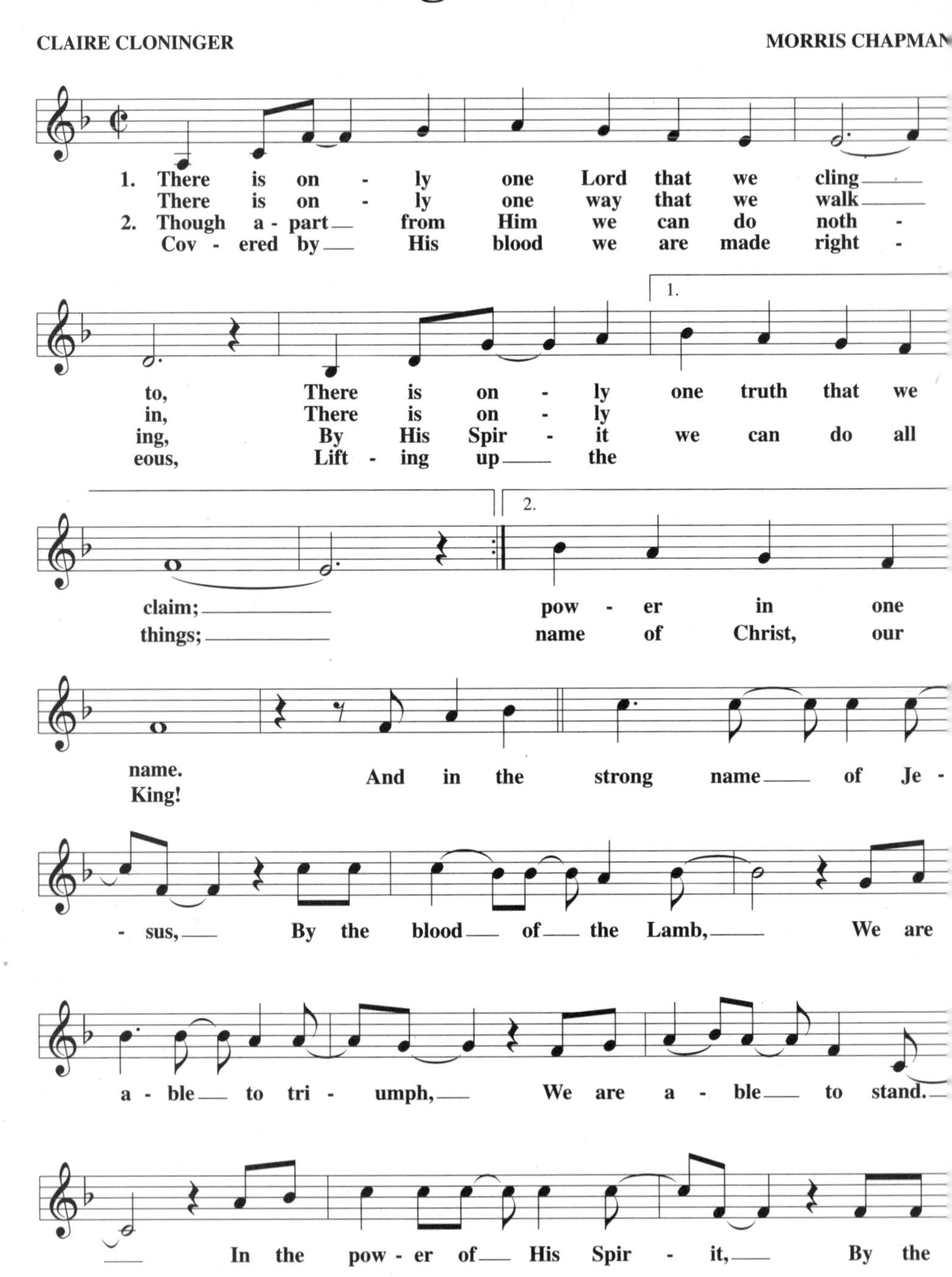

1. There is on - ly one Lord that we cling
   There is on - ly one way that we walk
2. Though a - part from Him we can do noth -
   Cov - ered by His blood we are made right -

to, There is on - ly one truth that we
in, There is on - ly
ing, By His Spir - it we can do all
eous, Lift - ing up the

claim; pow - er in one
things; name of Christ, our

name. And in the strong name of Je -
King!

- sus, By the blood of the Lamb, We are

a - ble to tri - umph, We are a - ble to stand.

In the pow - er of His Spir - it, By the

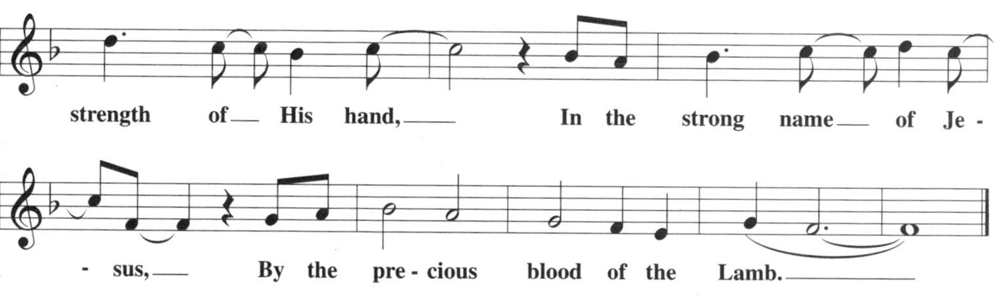

strength of — His hand, — In the strong name — of Je -
- sus, — By the pre - cious blood of the Lamb. —

Celebrate Jesus

121

GARY OLIVER

GARY OLIVER

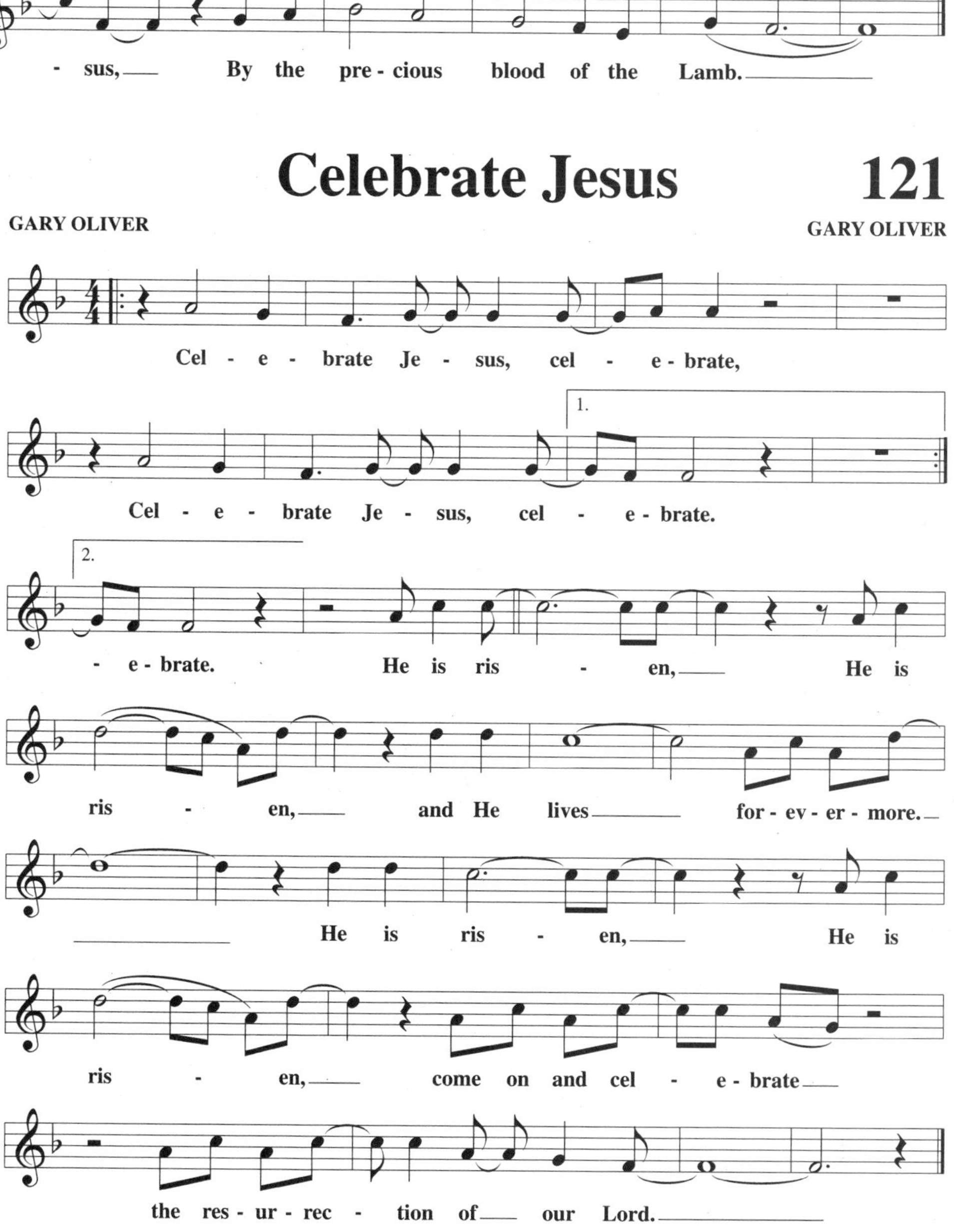

Cel - e - brate Je - sus, cel - e - brate,

Cel - e - brate Je - sus, cel - e - brate.

- e - brate. He is ris - en, — He is

ris - en, — and He lives — for - ev - er - more. —

He is ris - en, — He is

ris - en, — come on and cel - e - brate —

the res - ur - rec - tion of — our Lord. —

122

He Is Lord

TRADITIONAL

TRADITIONAL
Arranged by Tom Fettke

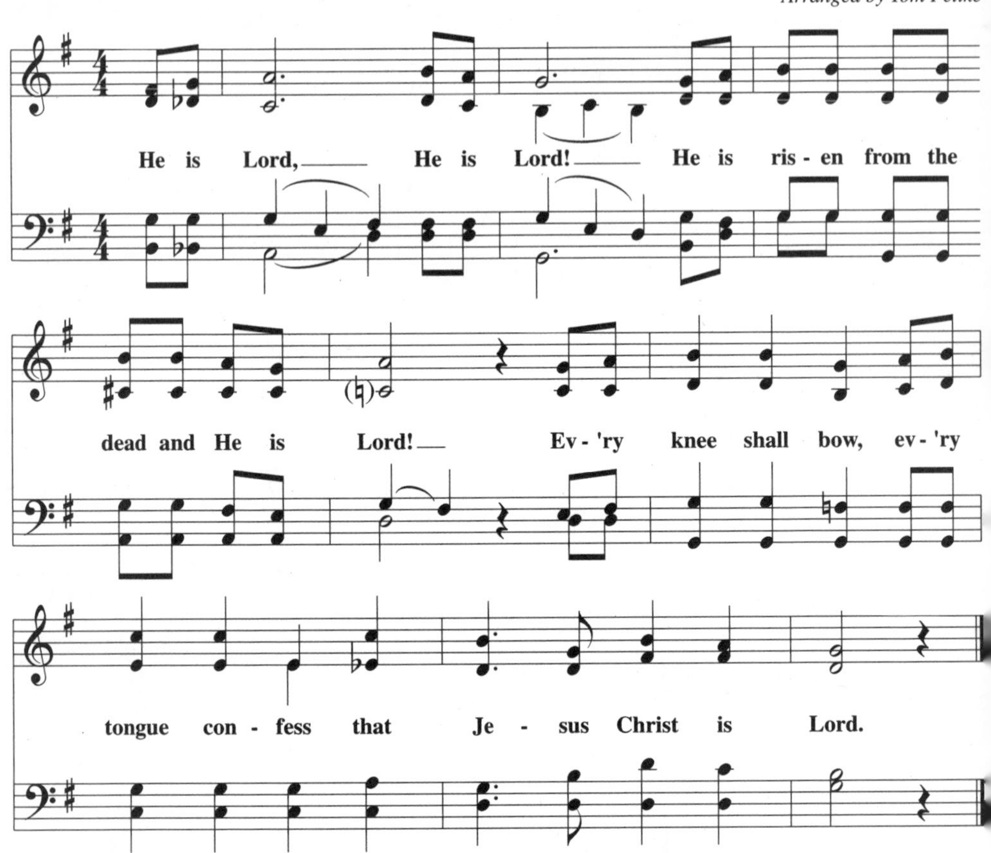

He is Lord, He is Lord! He is ris-en from the
dead and He is Lord! Ev-'ry knee shall bow, ev-'ry
tongue con-fess that Je-sus Christ is Lord.

123

Because He Lives

Words and Music by
WILLIAM J. and GLORIA GAITHER

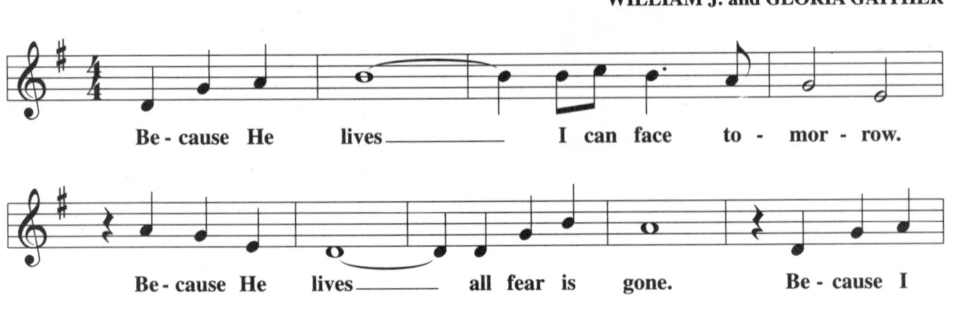

Be-cause He lives I can face to-mor-row.
Be-cause He lives all fear is gone. Be-cause I

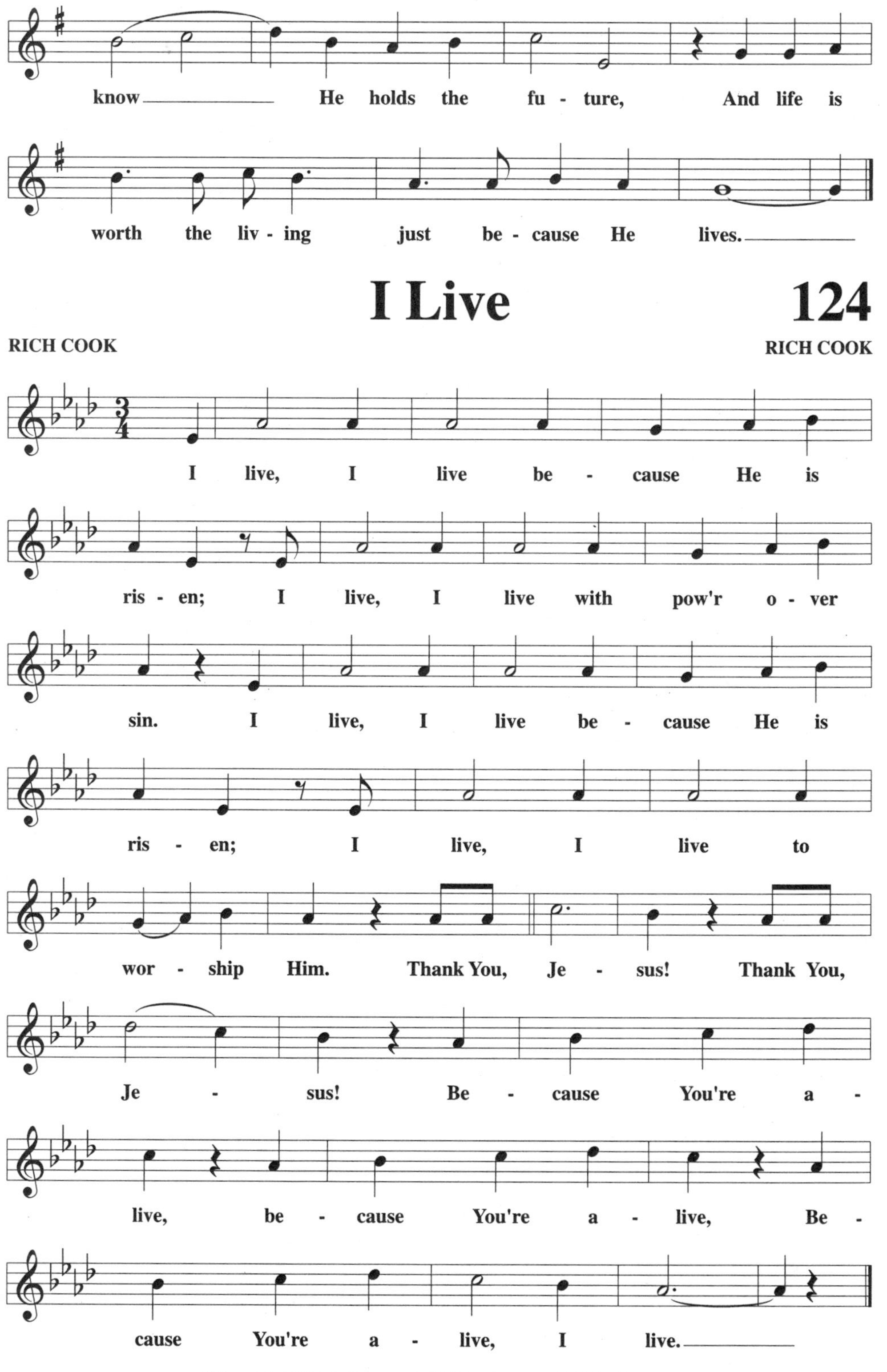

know ____ He holds the fu - ture, And life is

worth the liv - ing just be - cause He lives. ____

I Live

124

RICH COOK

RICH COOK

I live, I live be - cause He is

ris - en; I live, I live with pow'r o - ver

sin. I live, I live be - cause He is

ris - en; I live, I live to

wor - ship Him. Thank You, Je - sus! Thank You,

Je - sus! Be - cause You're a -

live, be - cause You're a - live, Be -

cause You're a - live, I live. ____

125 For This Purpose

GRAHAM KENDRICK   GRAHAM KENDRICK

For this pur-pose Christ was re-vealed,____

to de - stroy all the works of the e - vil one.____

Christ in us has o - ver - come, so with

glad-ness we sing____ and wel-come His king - dom in.____ O - ver

optional parts

sin   He has con - quered, Hal - le - lu - jah! He has con - quered, o - ver

death,   vic - to - rious, Hal - le - lu - jah! vic - to - rious; O - ver

sick - ness, He has tri - umphed, Hal - le - lu - jah! He has tri - umphed,

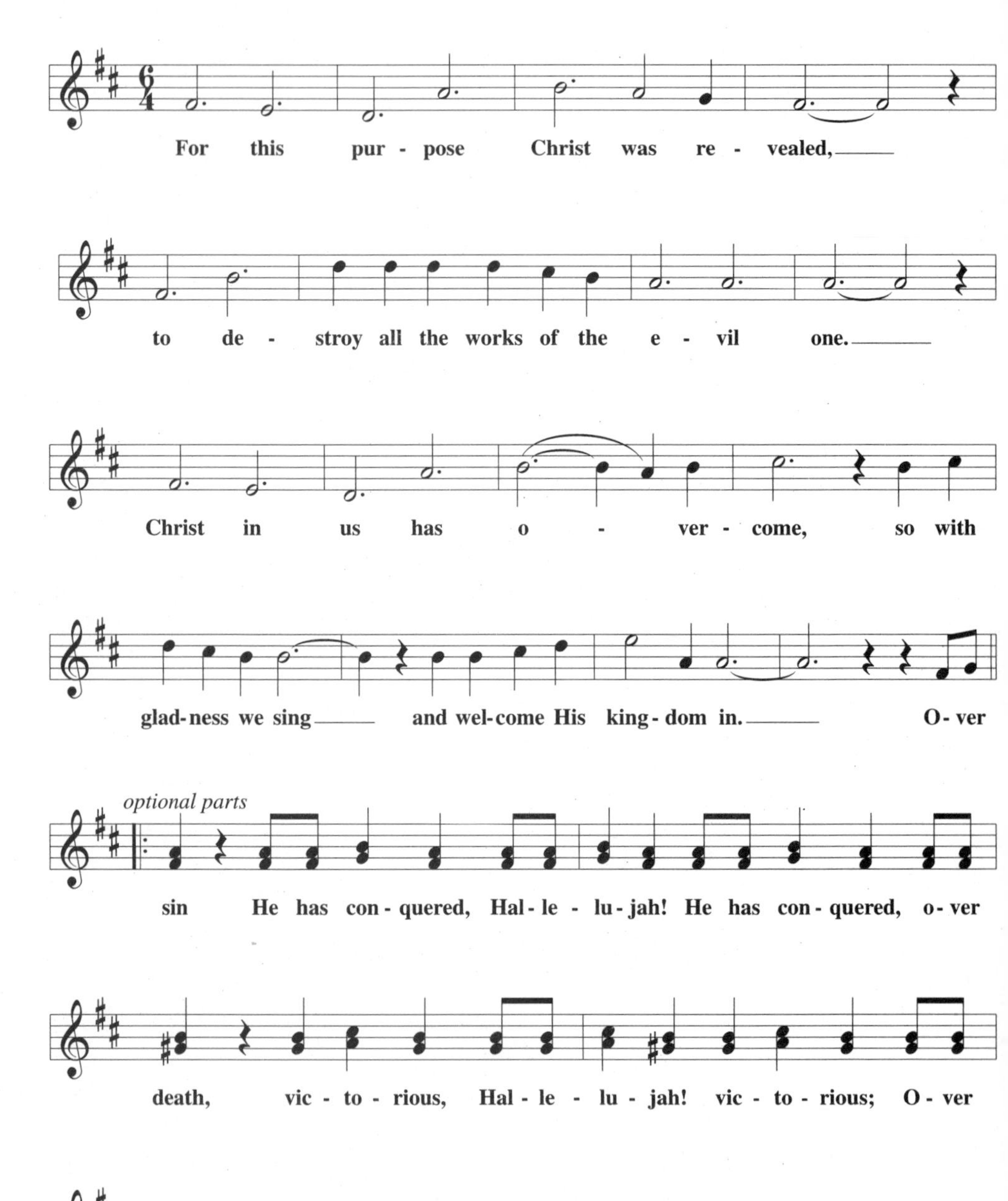

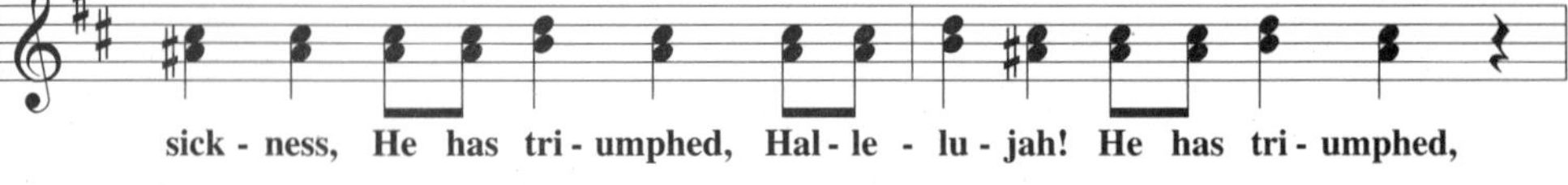

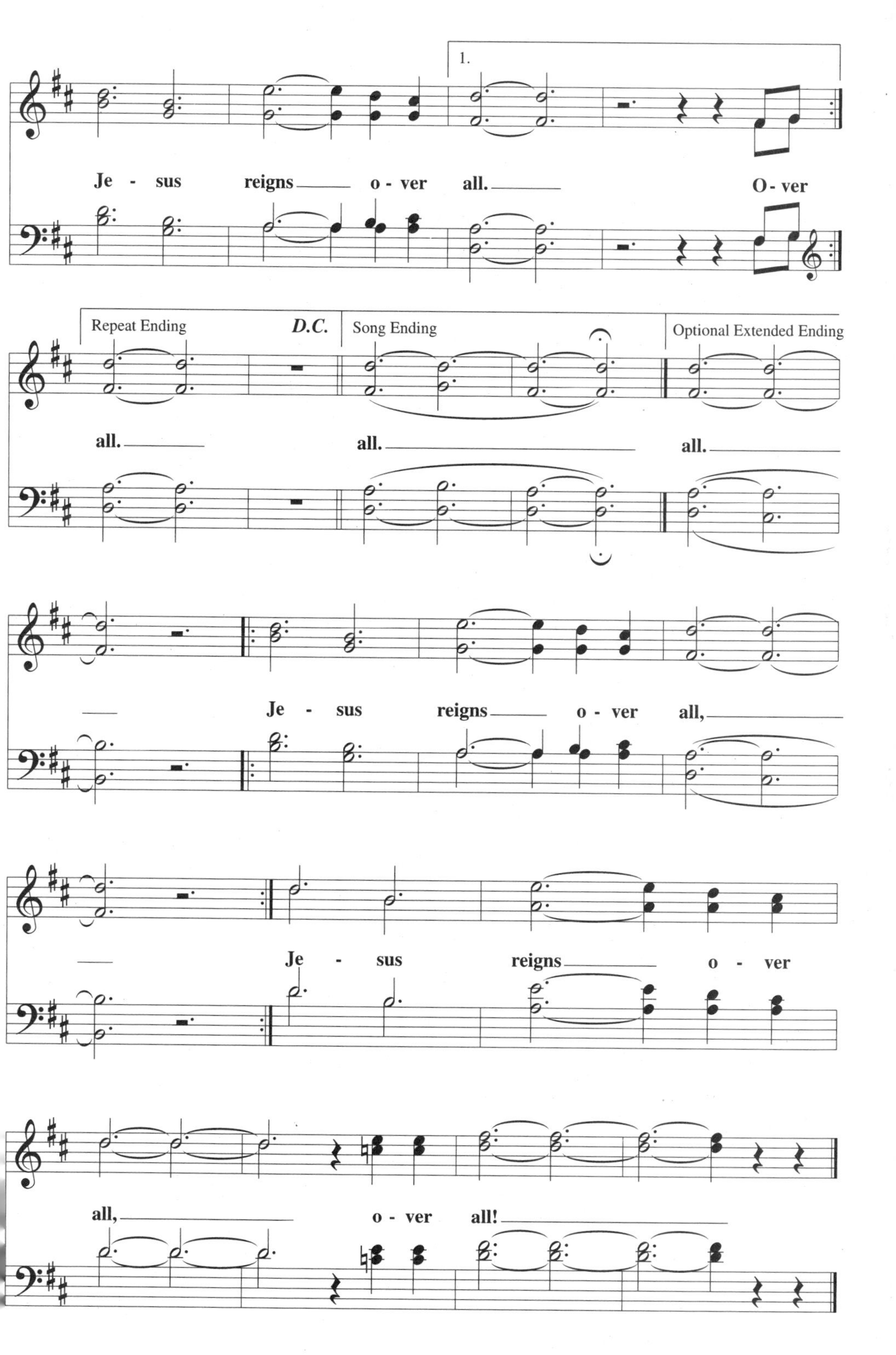
1.
Je - sus reigns o - ver all.
O - ver
Repeat Ending
D.C.
Song Ending
Optional Extended Ending
all.
all.
all.
Je - sus reigns o - ver all,
Je - sus reigns o - ver
all,
o - ver all!

126 Praise to the Holy One

STEVE FRY   STEVE FRY

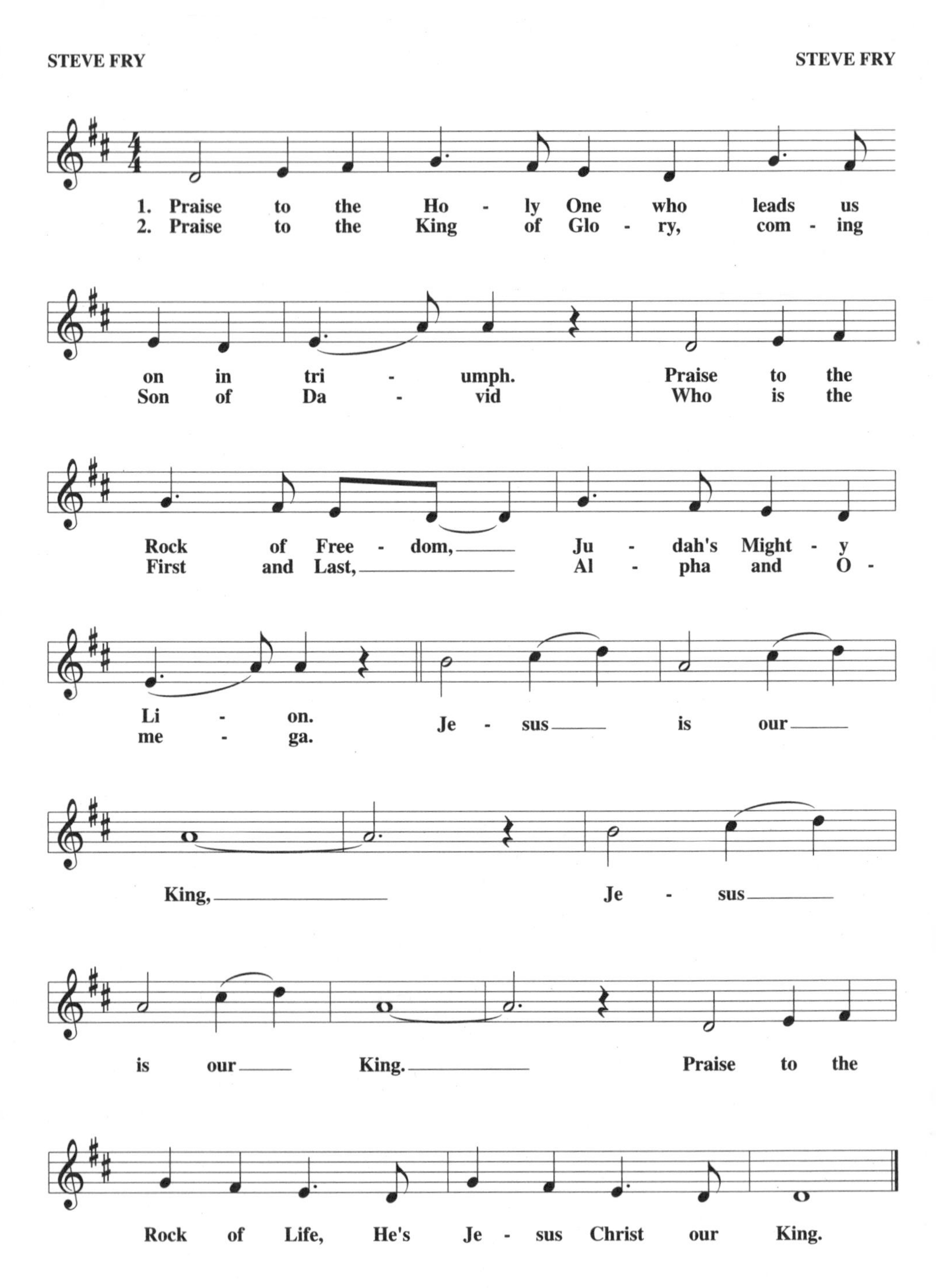

1. Praise to the Ho - ly One who leads us on in tri - umph. Praise to the Rock of Free - dom, Ju - dah's Might - y Li - on. Je - sus is our King, Je - sus is our King. Praise to the Rock of Life, He's Je - sus Christ our King.

2. Praise to the King of Glo - ry, com - ing Son of Da - vid Who is the First and Last, Al - pha and O - me - ga.

Lift Up Your Heads

127

STEVE FRY

STEVE FRY

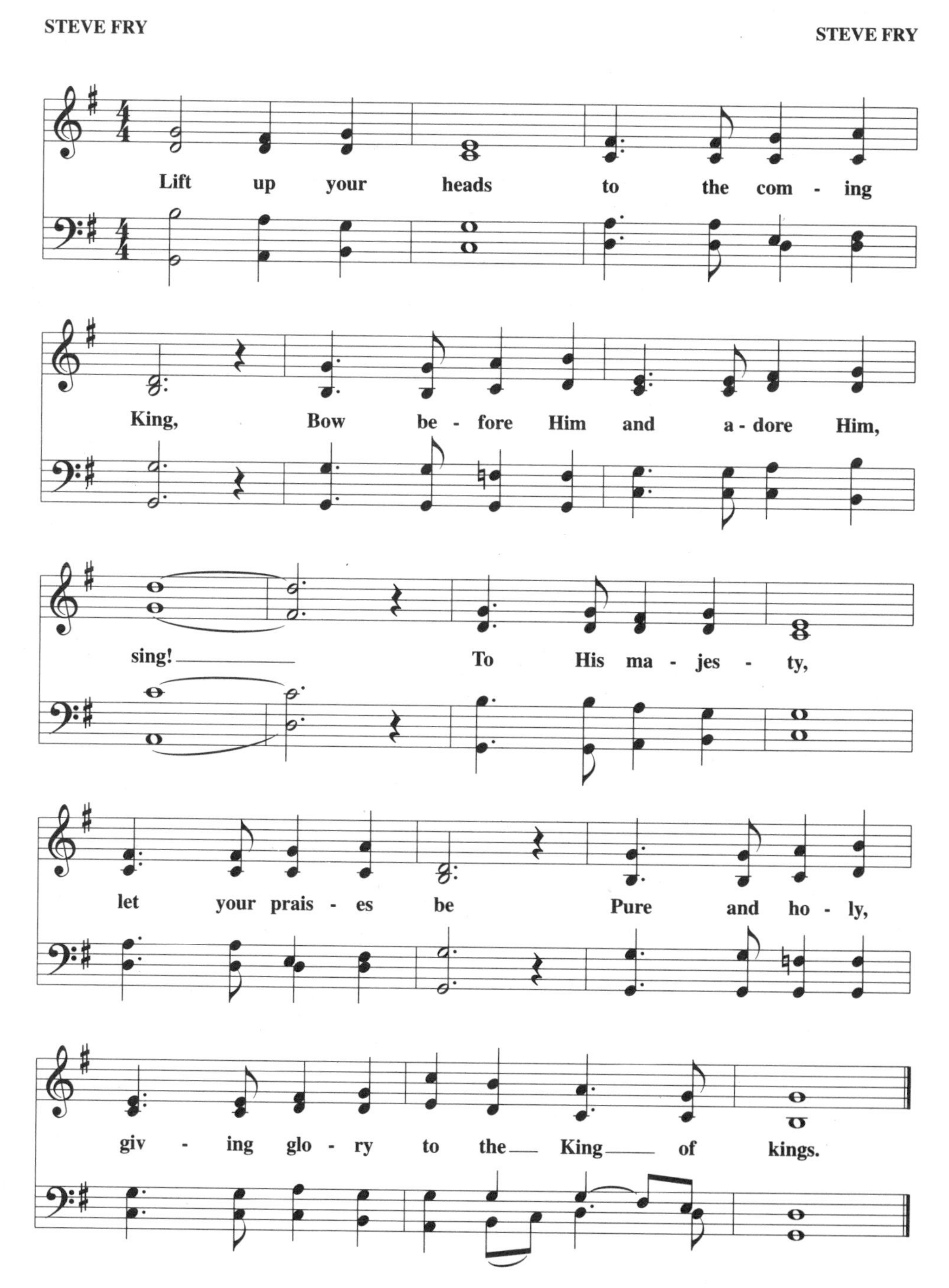

Lift up your heads to the com-ing King, Bow be-fore Him and a-dore Him, sing! To His ma-jes-ty, let your prais-es be Pure and ho-ly, giv-ing glo-ry to the King of kings.

128 The Trees of the Field

STEFFI GEISER RUBIN
Based on Isaiah 55:12

STUART DAUERMANN

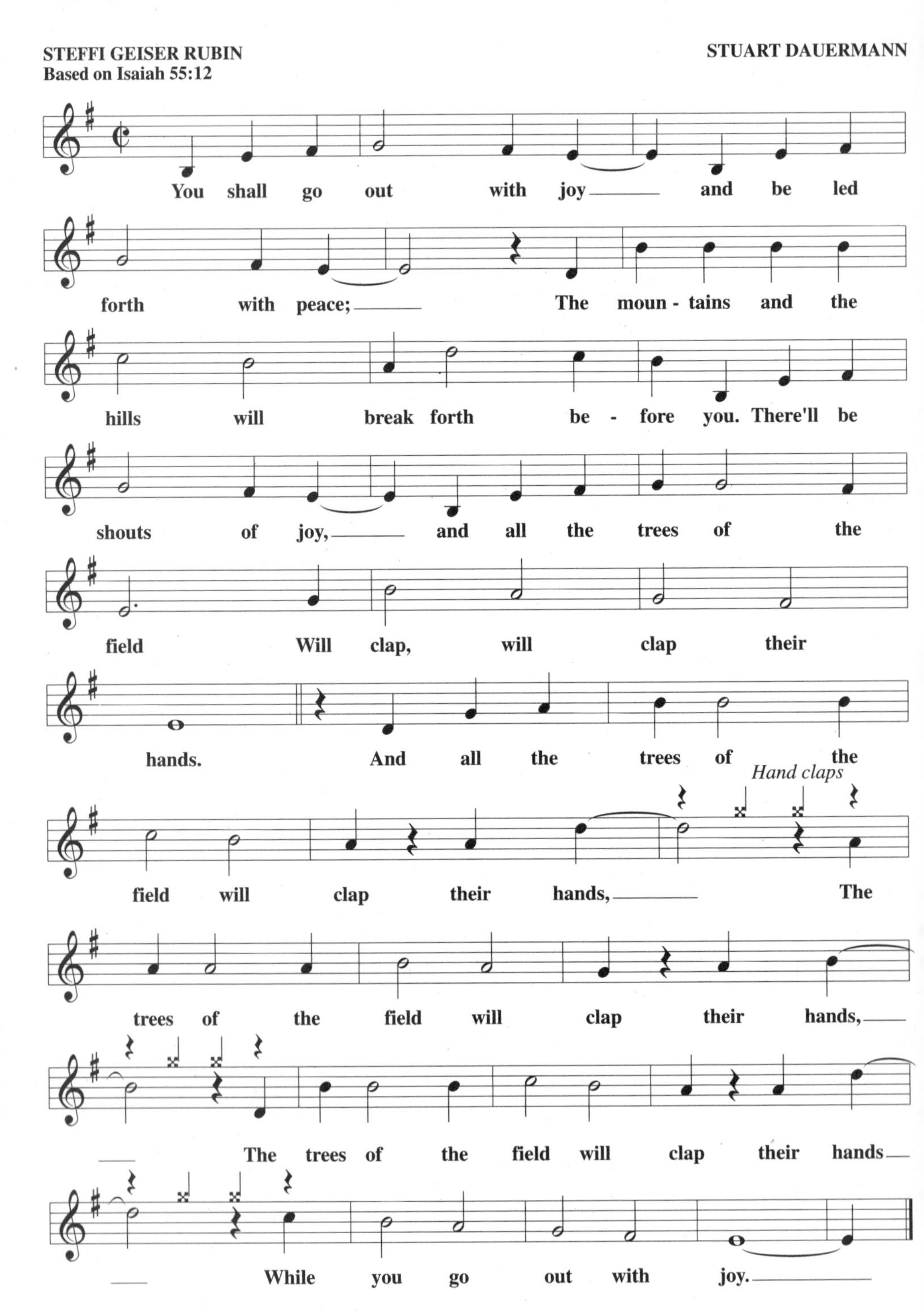

You shall go out with joy and be led forth with peace; The moun-tains and the hills will break forth be-fore you. There'll be shouts of joy, and all the trees of the field Will clap, will clap their hands. And all the trees of the

Hand claps

field will clap their hands, The trees of the field will clap their hands, The trees of the field will clap their hands While you go out with joy.

Therefore the Redeemed of the Lord   129

RUTH LAKE

RUTH LAKE

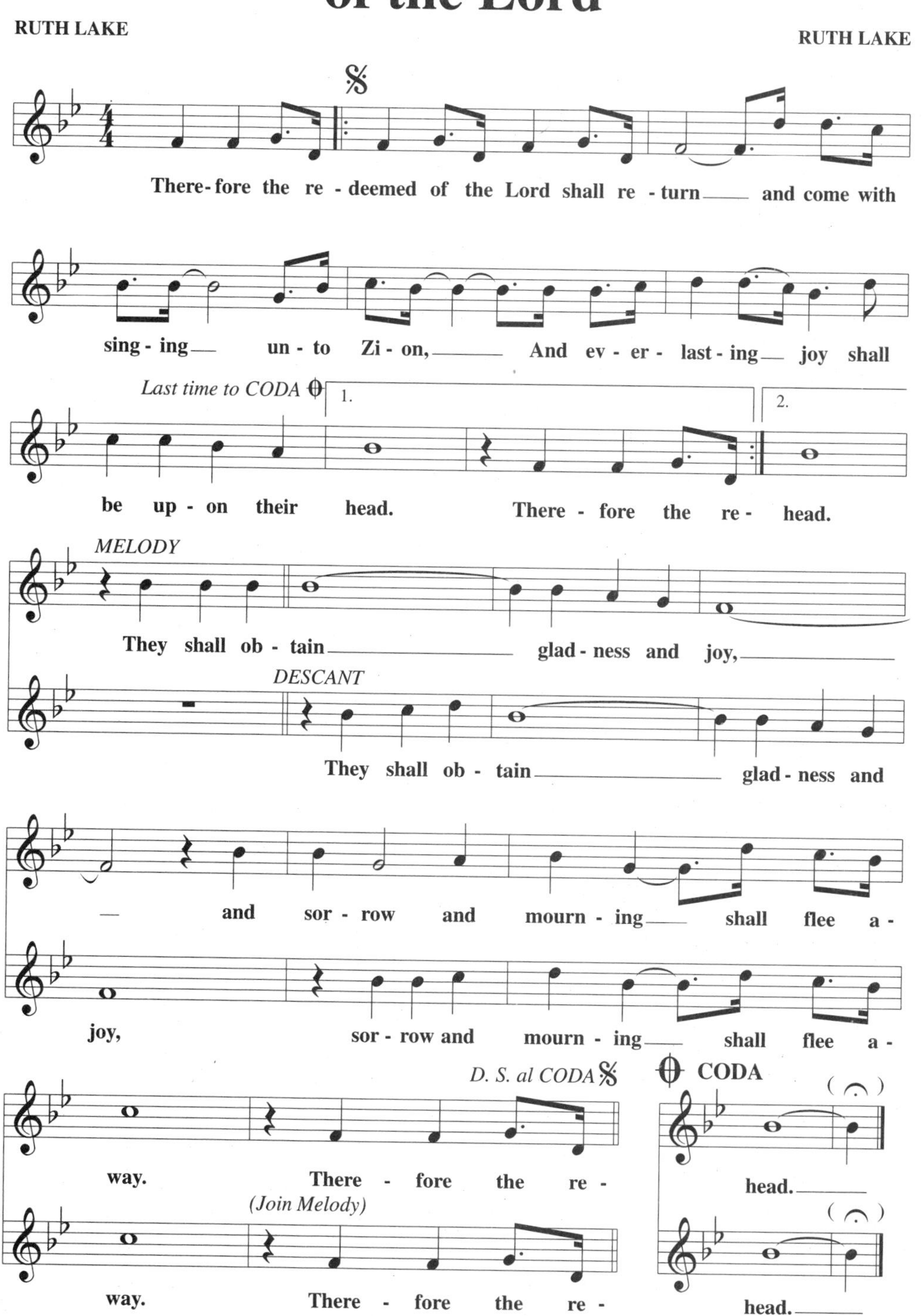

130 While We Are Waiting, Come

CLAIRE CLONINGER

DON CASON

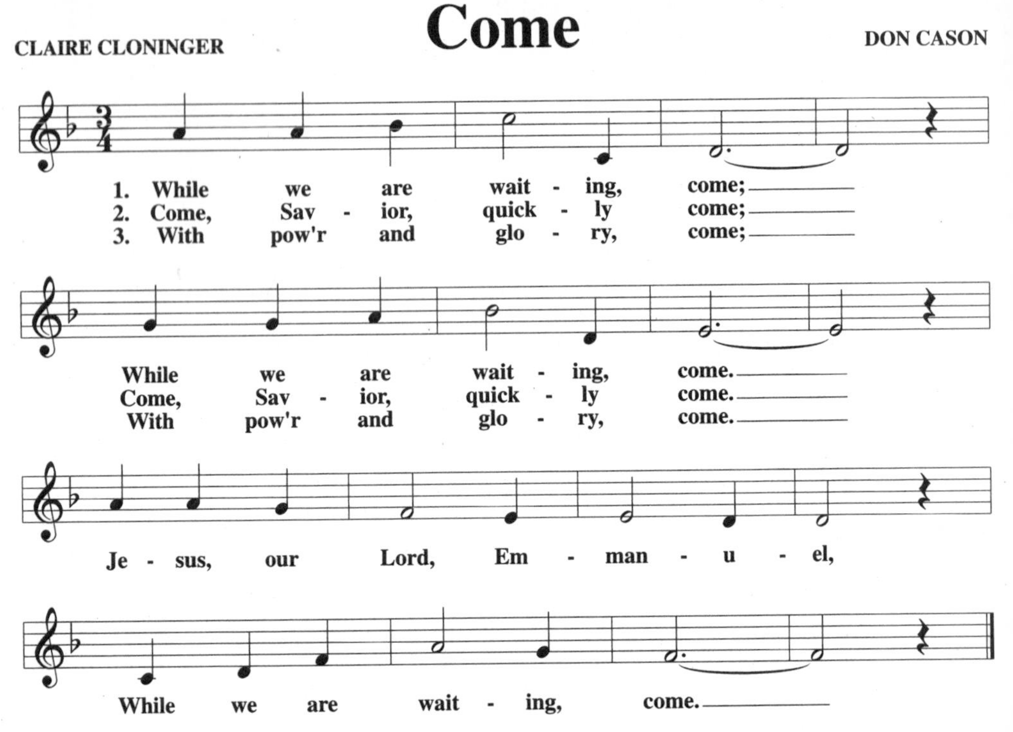

1. While we are wait - ing, come;
2. Come, Sav - ior, quick - ly come;
3. With pow'r and glo - ry, come;

While we are wait - ing, come.
Come, Sav - ior, quick - ly come.
With pow'r and glo - ry, come.

Je - sus, our Lord, Em - man - u - el,

While we are wait - ing, come.

131 Spirit of the Living God

DANIEL IVERSON

DANIEL IVERSON

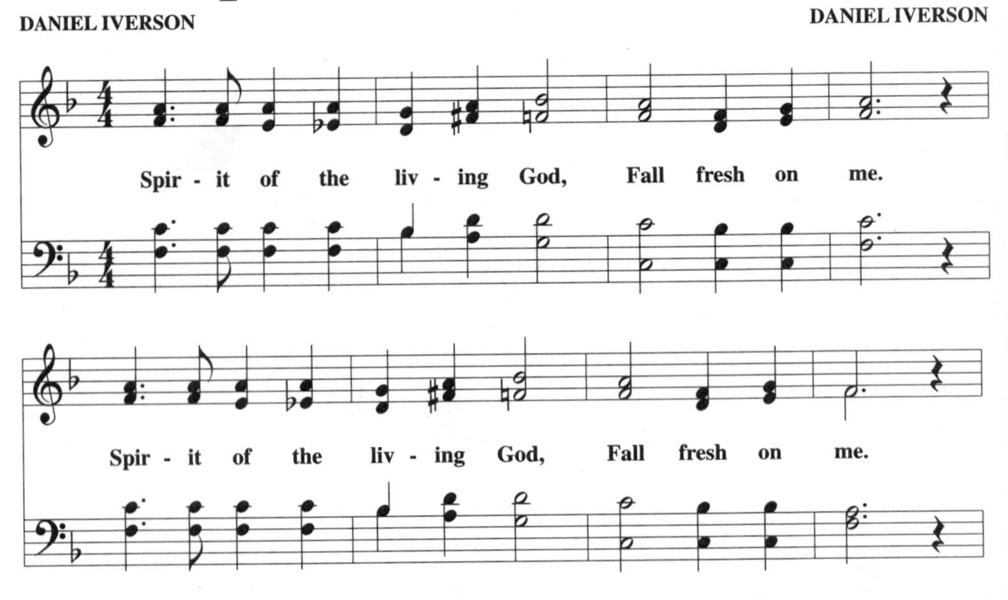

Spir - it of the liv - ing God, Fall fresh on me.

Spir - it of the liv - ing God, Fall fresh on me.

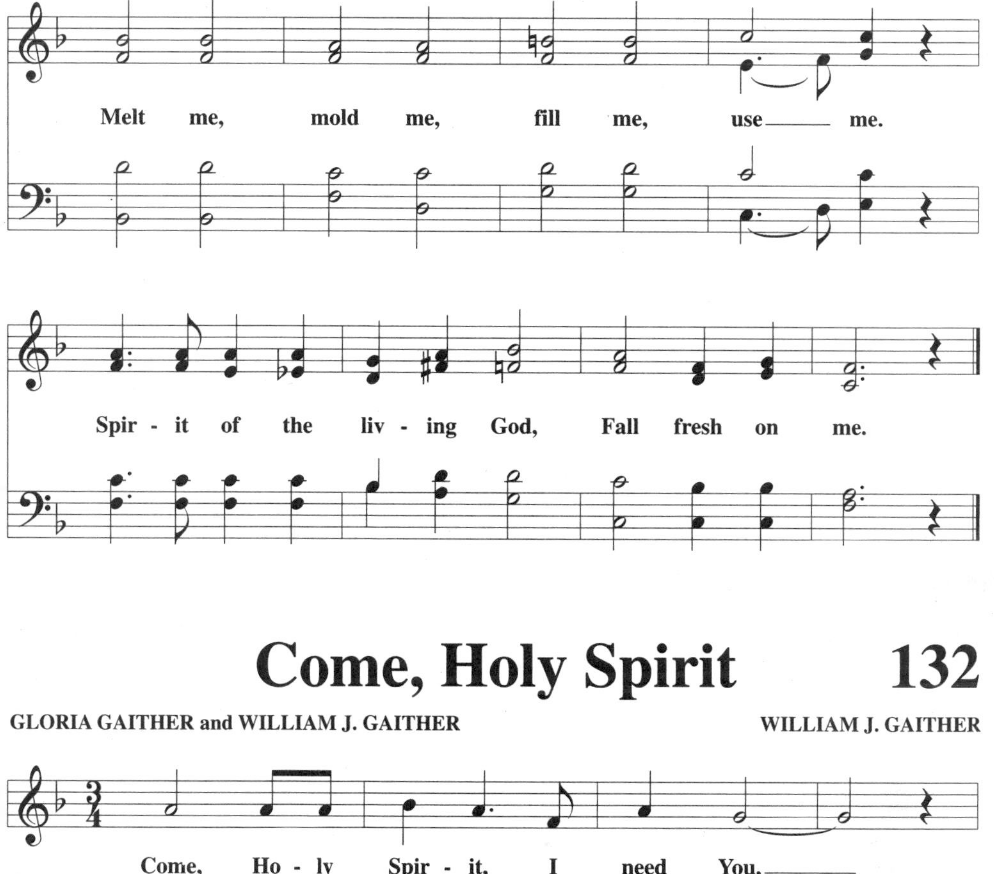

Melt me, mold me, fill me, use____ me.

Spir - it of the liv - ing God, Fall fresh on me.

Come, Holy Spirit 132

GLORIA GAITHER and WILLIAM J. GAITHER

WILLIAM J. GAITHER

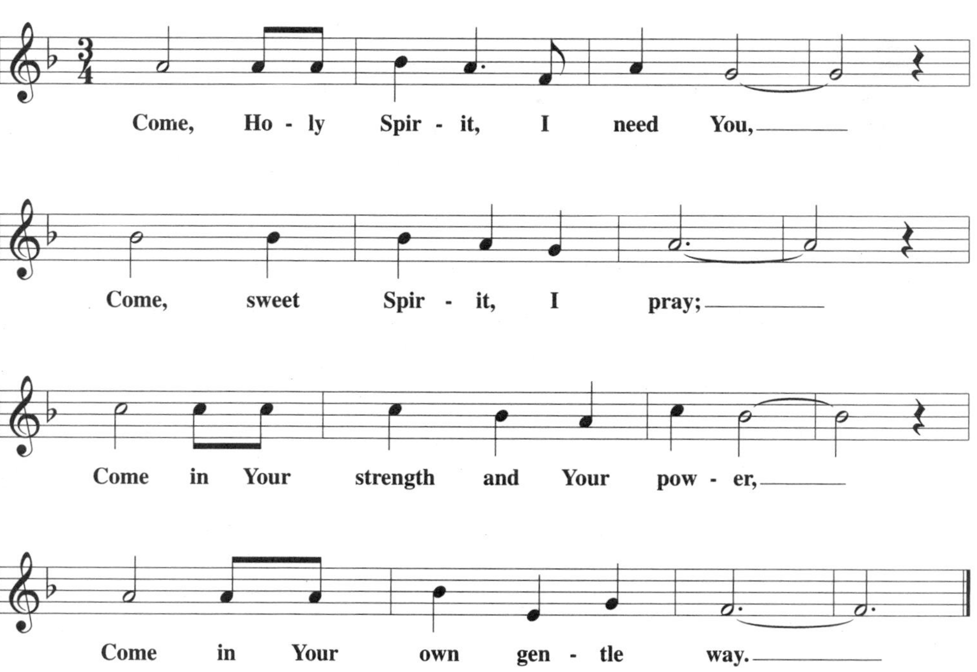

Come, Ho - ly Spir - it, I need You,____

Come, sweet Spir - it, I pray;____

Come in Your strength and Your pow - er,____

Come in Your own gen - tle way.____

Holy Spirit, Thou Art Welcome

133

Words and Music by
DOTTIE RAMBO and DAVID HUNTSINGER

Ho-ly Spir-it, Thou art wel-come in this place. Ho-ly Spir-it, Thou art wel-come in this place. Om-ni-po-tent Fa-ther of mer-cy and grace, Thou art wel-come in___ this place.___

Spirit Song

134

JOHN WIMBER

JOHN WIMBER

1. O let the Son of God en-fold you with His Spir-it and His
2. O come and sing the song of glad-ness as your hearts are filled with

love, Let Him fill your life and sat-is-fy___ your soul.
joy, Lift your hands in sweet sur-ren-der to___ His name.

O let Him have the things that hold you and His Spir-it, like a
O give Him all your tears and sad-ness, give Him all your years of

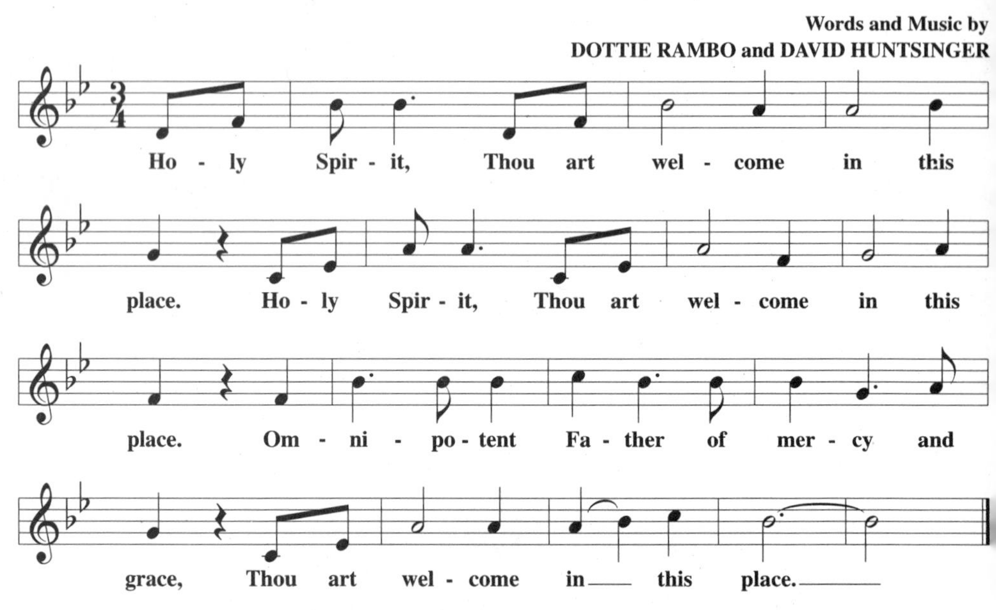

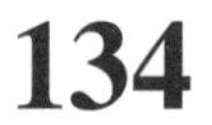

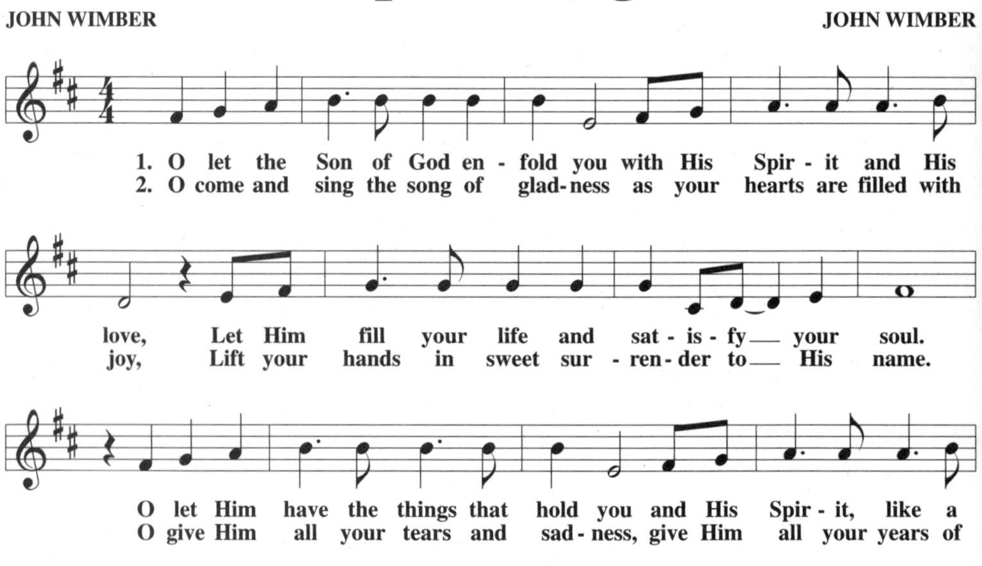

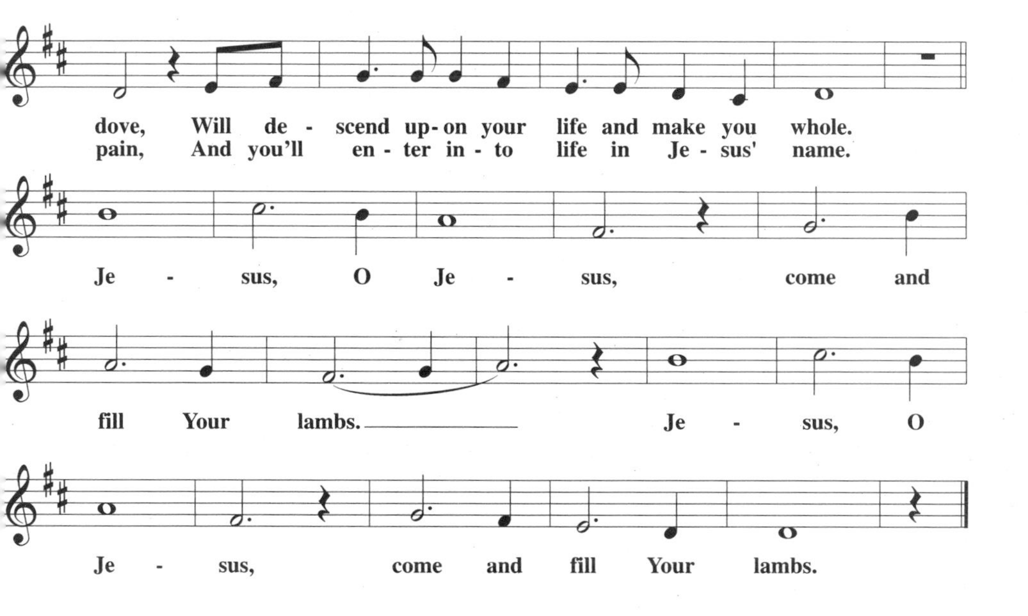

dove, Will de - scend up-on your life and make you whole.
pain, And you'll en - ter in - to life in Je - sus' name.

Je - sus, O Je - sus, come and

fill Your lambs. _____ Je - sus, O

Je - sus, come and fill Your lambs.

Spirit of God
135

Words and Music by
BARBARA ROSS and ROBERT TILL

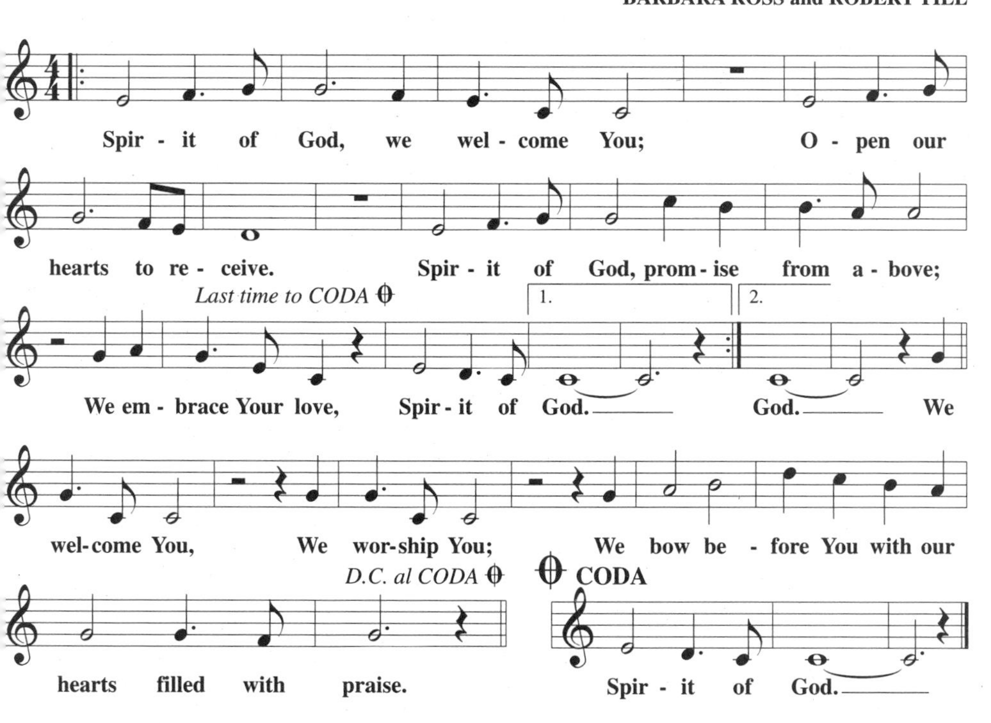

Spir - it of God, we wel - come You; O - pen our

hearts to re - ceive. Spir - it of God, prom - ise from a - bove;

Last time to CODA ⊕

1.
2.

We em - brace Your love, Spir - it of God. _____ God. _____ We

wel-come You, We wor-ship You; We bow be - fore You with our

D.C. al CODA ⊕   ⊕ CODA

hearts filled with praise.   Spir - it of God. _____

136 Sweet, Sweet Spirit

DORIS AKERS

DORIS AKERS

There's a sweet, sweet Spir - it in this place,⎯ And I
sweet ex - pres - sions on each face,⎯ And I

know that it's the Spir - it of⎯the Lord;⎯ There are
know that it's the pres - ence of⎯the Lord.⎯

Sweet Ho - ly Spir - it, Sweet heav - en - ly Dove, Stay right here

with⎯us, fill - ing us with⎯Your love; And for these bless - ings We

lift our hearts in praise; With-out a doubt we'll know⎯ that we have

been re - vived,⎯ when we shall leave this place.⎯

Make Us One 137

AROL CYMBALA

CAROL CYMBALA

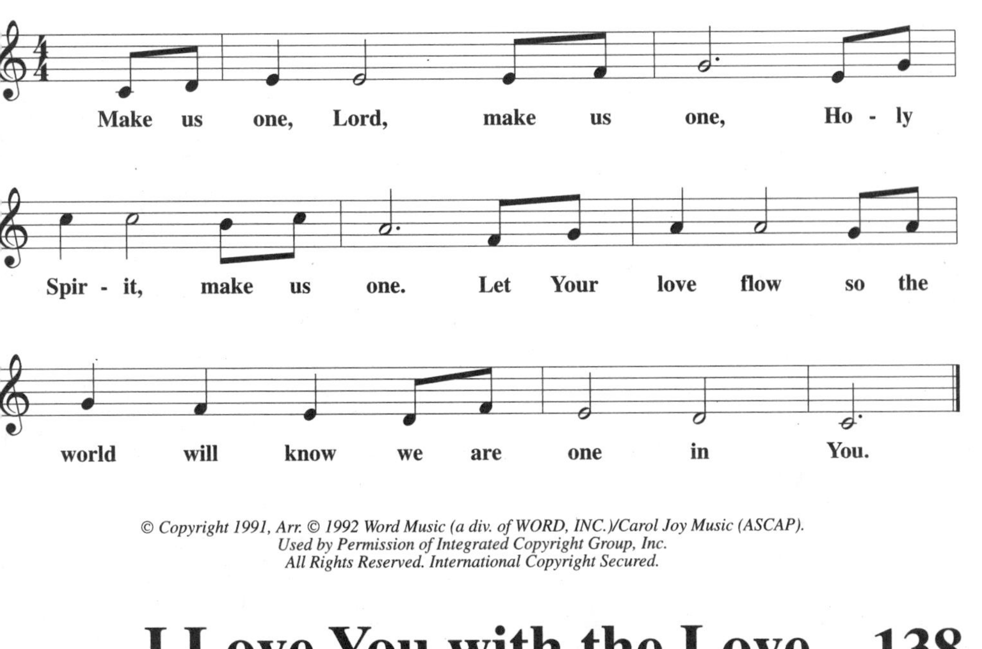

Make us one, Lord, make us one, Ho - ly
Spir - it, make us one. Let Your love flow so the
world will know we are one in You.

I Love You with the Love of the Lord 138

IM GILBERT

JIM GILBERT

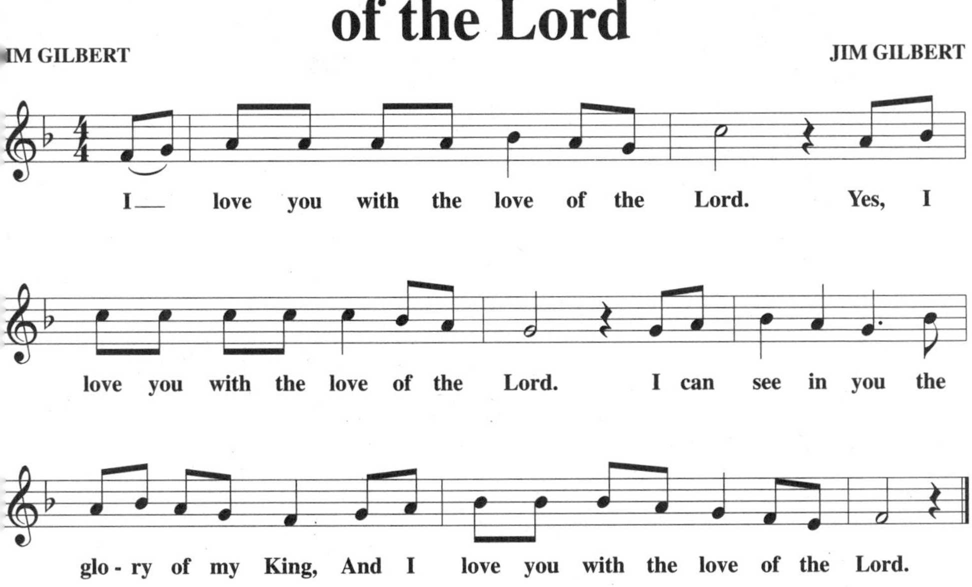

I— love you with the love of the Lord. Yes, I
love you with the love of the Lord. I can see in you the
glo - ry of my King, And I love you with the love of the Lord.

139 People of God

WAYNE WATSON

WAYNE WATSON

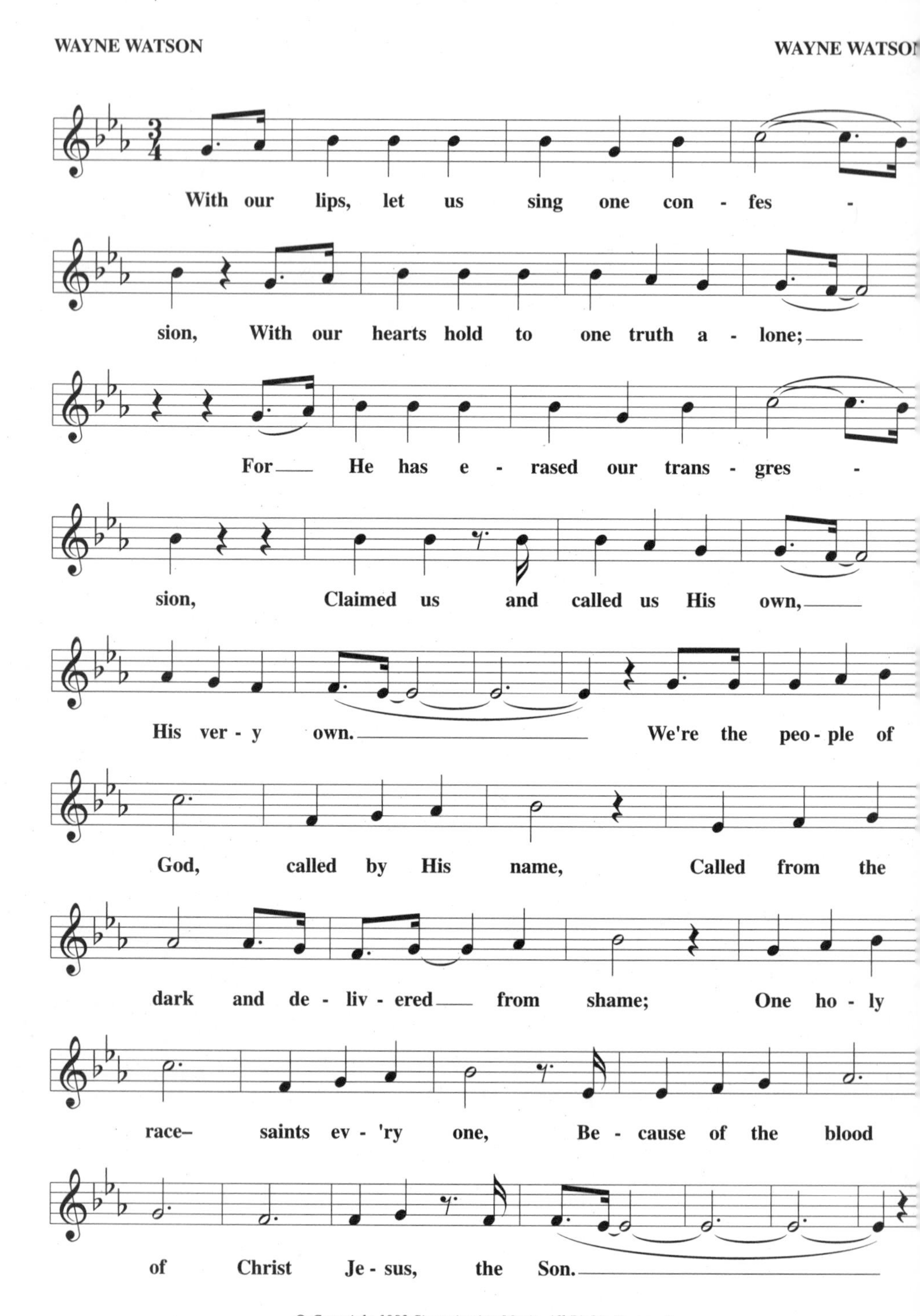

With our lips, let us sing one con - fes -
sion, With our hearts hold to one truth a - lone;____
For____ He has e - rased our trans - gres -
sion, Claimed us and called us His own,____
His ver - y own._____ We're the peo - ple of
God, called by His name, Called from the
dark and de - liv - ered____ from shame; One ho - ly
race– saints ev - 'ry one, Be - cause of the blood
of Christ Je - sus, the Son._____

Bind Us Together

OB GILLMAN

BOB GILLMAN

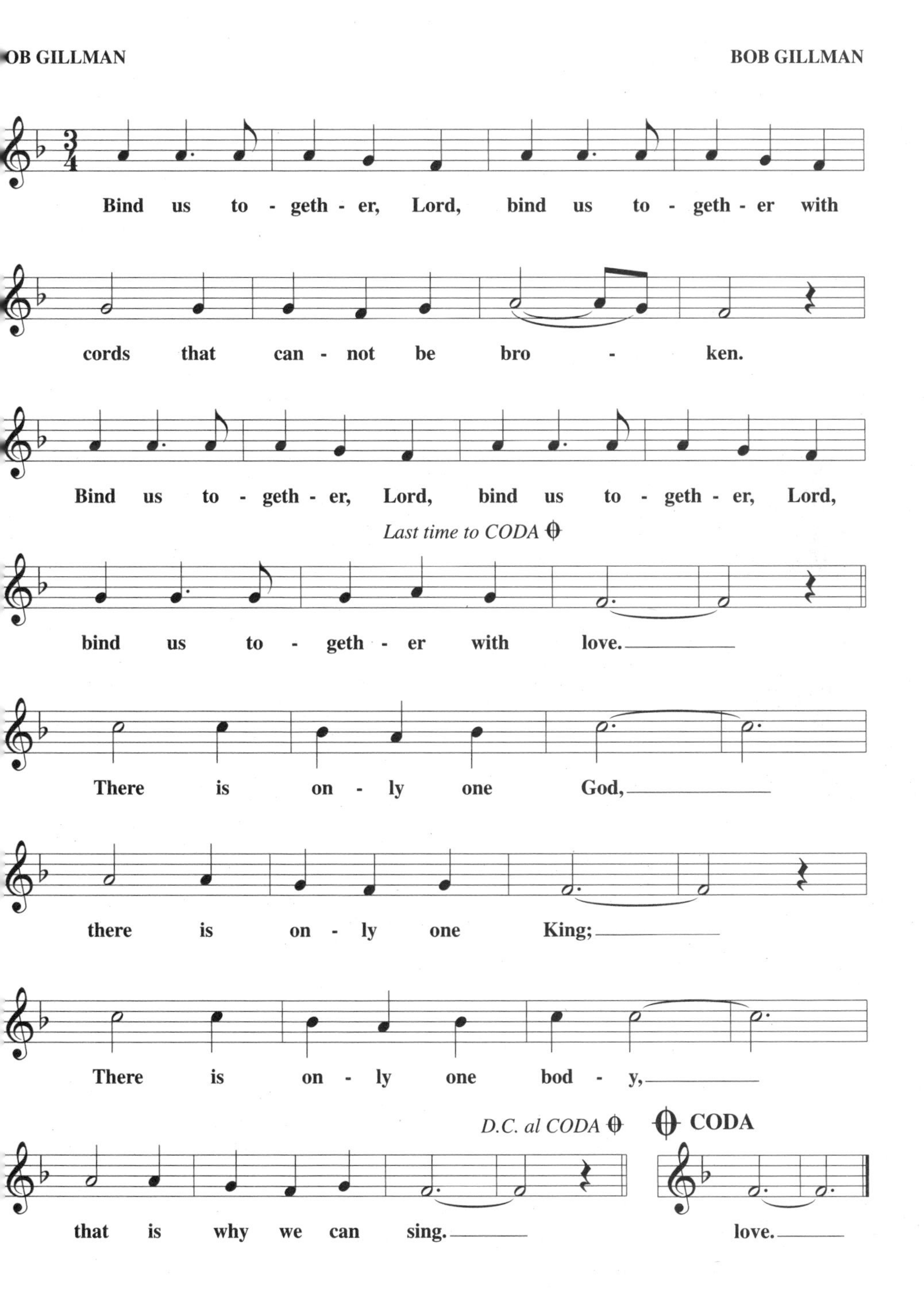

141 Holy, Holy

JIMMY OWENS

JIMMY OWENS

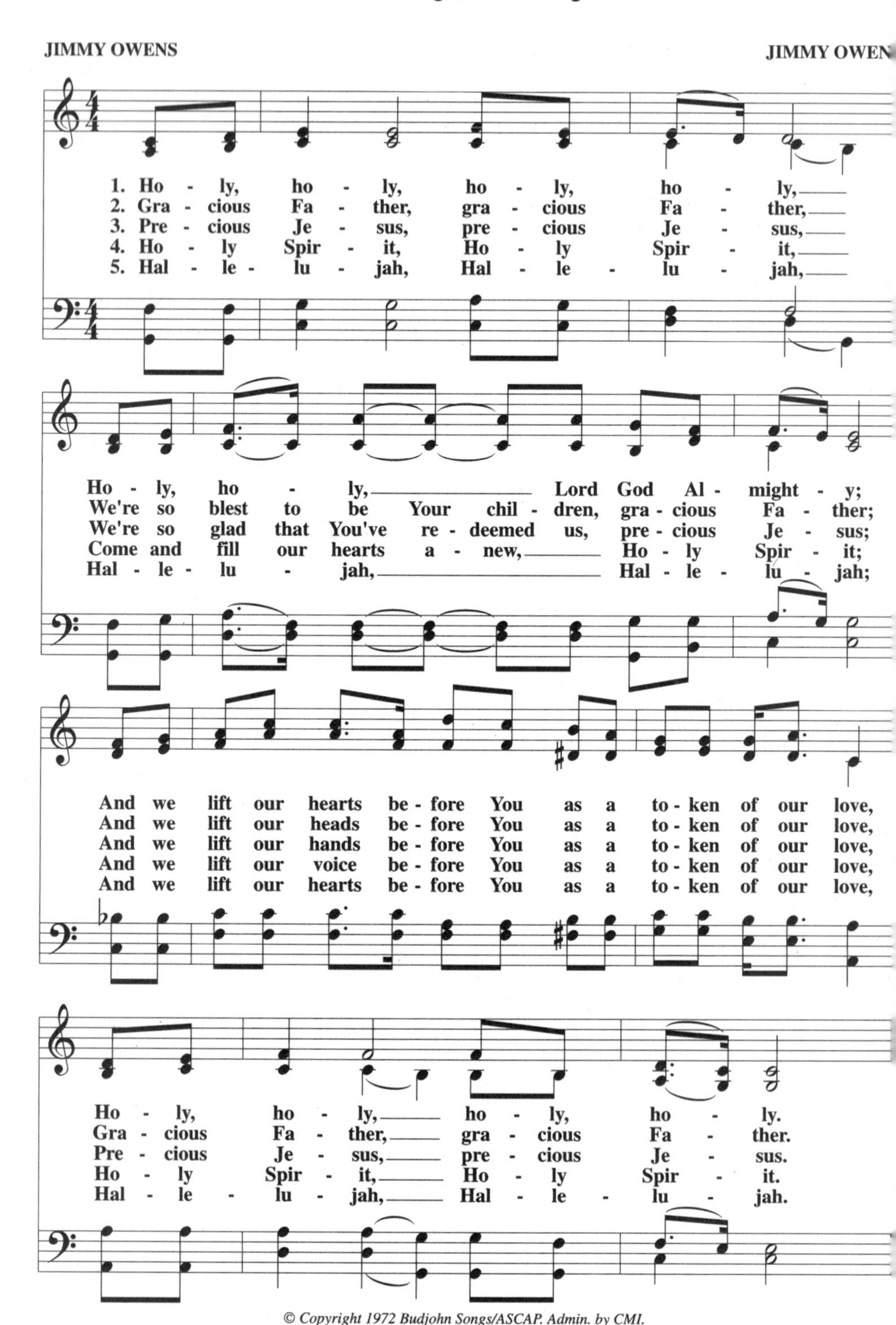

1. Ho - ly, ho - ly, ho - ly, ho - ly,____
2. Gra - cious Fa - ther, gra - cious Fa - ther,____
3. Pre - cious Je - sus, pre - cious Je - sus,____
4. Ho - ly Spir - it, Ho - ly Spir - it,____
5. Hal - le - lu - jah, Hal - le - lu - jah,____

Ho - ly, ho - ly,____ Lord God Al - might - y;
We're so blest to be Your chil - dren, gra - cious Fa - ther,
We're so glad that You've re - deemed us, pre - cious Je - sus;
Come and fill our hearts a - new,____ Ho - ly Spir - it;
Hal - le - lu - jah,____ Hal - le - lu - jah;

And we lift our hearts be - fore You as a to - ken of our love,
And we lift our heads be - fore You as a to - ken of our love,
And we lift our hands be - fore You as a to - ken of our love,
And we lift our voice be - fore You as a to - ken of our love,
And we lift our hearts be - fore You as a to - ken of our love,

Ho - ly, ho - ly,____ ho - ly, ho - ly.
Gra - cious Fa - ther,____ gra - cious Fa - ther.
Pre - cious Je - sus,____ pre - cious Je - sus.
Ho - ly Spir - it,____ Ho - ly Spir - it.
Hal - le - lu - jah,____ Hal - le - lu - jah.

Shine, Jesus Shine

142

GRAHAM KENDRICK

GRAHAM KENDRICK

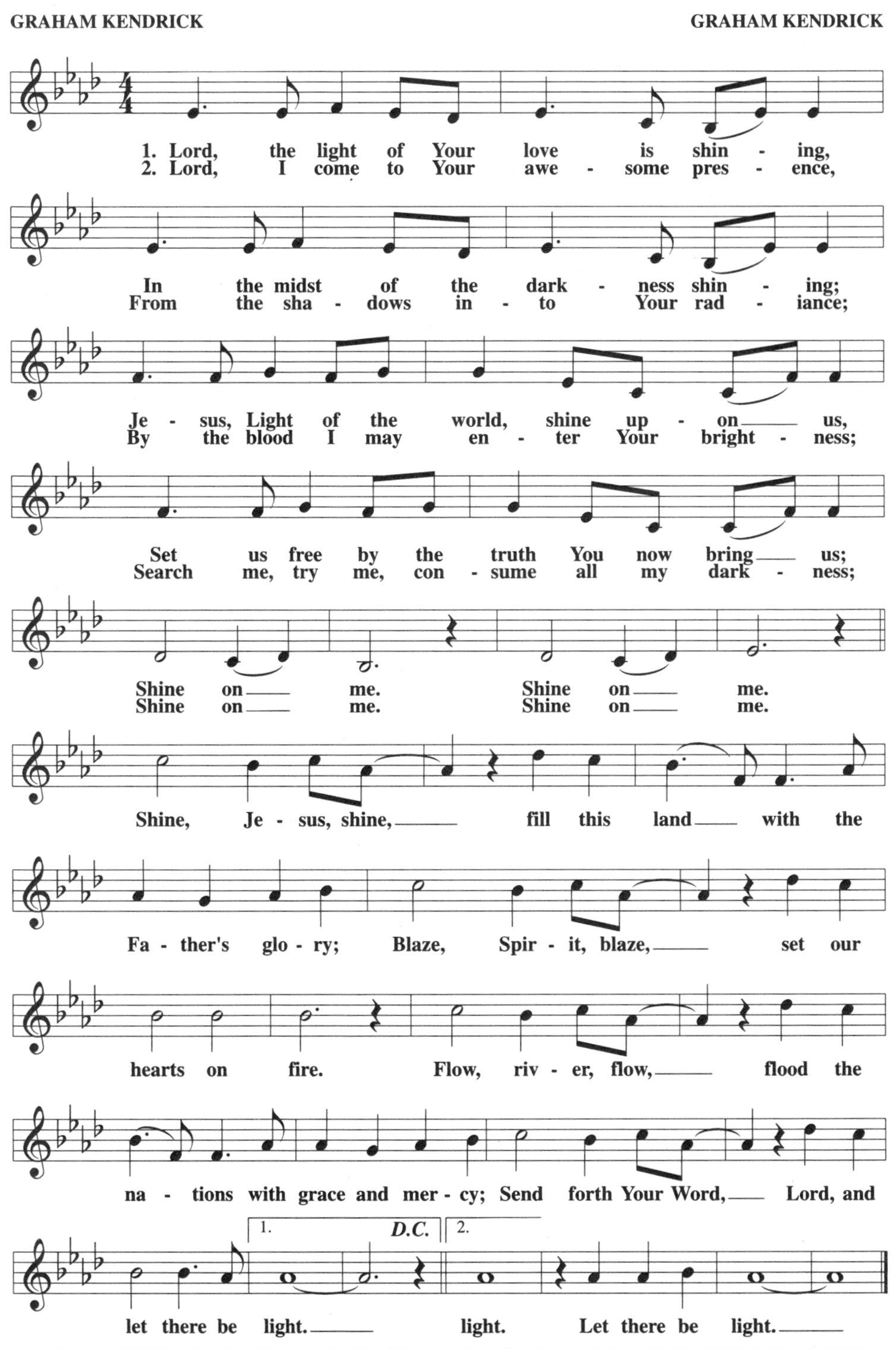

1. Lord, the light of Your love is shin - ing,
2. Lord, I come to Your awe - some pres - ence,

In the midst of the dark - ness shin - ing;
From the sha - dows in - to Your rad - iance;

Je - sus, Light of the world, shine up - on us,
By the blood I may en - ter Your bright - ness;

Set us free by the truth You now bring us;
Search me, try me, con - sume all my dark - ness;

Shine on me. Shine on me.
Shine on me. Shine on me.

Shine, Je - sus, shine, fill this land with the

Fa - ther's glo - ry; Blaze, Spir - it, blaze, set our

hearts on fire. Flow, riv - er, flow, flood the

na - tions with grace and mer - cy; Send forth Your Word, Lord, and

1. | D.C. | 2.

let there be light. light. Let there be light.

143 Carry the Light

TWILA PARIS

TWILA PARIS

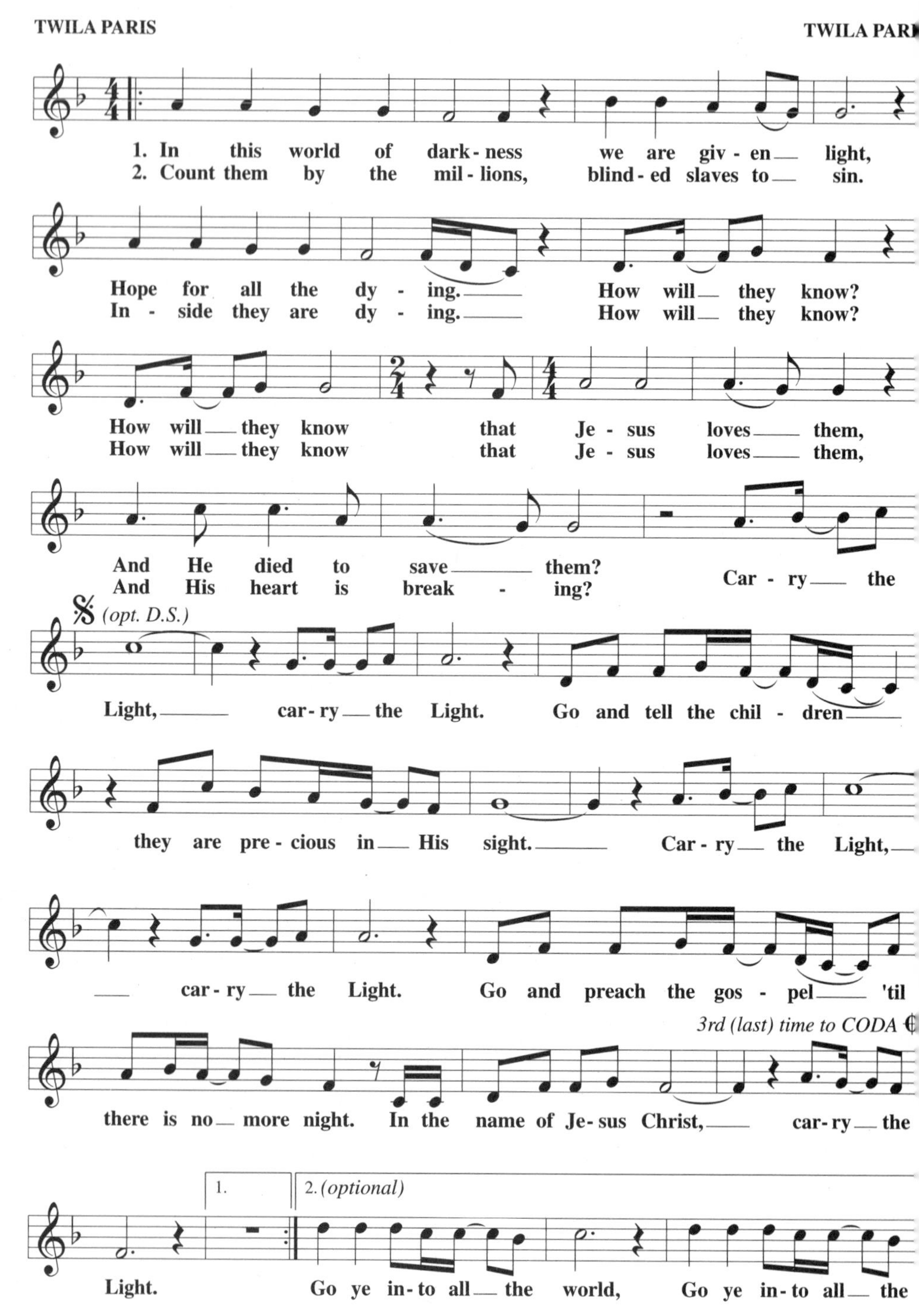

1. In this world of dark-ness we are giv-en light,
2. Count them by the mil-lions, blind-ed slaves to sin.

Hope for all the dy - ing. How will they know?
In - side they are dy - ing. How will they know?

How will they know that Je - sus loves them,
How will they know that Je - sus loves them,

And He died to save them? Car-ry the
And His heart is break - ing?

(opt. D.S.)

Light, car-ry the Light. Go and tell the chil - dren

they are pre-cious in His sight. Car-ry the Light,

car-ry the Light. Go and preach the gos-pel 'til

3rd (last) time to CODA

there is no more night. In the name of Je-sus Christ, car-ry the

1.

2. (optional)

Light. Go ye in-to all the world, Go ye in-to all the

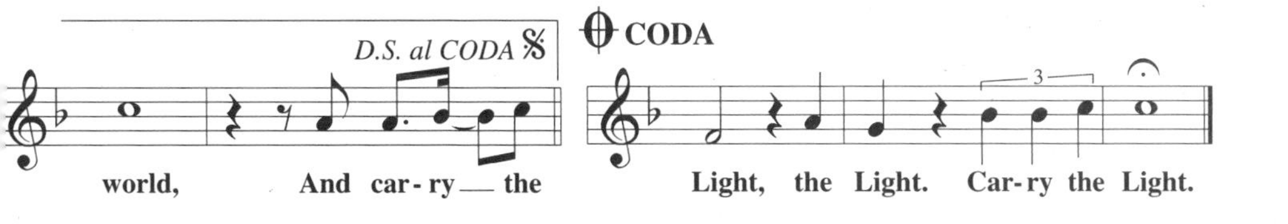

D.S. al CODA %   ⊕ CODA

world,   And car-ry — the   Light, the Light. Car-ry the Light.

Song for the Nations   144

CHRIS CHRISTENSEN   CHRIS CHRISTENSEN

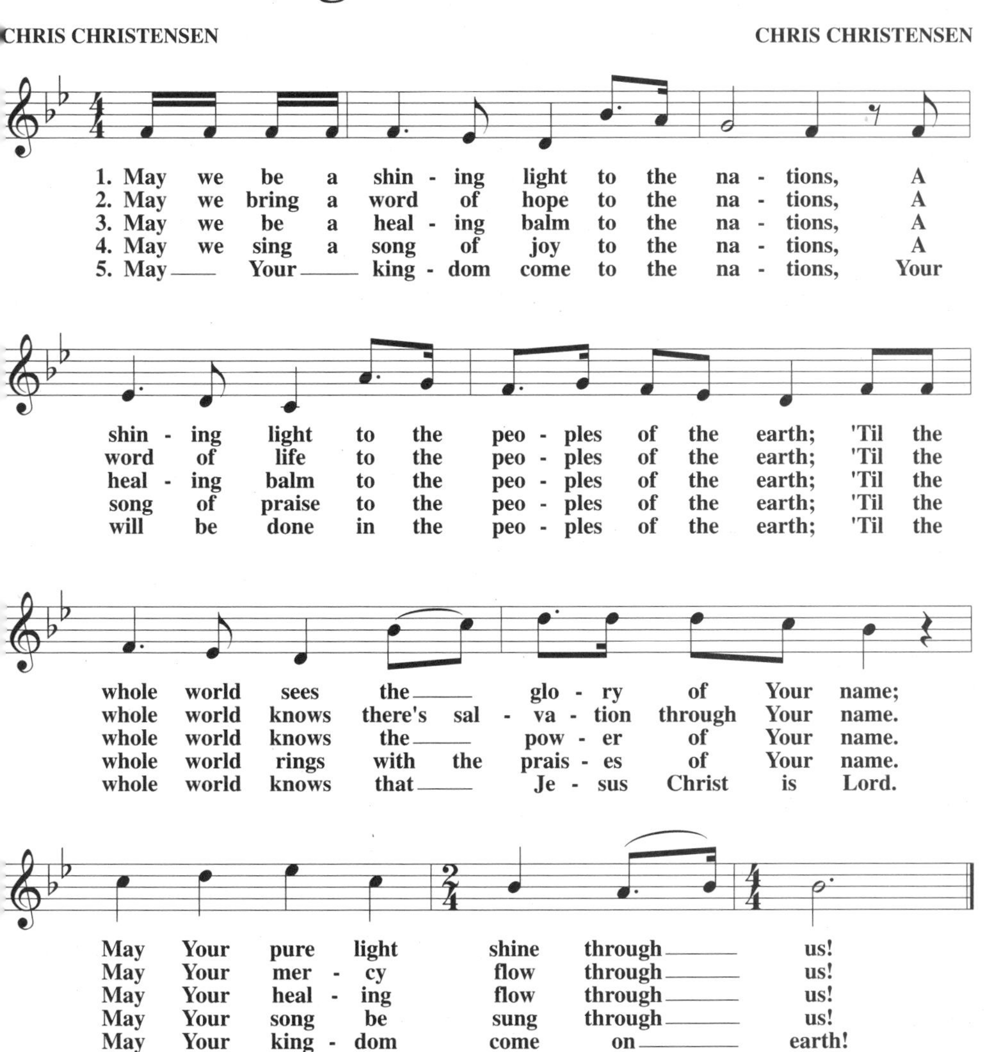

1. May   we   be   a   shin - ing   light   to   the   na - tions,   A
2. May   we   bring   a   word   of   hope   to   the   na - tions,   A
3. May   we   be   a   heal - ing   balm   to   the   na - tions,   A
4. May   we   sing   a   song   of   joy   to   the   na - tions,   A
5. May   Your   king - dom   come   to   the   na - tions,   Your

shin - ing   light   to   the   peo - ples   of   the   earth;   'Til   the
word   of   life   to   the   peo - ples   of   the   earth;   'Til   the
heal - ing   balm   to   the   peo - ples   of   the   earth;   'Til   the
song   of   praise   to   the   peo - ples   of   the   earth;   'Til   the
will   be   done   in   the   peo - ples   of   the   earth;   'Til   the

whole   world   sees   the —   glo - ry   of   Your   name;
whole   world   knows   there's   sal - va - tion   through   Your   name.
whole   world   knows   the —   pow - er   of   Your   name.
whole   world   rings   with   the   prais - es   of   Your   name.
whole   world   knows   that —   Je - sus   Christ   is   Lord.

May   Your   pure   light   shine   through — us!
May   Your   mer - cy   flow   through — us!
May   Your   heal - ing   flow   through — us!
May   Your   song   be   sung   through — us!
May   Your   king - dom   come   on — earth!

© Copyright 1986, Arr. © 1992 Integrity's Hosanna! Music,
c/o Integrity Music, Inc., P.O. Box 16813, Mobile, AL 36616.
All Rights Reserved. International Copyright Secured. Used by Permission.

145 All That I Need

TWILA PARIS

TWILA PARIS

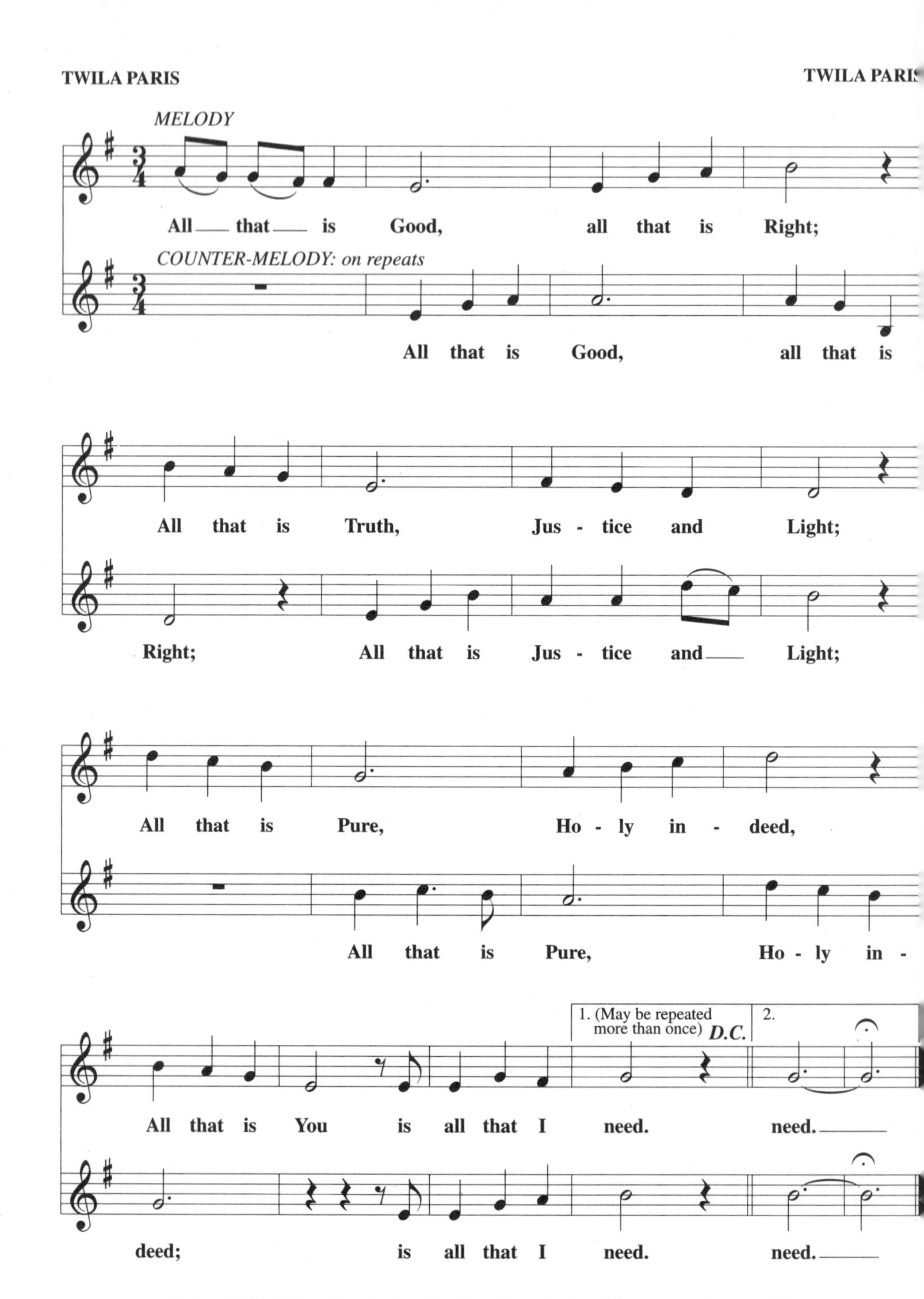

MELODY

All — that — is Good, all that is Right;

COUNTER-MELODY: on repeats

All that is Good, all that is

All that is Truth, Jus - tice and Light;

Right; All that is Jus - tice and — Light;

All that is Pure, Ho - ly in - deed,

All that is Pure, Ho - ly in -

1. (May be repeated more than once) *D.C.* 2.

All that is You is all that I need. need. ___

deed; is all that I need. need. ___

Revive Us, Oh Lord

146

Words and Music by
STEVE CAMP and CARMAN LICCIARDELLO

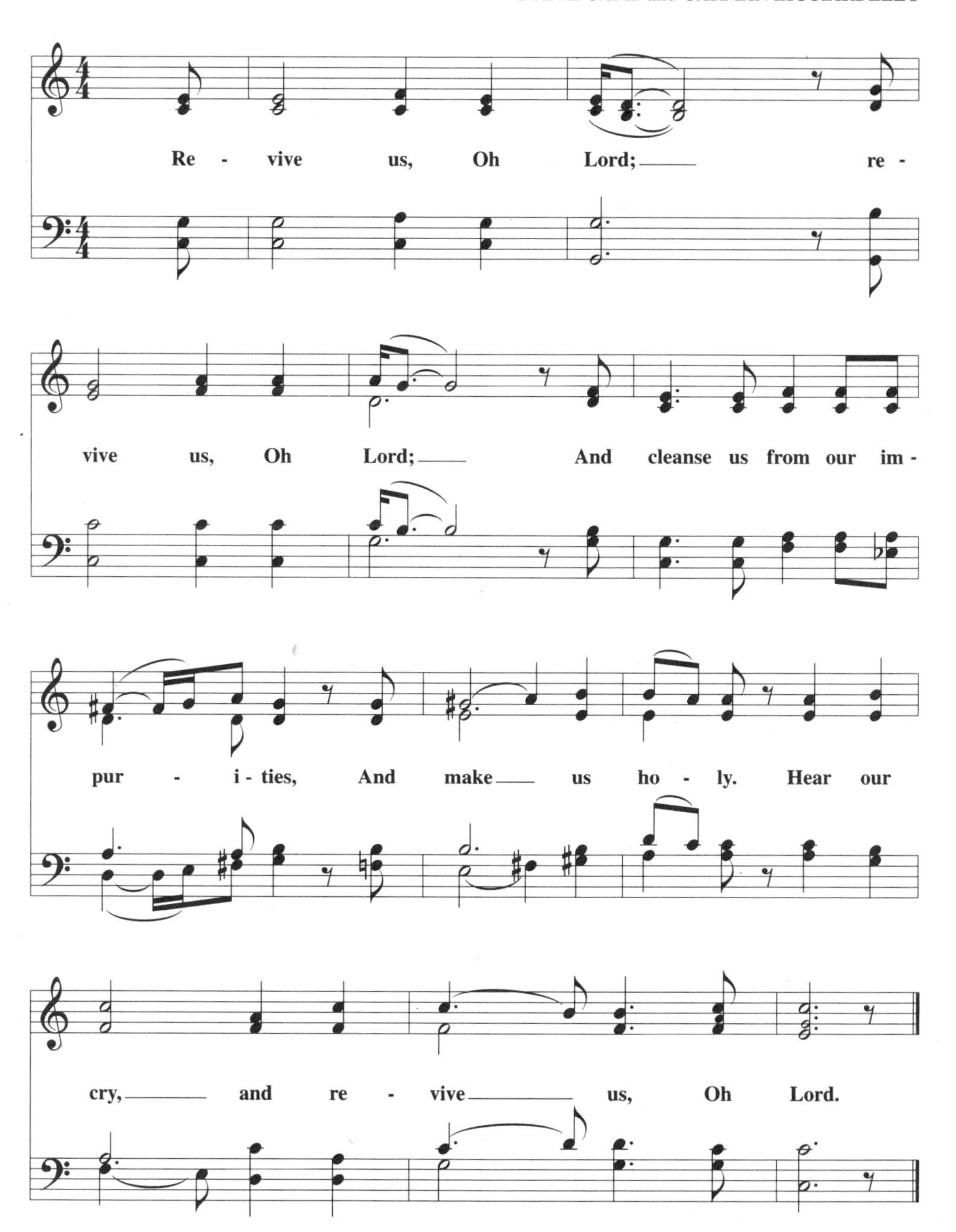

147 I Will Celebrate

LINDA DUVALL   LINDA DUVALL

I will cel - e - brate, — sing un-to the Lord, — I will sing to Him a

new song. I will praise Him, I will sing to Him a

new song. I will praise Him, I will sing to Him a new song.

Hal - le - lu - jah, hal - le - lu - jah, hal - le - lu - jah, hal - le - lu - jah,

hal - le - lu, hal - le - lu - jah.

1. lu - jah.

2. I will

praise Him, I will sing to Him a new song.

I will praise Him, I will sing to Him a

new song. I will sing to Him a new song.

I Will Arise

148

LESLIE BROWN

LESLIE BROWN

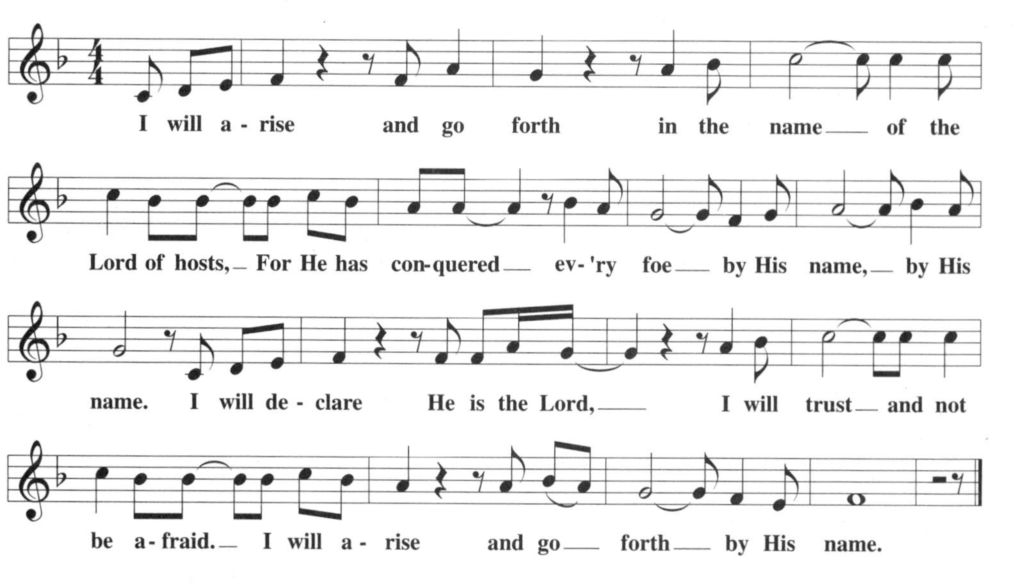

I will a - rise and go forth in the name of the Lord of hosts, For He has con-quered ev-'ry foe by His name, by His name. I will de - clare He is the Lord, I will trust and not be a-fraid. I will a - rise and go forth by His name.

Let God Arise

149

ELIZABETH BACON
Based on Psalm 68:1

ELIZABETH BACON

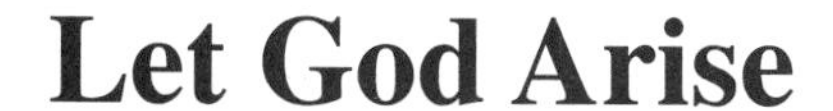
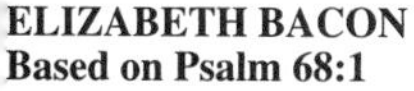

(1. 2.) Let God a - rise, let His en - e - mies be scat - tered; Let
(3.) Our God a - rose, and His en - e - mies were scat - tered; Our

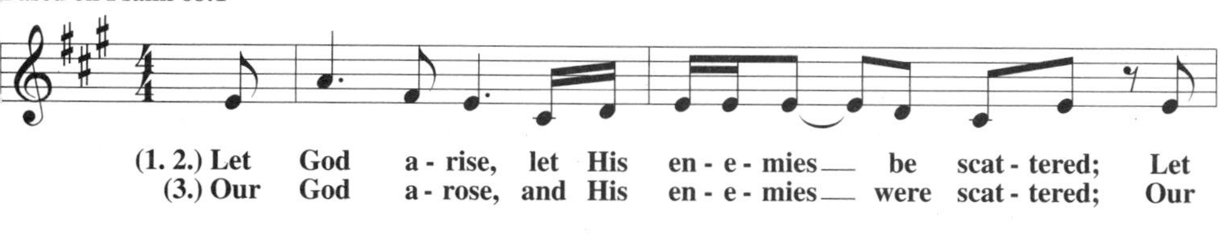

God a - rise, let His en-e-mies be scat-tered; Let God a - rise, let His
God a - rose, and His en-e-mies were scat-tered; Our God a - rose, and His

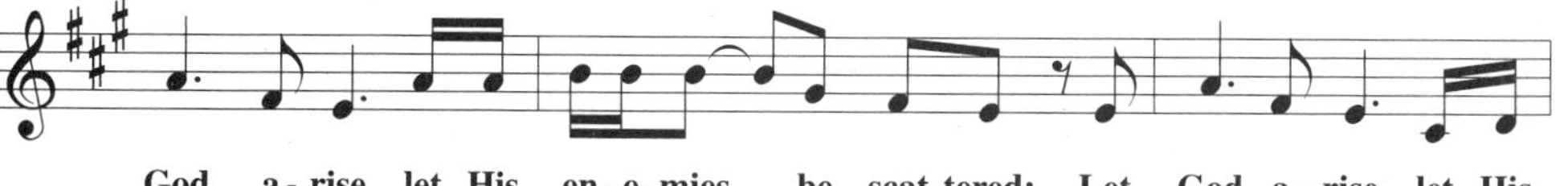

en - e - mies be scat - tered; Let God, let God a - rise.
en - e - mies were scat - tered; Our God, our God a - rose.

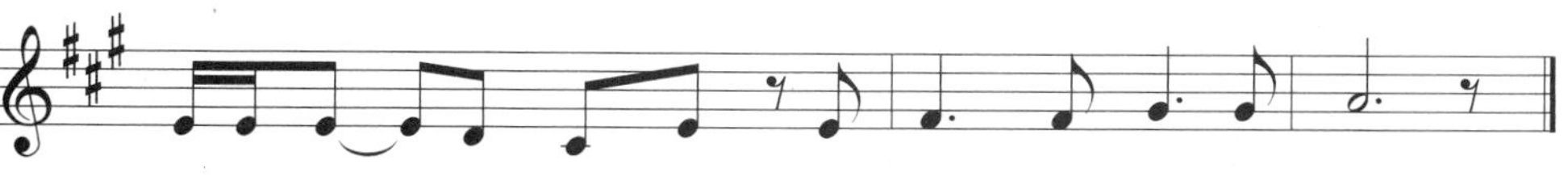

150 Rejoice

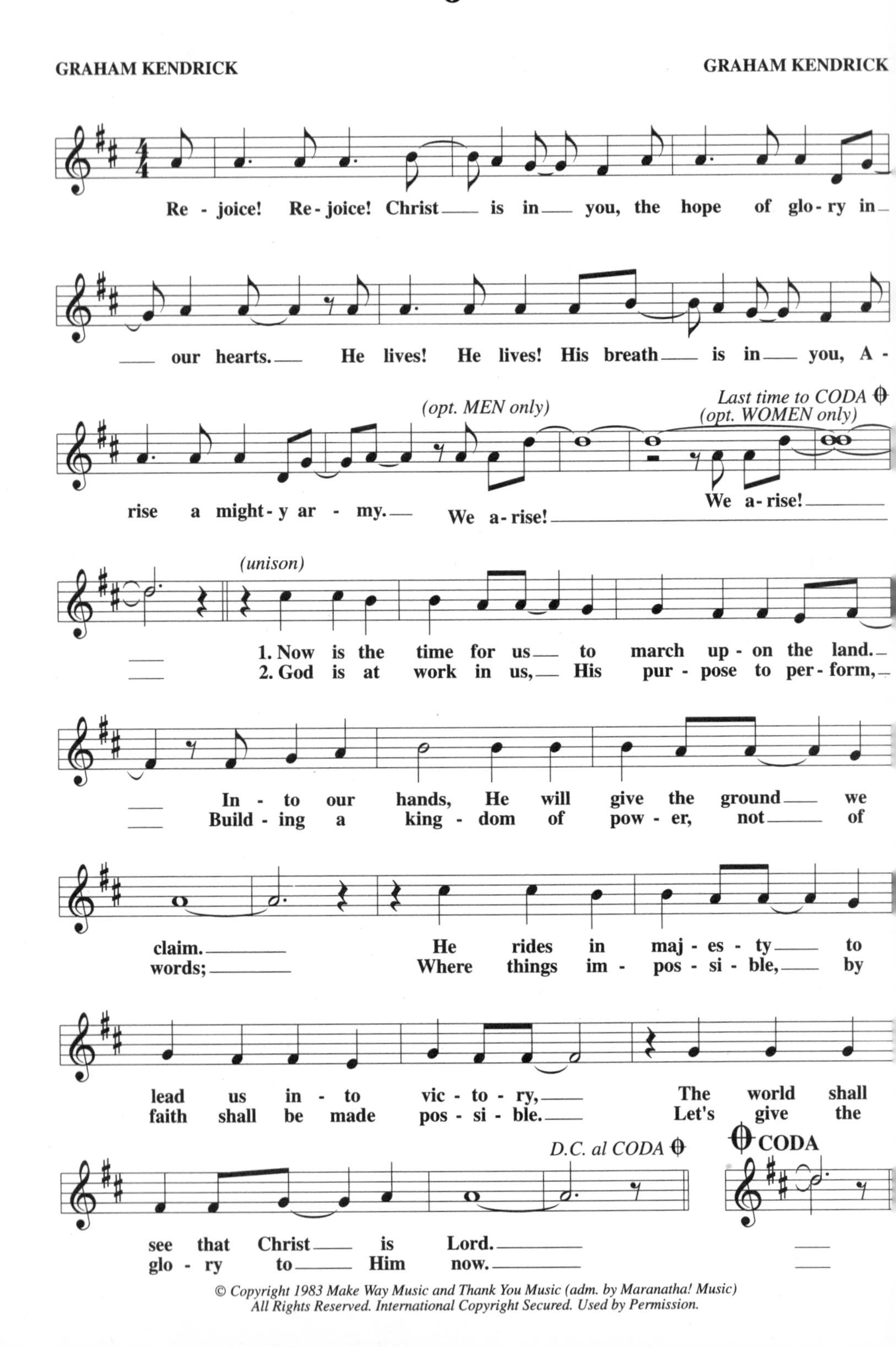
GRAHAM KENDRICK
GRAHAM KENDRICK
Re - joice! Re - joice! Christ is in you, the hope of glo - ry in our hearts.
He lives! He lives! His breath is in you, A - rise a might - y ar - my.
(opt. MEN only)
We a - rise!
Last time to CODA
(opt. WOMEN only)
We a - rise!
(unison)
1. Now is the time for us to march up - on the land. In - to our hands, He will give the ground we claim. He rides in maj - es - ty to lead us in - to vic - to - ry, The world shall see that Christ is Lord.
2. God is at work in us, His pur - pose to per - form, Build - ing a king - dom of pow - er, not of words; Where things im - pos - si - ble, by faith shall be made pos - si - ble. Let's give the glo - ry to Him now.
D.C. al CODA
CODA
© Copyright 1983 Make Way Music and Thank You Music (adm. by Maranatha! Music)
All Rights Reserved. International Copyright Secured. Used by Permission.

Blow the Trumpet in Zion 151

CRAIG TERNDRUP
Based on Joel 2:1

CRAIG TERNDRUP

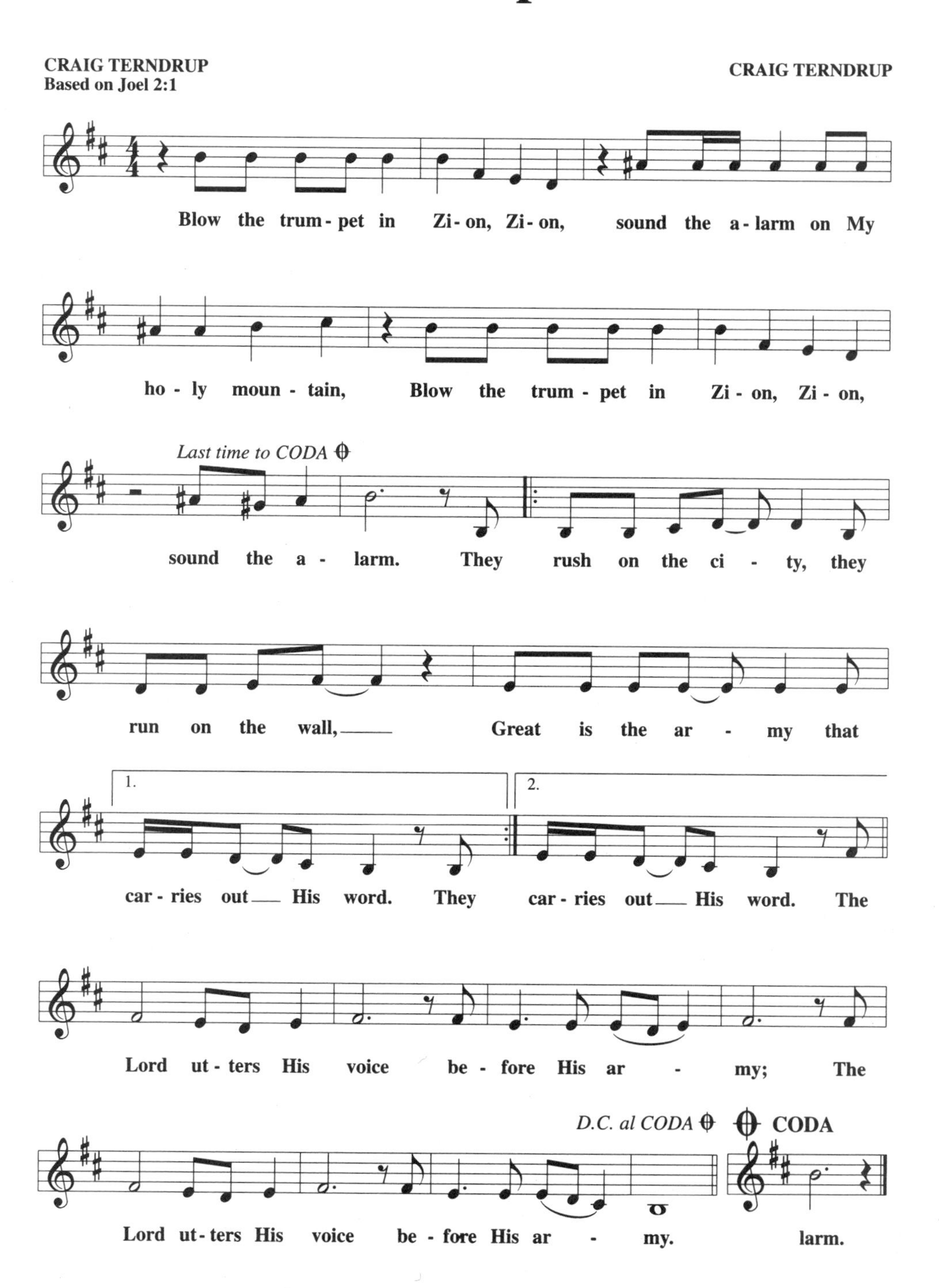

152 Thou Art a Shield for Me

FREDA TAPP

FREDA TAPP

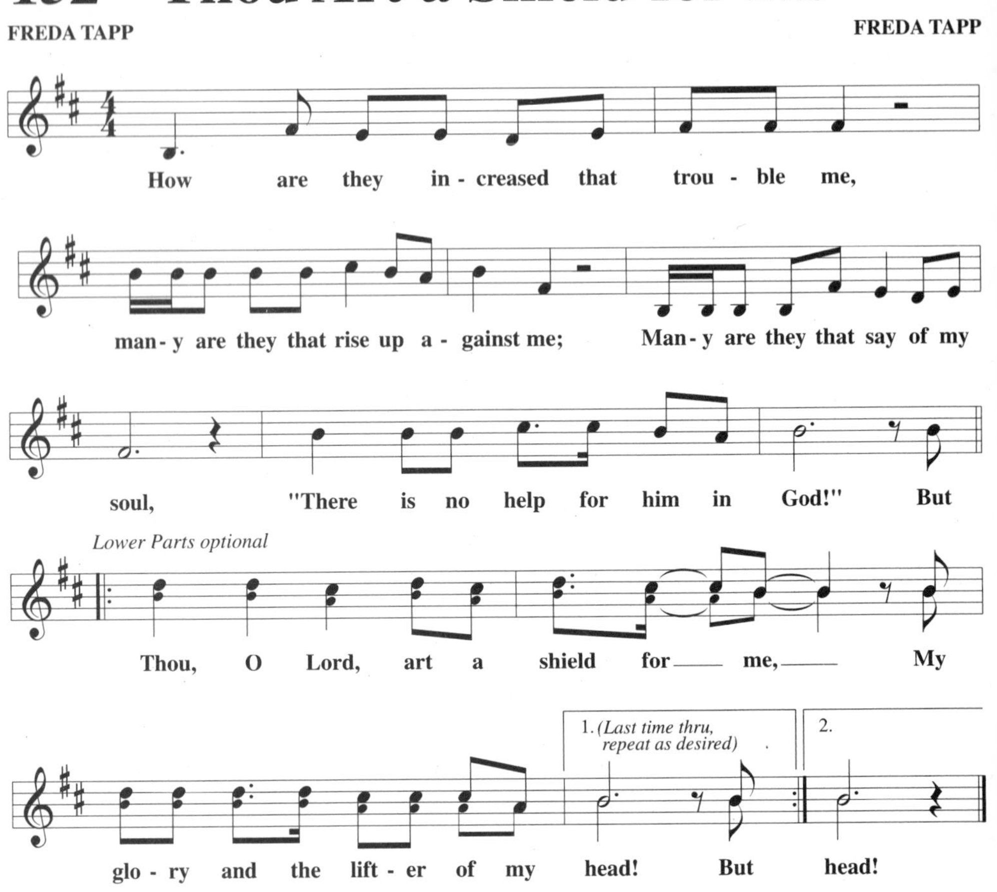

How are they in-creased that trou-ble me, man-y are they that rise up a-gainst me; Man-y are they that say of my soul, "There is no help for him in God!" But

Lower Parts optional

Thou, O Lord, art a shield for ___ me, ___ My

1.(*Last time thru, repeat as desired*)   2.

glo-ry and the lift-er of my head! But head!

153 Let God Arise

JOHN SELLERS

JOHN SELLERS

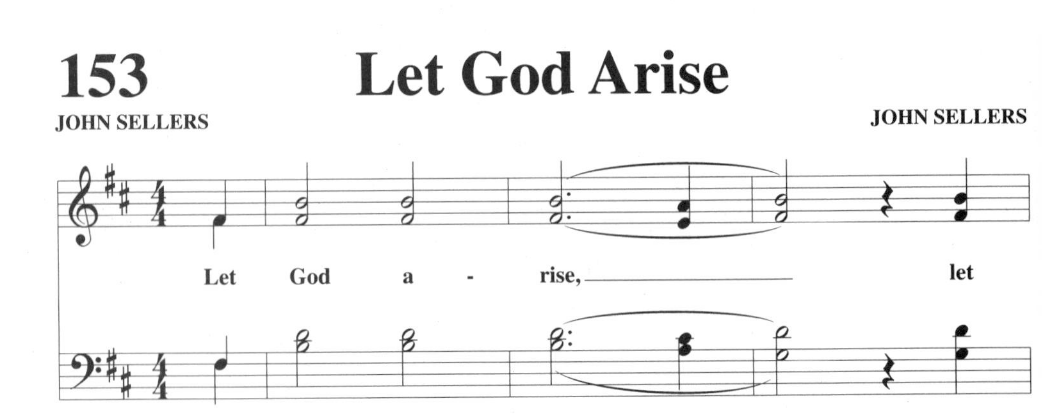

Let God a - rise, ___ let

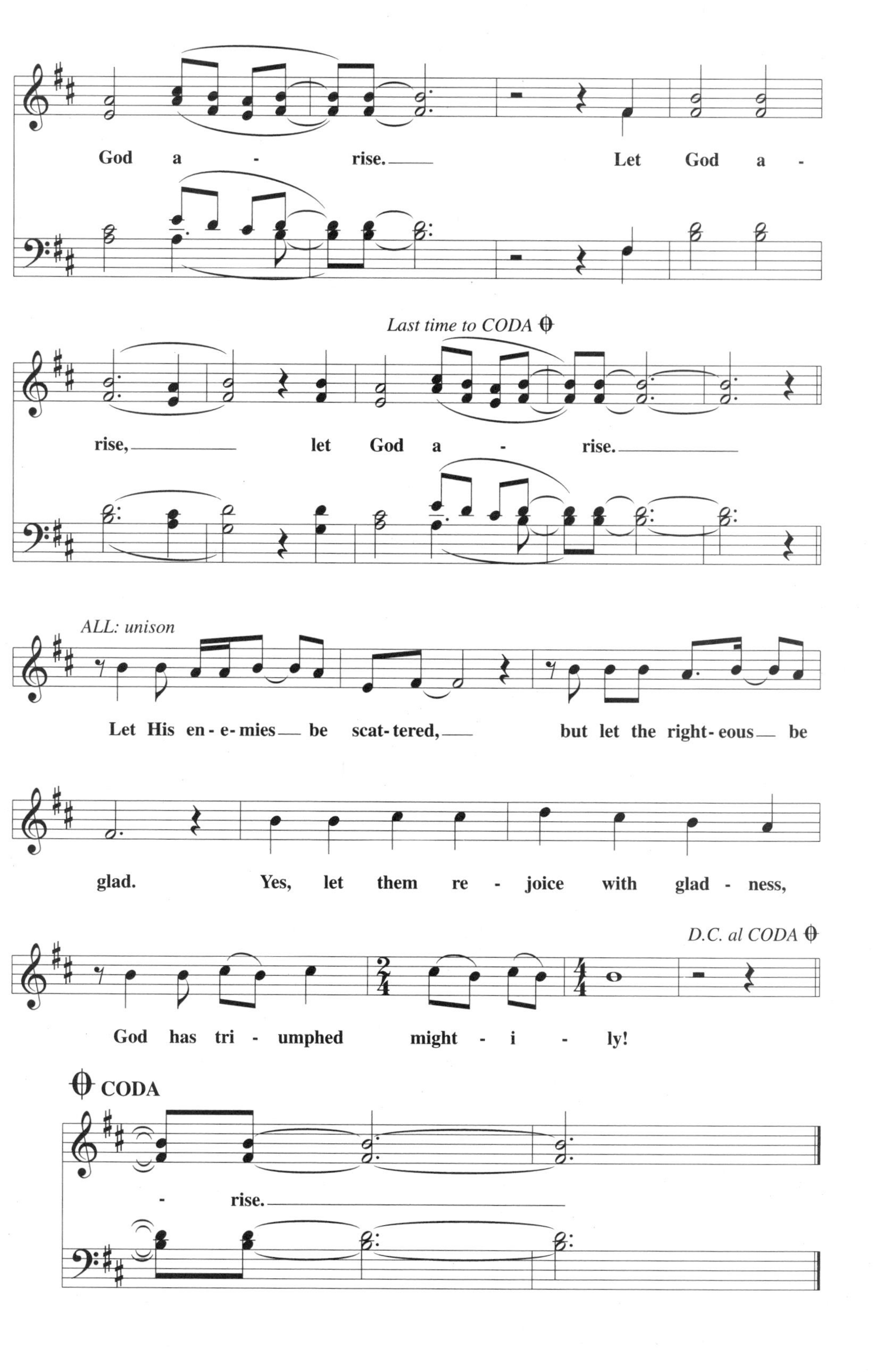
God a - rise.
Let God a -
Last time to CODA
rise, let God a - rise.
ALL: unison
Let His en - e - mies be scat - tered,
but let the right - eous be
glad.
Yes, let them re - joice with glad - ness,
D.C. al CODA
God has tri - umphed might - i - ly!
CODA
- rise.

154
For the Lord Is Marching On

BONNIE LOW   BONNIE LOW

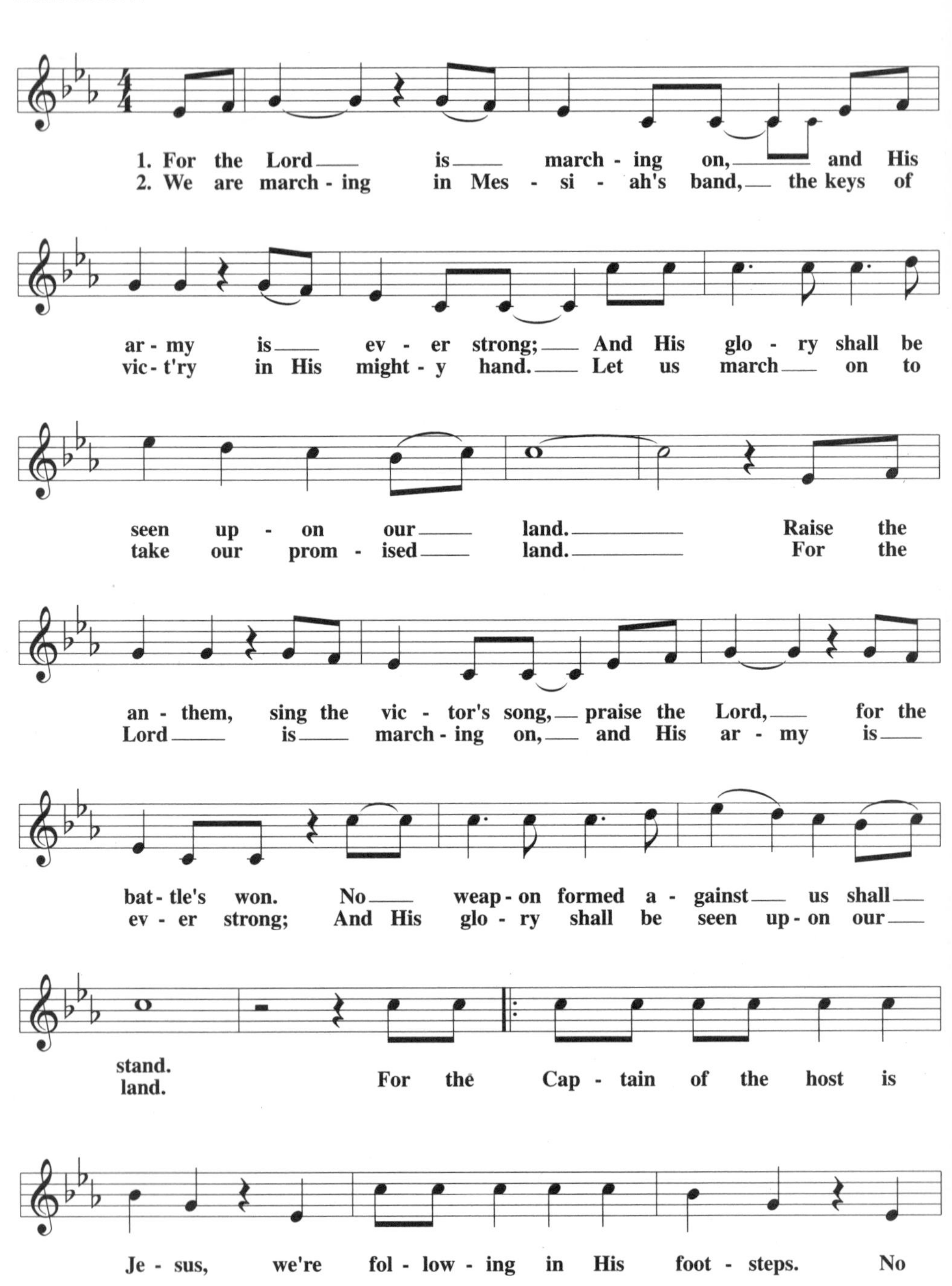

1. For the Lord___ is___ march-ing on,___ and His
2. We are march-ing in Mes-si-ah's band,___ the keys of

ar-my is___ ev-er strong;___ And His glo-ry shall be
vic-t'ry in His might-y hand.___ Let us march___ on to

seen up-on our___ land.___ Raise the
take our prom-ised___ land.___ For the

an-them, sing the vic-tor's song,___ praise the Lord,___ for the
Lord___ is___ march-ing on,___ and His ar-my is

bat-tle's won. No___ weap-on formed a-gainst___ us shall___
ev-er strong; And His glo-ry shall be seen up-on our___

stand.
land. For the Cap-tain of the host is

Je-sus, we're fol-low-ing in His foot-steps. No

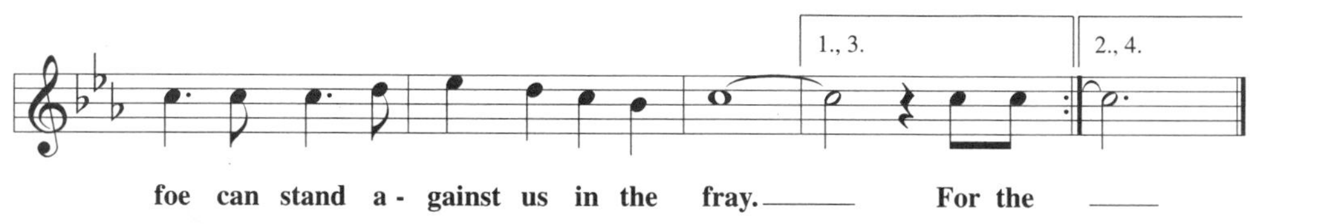

foe can stand a-gainst us in the fray._____ For the _____

Victory Song   155
(Through Our God)

DALE GARRATT

DALE GARRATT

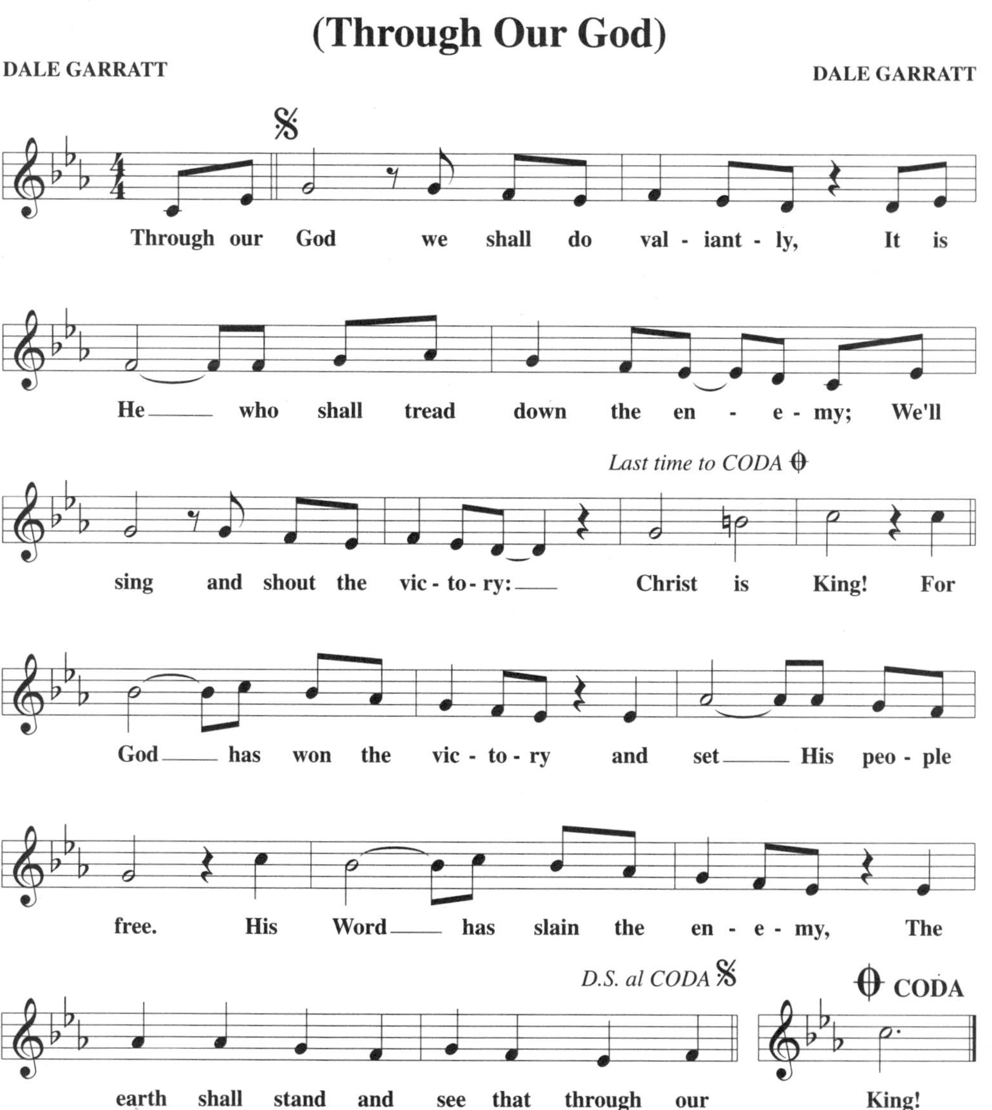

Through our God we shall do val-iant-ly, It is

He_____ who shall tread down the en-e-my; We'll

Last time to CODA ✛

sing and shout the vic-to-ry:_____ Christ is King! For

God_____ has won the vic-to-ry and set_____ His peo-ple

free. His Word_____ has slain the en-e-my, The

D.S. al CODA 𝄋

✛ CODA

earth shall stand and see that through our

King!

156 Mighty Warrior

DEBBYE GRAAFSMA

DEBBYE GRAAFSMA

Might - y War - rior____ dressed for bat - tle,____

ho - ly Lord of all___ is He. Com - man - der in chief,

bring us to at - ten - tion,____ Lead us in - to bat - tle to

crush the en - e - my.____ 1. Sa - tan
2. Je - sus

1. has no au - thor - i - ty here in this place. He
2. has all au - thor - i - ty here in this place. He

1. has no au - thor - i - ty here. For this hab - i - ta - tion___ was
2. has all au - thor - i - ty here. For this hab - i - ta - tion___ was

1. fash - ioned for the Lord's pres - ence; no au - thor - i - ty here.
2. fash - ioned for the Lord's pres - ence; all au - thor - i - ty here.

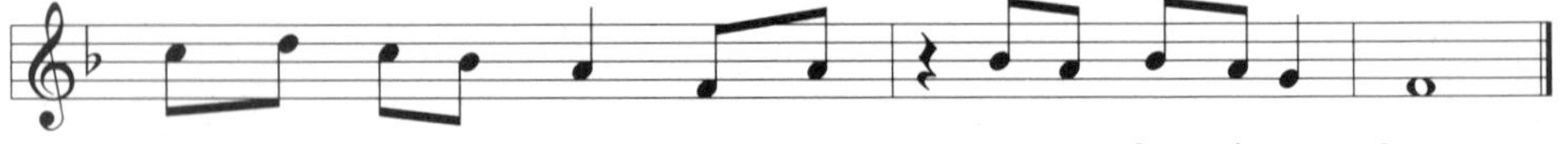

Above All Else 157

KIRK DEARMAN   KIRK DEARMAN

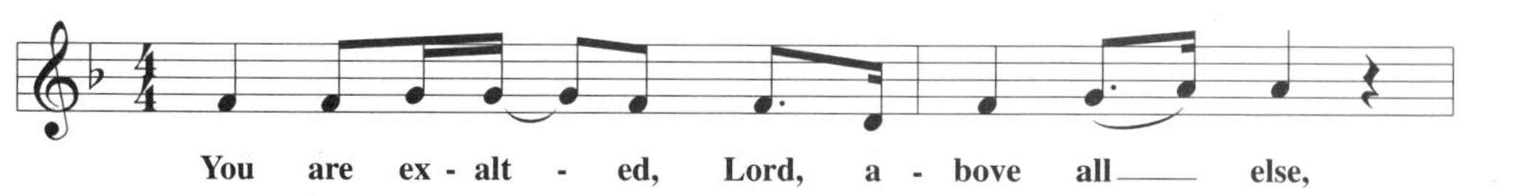

You are ex - alt - ed, Lord, a - bove all____ else,

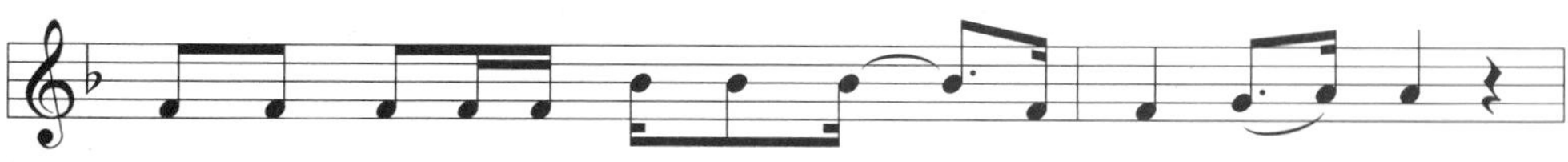

We place You at the high - est place,____ a - bove all____ else.

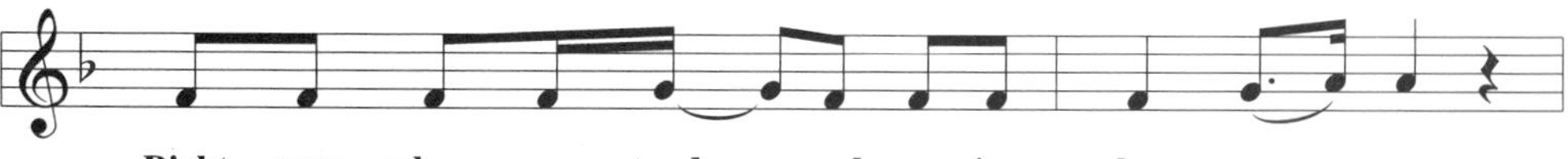

Right now where we stand,____ and ev - 'ry - where we____ go,

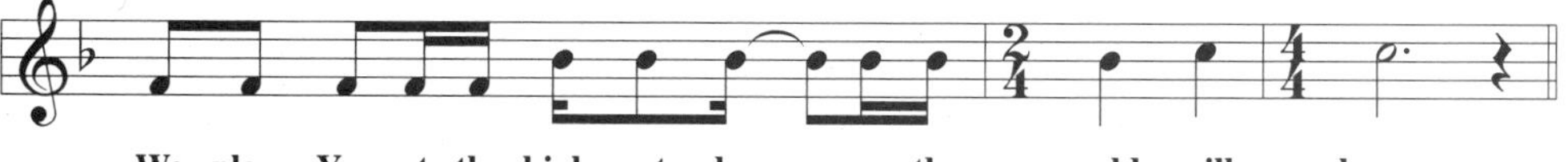

We place You at the high - est place__ so the world will know;

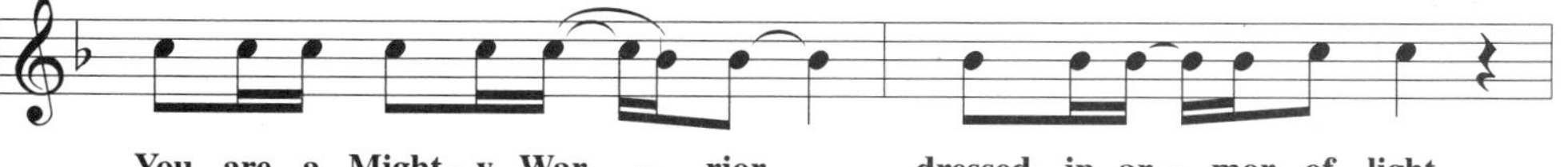

You are a Might - y War - rior,____ dressed in ar - mor of light,

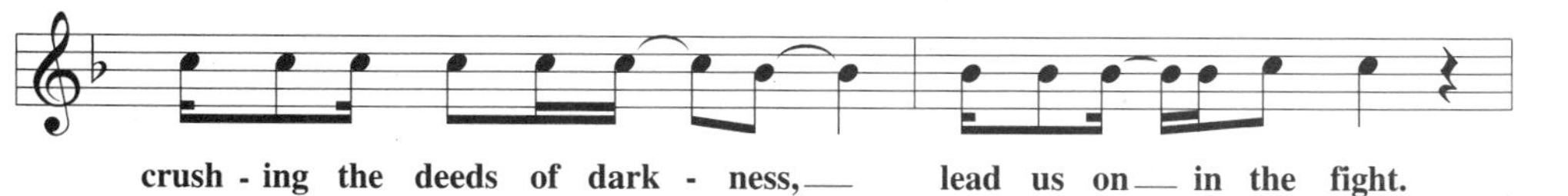

crush - ing the deeds of dark - ness,____ lead us on__ in the fight.

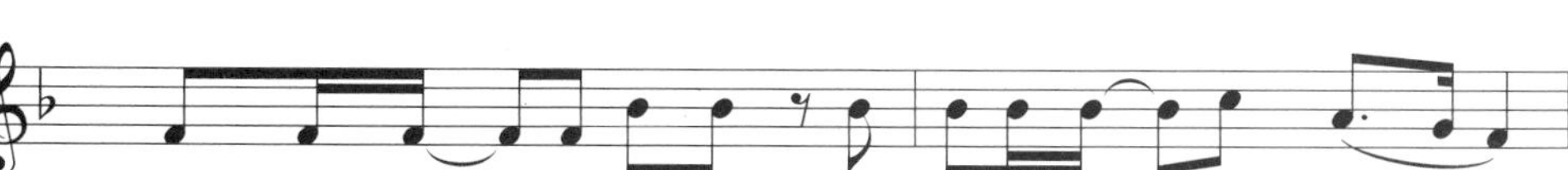

Through the blood____ of Je - sus, vic - to - ri - ous____ we stand,____

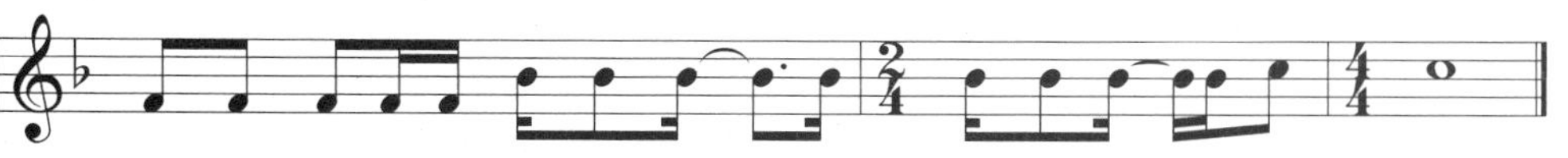

We place You at the high - est place__ a - bove all else__ in this land.

158 The Battle Belongs to the Lord

JAMIE OWENS - COLLINS JAMIE OWENS - COLLINS

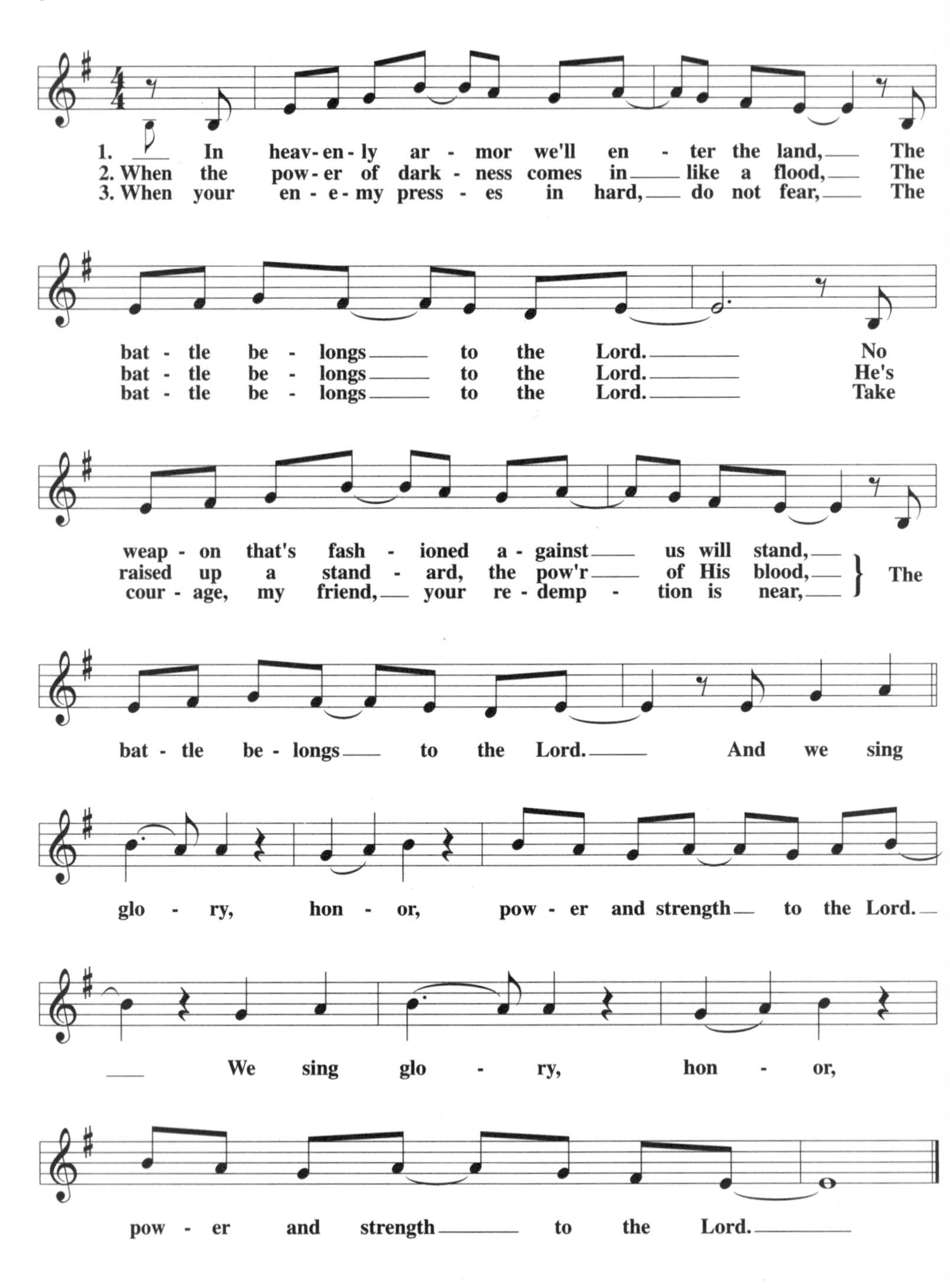

1. In heav-en-ly ar - mor we'll en - ter the land,___ The
2. When the pow-er of dark - ness comes in___ like a flood,___ The
3. When your en-e-my press - es in hard,___ do not fear,___ The

bat - tle be - longs___ to the Lord.___ No
bat - tle be - longs___ to the Lord.___ He's
bat - tle be - longs___ to the Lord.___ Take

weap - on that's fash - ioned a - gainst___ us will stand,___
raised up a stand - ard, the pow'r___ of His blood,___ } The
cour - age, my friend,___ your re - demp - tion is near,___

bat - tle be - longs___ to the Lord.___ And we sing

glo - ry, hon - or, pow - er and strength___ to the Lord.

___ We sing glo - ry, hon - or,

pow - er and strength___ to the Lord.___

Making War in the Heavenlies

159

GEORGE SEARCY
Based on 2 Cor. 10:5

GEORGE SEARCY

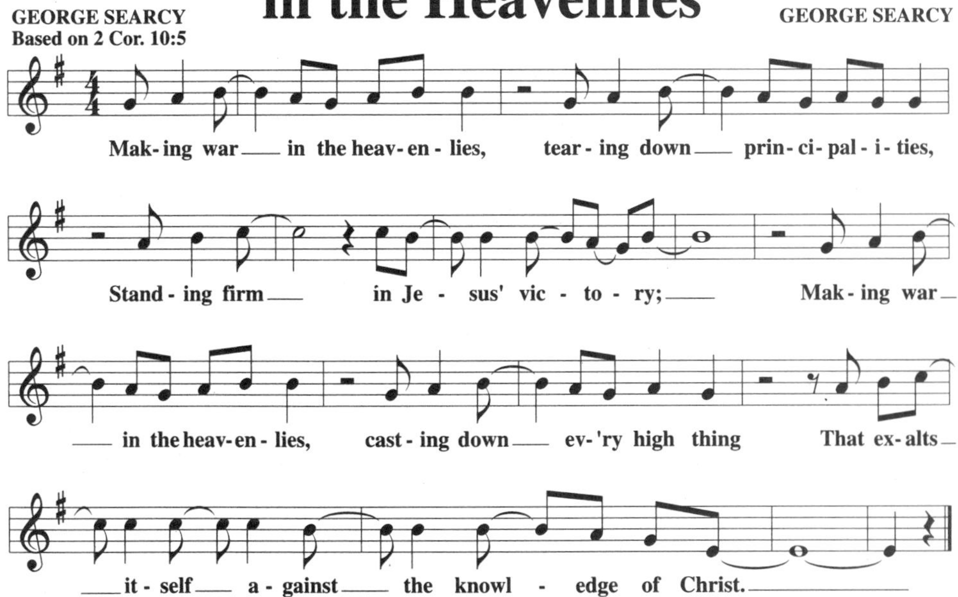

Mak-ing war — in the heav-en-lies, tear-ing down — prin-ci-pal-i-ties, Stand-ing firm — in Je-sus' vic-to-ry; — Mak-ing war — in the heav-en-lies, cast-ing down — ev-'ry high thing That ex-alts — it-self — a-gainst — the knowl-edge of Christ. —

We Will Overcome

160

CAROL CYMBALA

CAROL CYMBALA

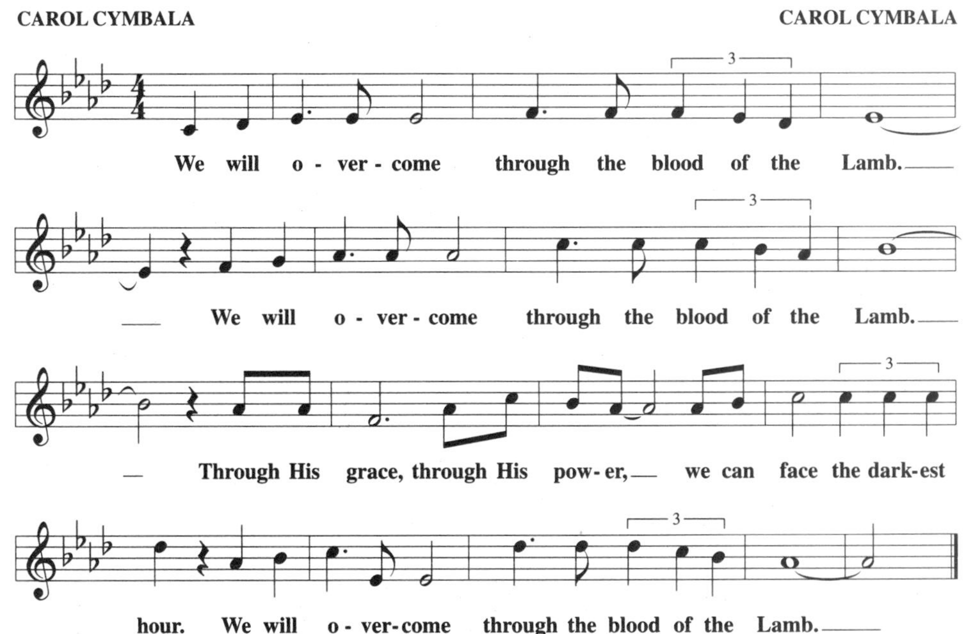

We will o-ver-come through the blood of the Lamb. —
— We will o-ver-come through the blood of the Lamb. —
— Through His grace, through His pow-er, — we can face the dark-est hour. We will o-ver-come through the blood of the Lamb. —

161

We Will Triumph in the Lord

DANIEL GARDNER   DANIEL GARDNER

We will tri-umph in the Lord, we will tri-umph like nev-er be-
fore; For great-er is He that makes me o-ver-come. We will
walk in the pow-er of His might, we will shine forth His glo-ri-ous
light; For great-er is He that makes me o-ver-come.

162

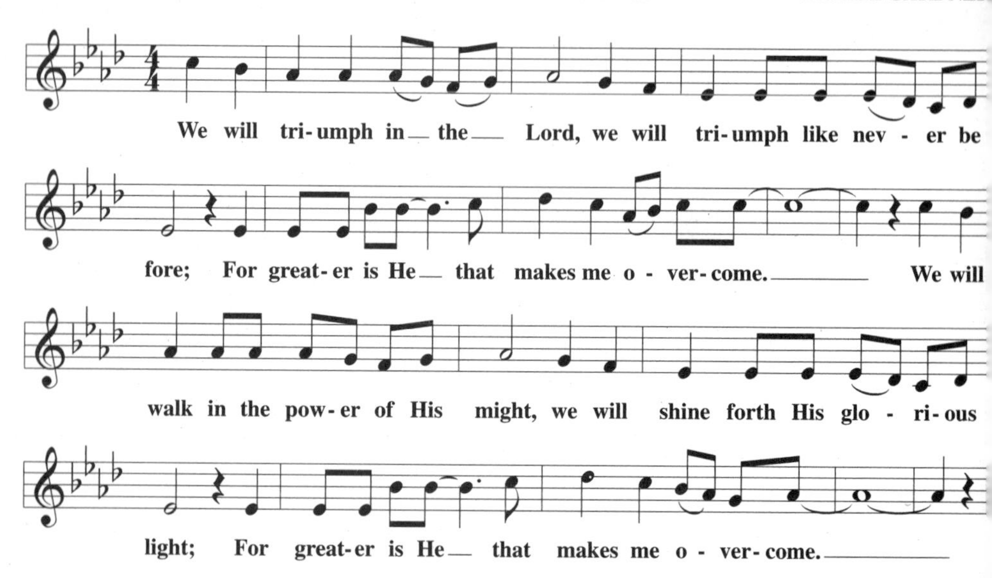

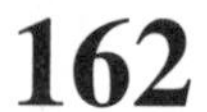

We Celebrate

Words and Music by
PAULA TILL, ROBERT TILL
and SAMMY DAVENPORT

1. We cel - e - brate the joy of our sal - va - tion, re-
(2.) cel - e - brate the joy of our sal - va - tion, re-

joic-ing in the Spir-it of the Lord. He gave His life to
joic-ing in the Spir-it of the Lord. He gives us pow'r to

o - pen up His king - dom, we en - ter in as
tri - umph in the bat - tle, He clothes us with the

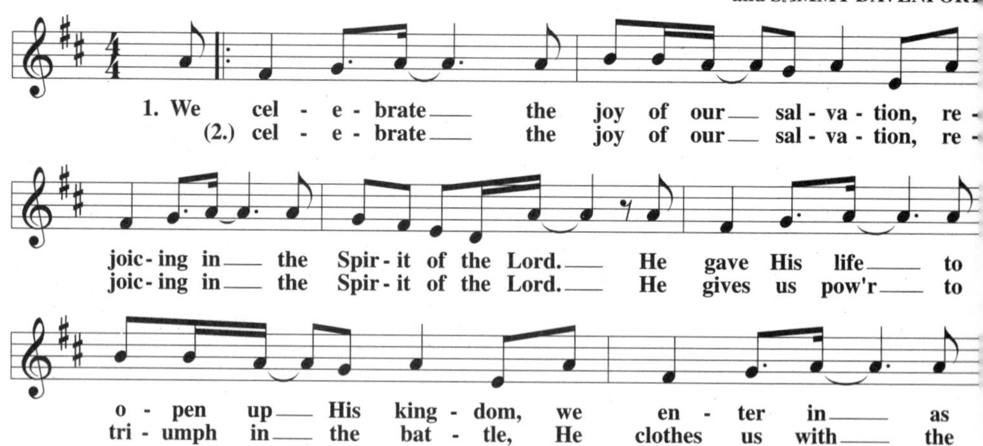

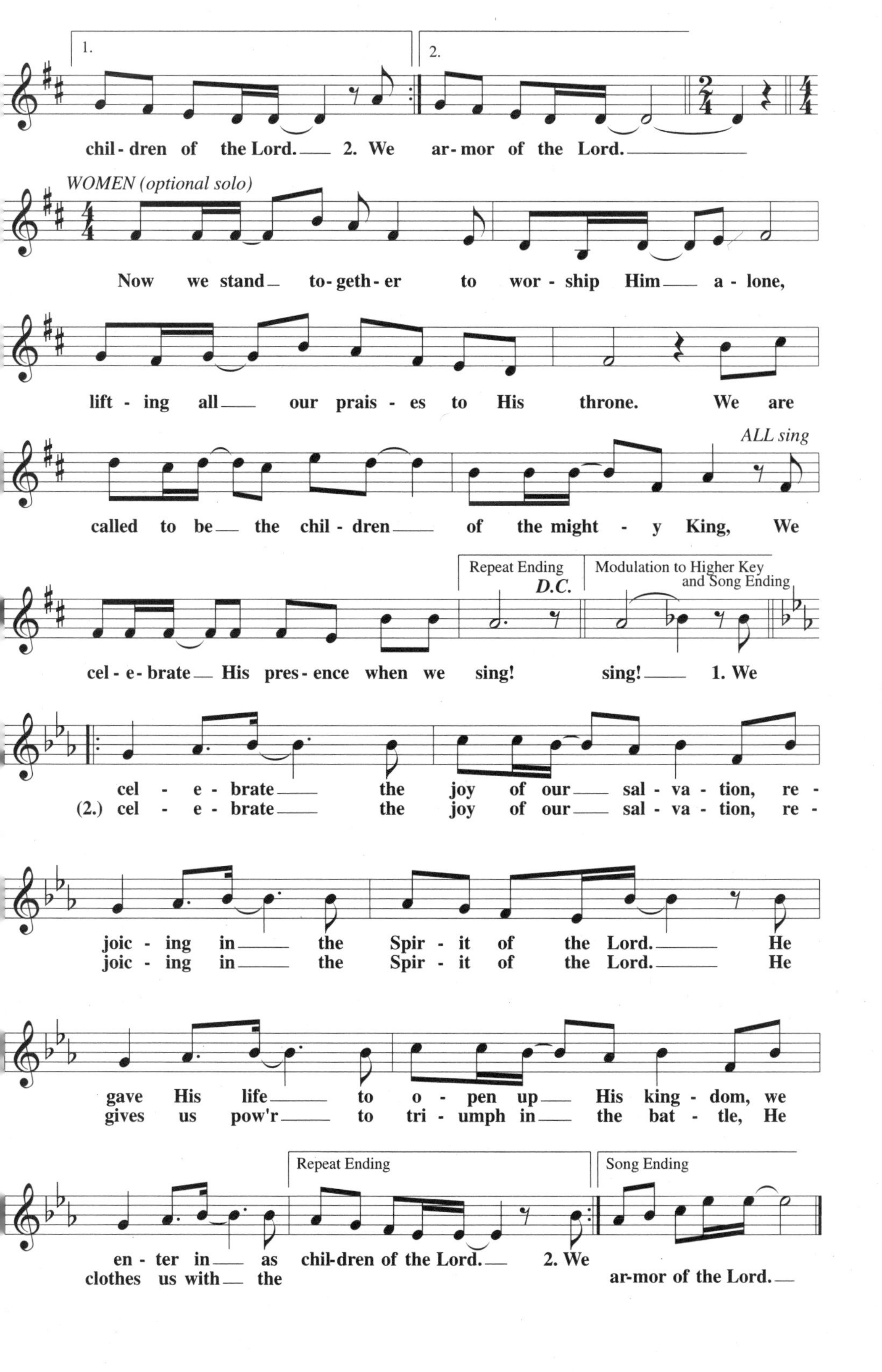
1.
2.
chil - dren of the Lord. 2. We
ar - mor of the Lord.
WOMEN (optional solo)
Now we stand to - geth - er to wor - ship Him a - lone,
lift - ing all our prais - es to His throne. We are
ALL sing
called to be the chil - dren of the might - y King, We
Repeat Ending
D.C.
Modulation to Higher Key and Song Ending
cel - e - brate His pres - ence when we sing! sing! 1. We
cel - e - brate the joy of our sal - va - tion, re -
(2.) cel - e - brate the joy of our sal - va - tion, re -
joic - ing in the Spir - it of the Lord. He
joic - ing in the Spir - it of the Lord. He
gave His life to o - pen up His king - dom, we
gives us pow'r to tri - umph in the bat - tle, He
Repeat Ending
Song Ending
en - ter in as chil-dren of the Lord. 2. We
clothes us with the ar-mor of the Lord.

163 Lamb of Glory

Words and Music by
GREG NELSON and PHILL McHUGH

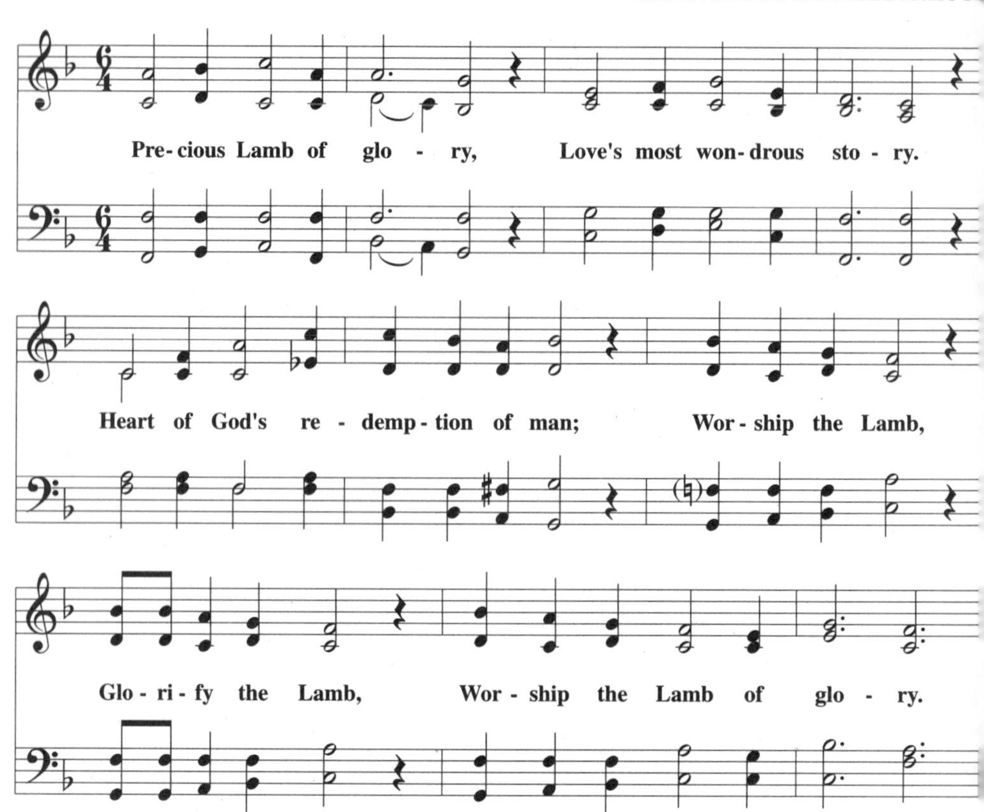

Pre-cious Lamb of glo-ry, Love's most won-drous sto-ry.

Heart of God's re-demp-tion of man; Wor-ship the Lamb,

Glo-ri-fy the Lamb, Wor-ship the Lamb of glo-ry.

164 Behold the Lamb

DOTTIE RAMBO   DOTTIE RAMBO

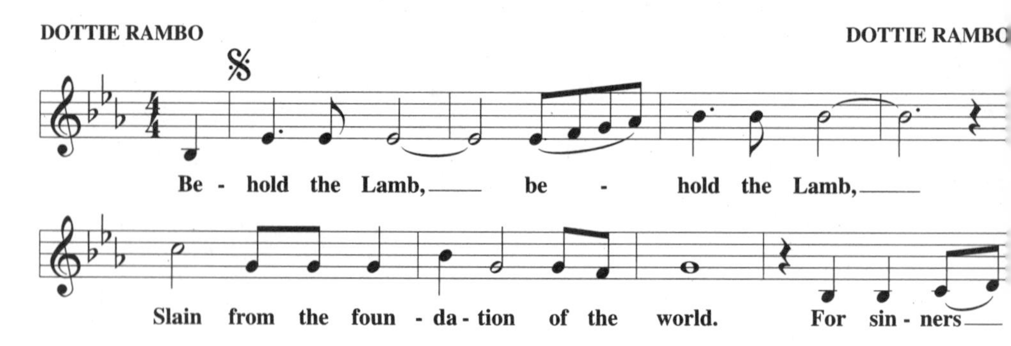

Be-hold the Lamb, be-hold the Lamb,

Slain from the foun-da-tion of the world. For sin-ners

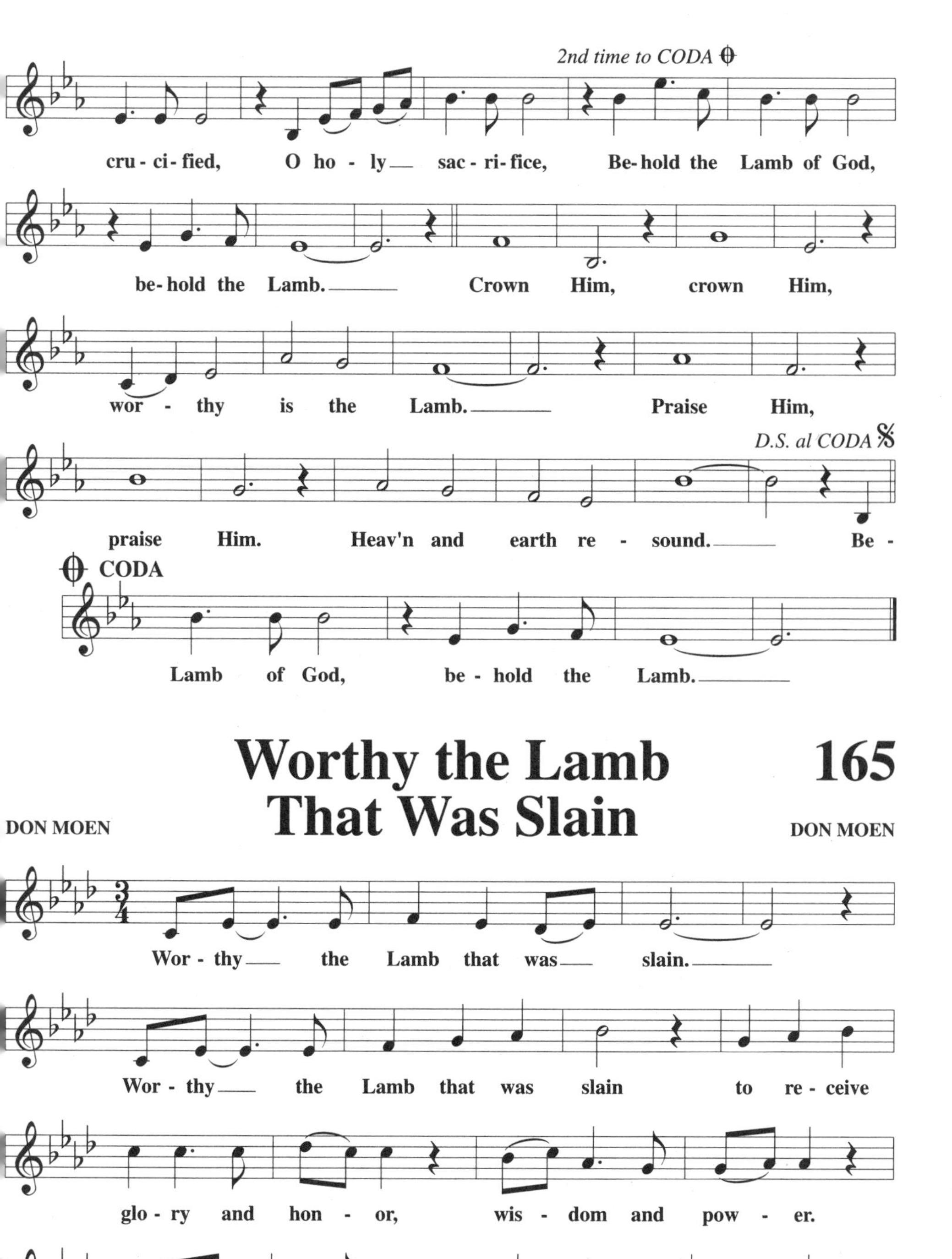

Worthy the Lamb That Was Slain 165

DON MOEN

DON MOEN

166 We Remember You

KIRK DEARMAN

KIRK DEARMAN

As we drink this cup, we wor-ship You; As we eat this bread, we

hon-or You; And we of-fer You our lives as You have of-fered Yours for

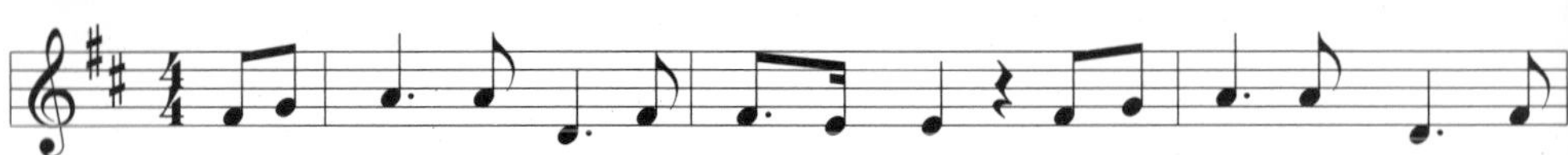

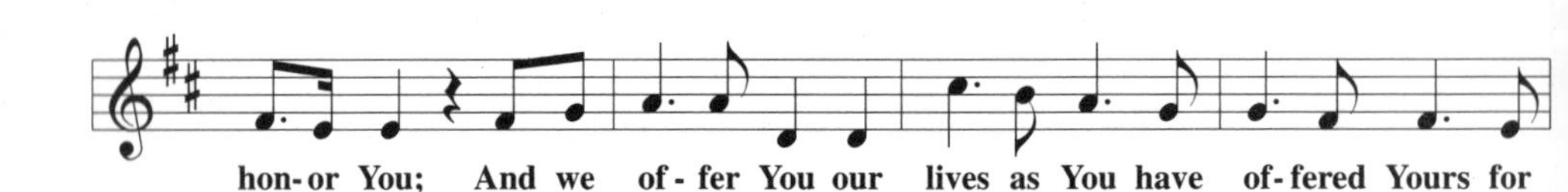

us. We re-mem-ber all You've done for us,___ We re-

mem-ber Your cov-e-nant with us,___ We re-

mem-ber, and wor-ship You, O___ Lord.___

167 Commune with Me

KIRK DEARMAN

KIRK DEARMAN

1. Com - mune with me, com - mune with me Be -
2. I wor - ship You, I wor - ship You Be -
3. I'll meet You there, I'll meet You there Be -

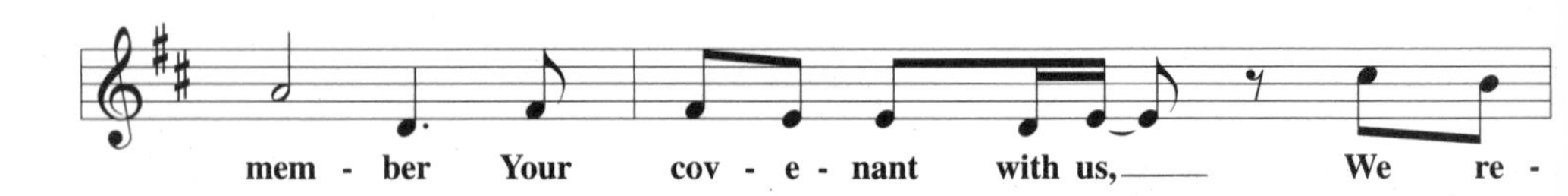

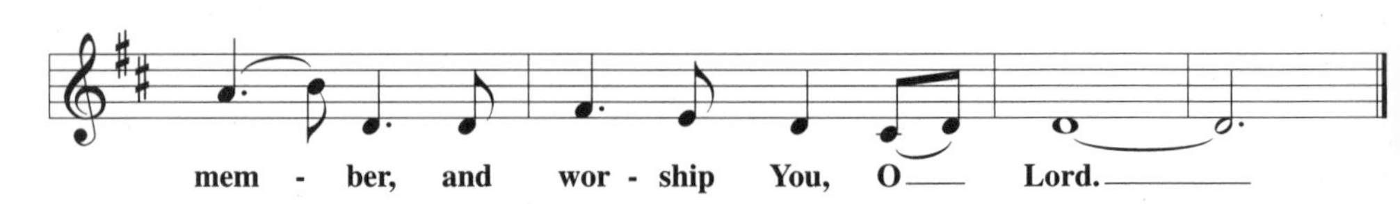

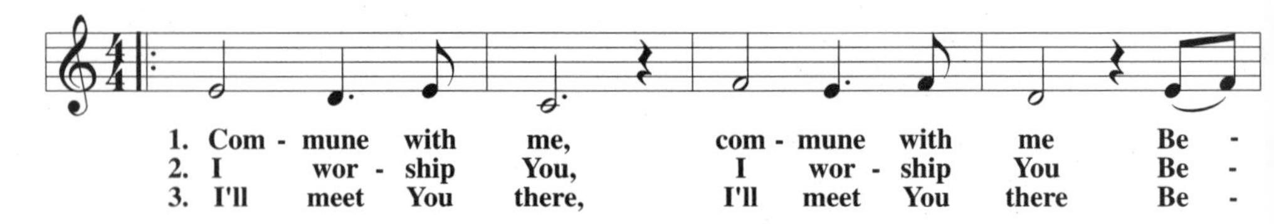

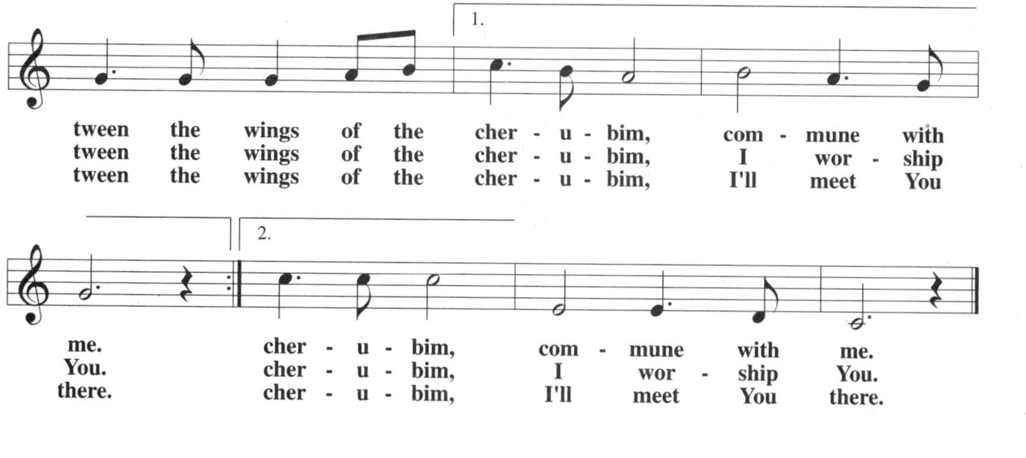

tween the wings of the cher - u - bim, com - mune with
tween the wings of the cher - u - bim, I wor - ship
tween the wings of the cher - u - bim, I'll meet You

me. cher - u - bim, com - mune with me.
You. cher - u - bim, I wor - ship You.
there. cher - u - bim, I'll meet You there.

I Will Enter His Gates   168
(He Has Made Me Glad)

LEONA VON BRETHORST
Based on Psalm 100:2, 4

LEONA VON BRETHORST

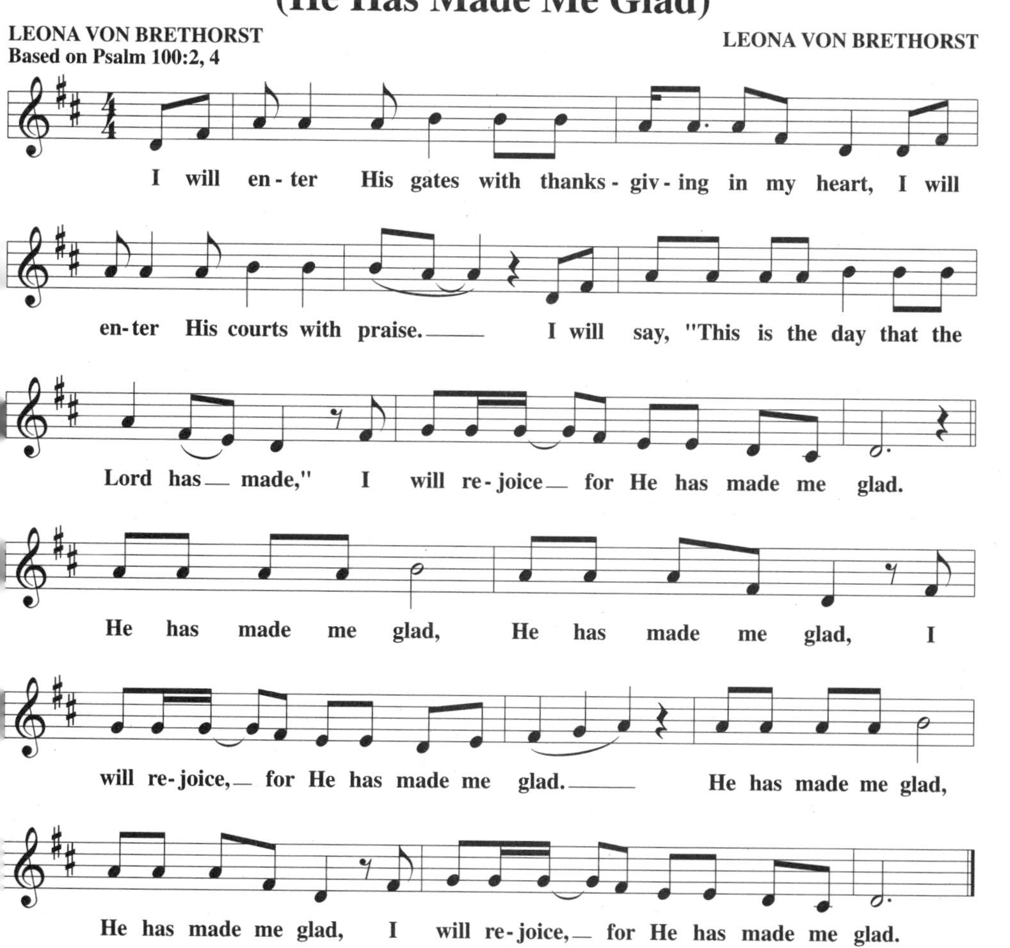

I will en- ter His gates with thanks- giv- ing in my heart, I will

en- ter His courts with praise. I will say, "This is the day that the

Lord has made," I will re - joice for He has made me glad.

He has made me glad, He has made me glad, I

will re - joice, for He has made me glad. He has made me glad,

He has made me glad, I will re - joice, for He has made me glad.

169

It Is a Good Thing
to Give Thanks

JUDY HORNER MONTEMAYOR

JUDY HORNER MONTEMAYOR

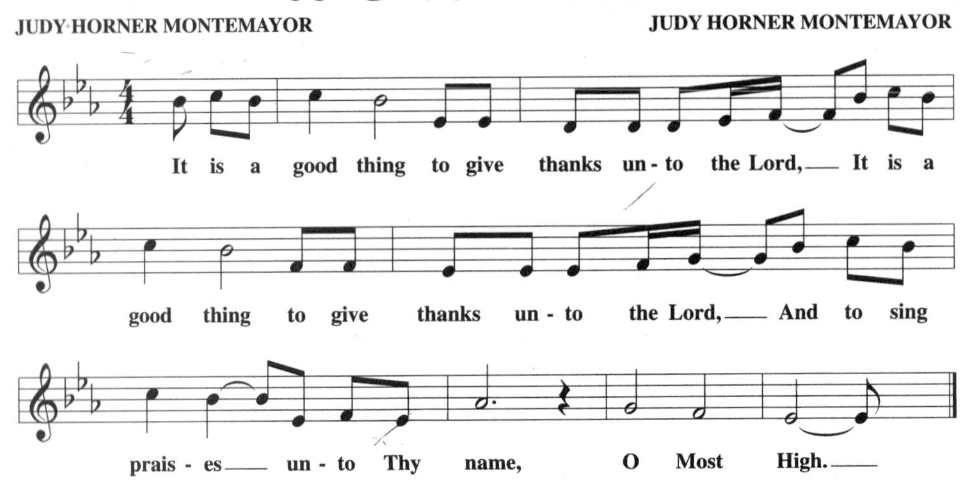

It is a good thing to give thanks un-to the Lord,___ It is a

good thing to give thanks un-to the Lord,___ And to sing

prais-es___ un-to Thy name, O Most High.___

170

Give Thanks

HENRY SMITH

HENRY SMITH

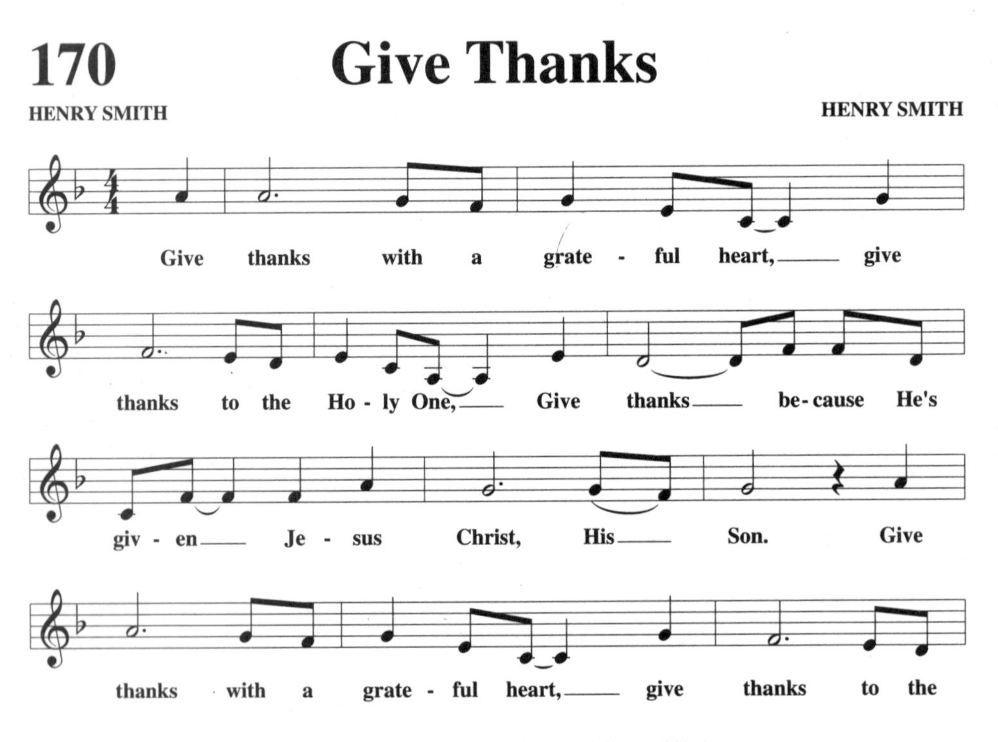

Give thanks with a grate-ful heart,___ give

thanks to the Ho-ly One,___ Give thanks___ be-cause He's

giv-en___ Je-sus Christ, His___ Son. Give

thanks with a grate-ful heart,___ give thanks to the

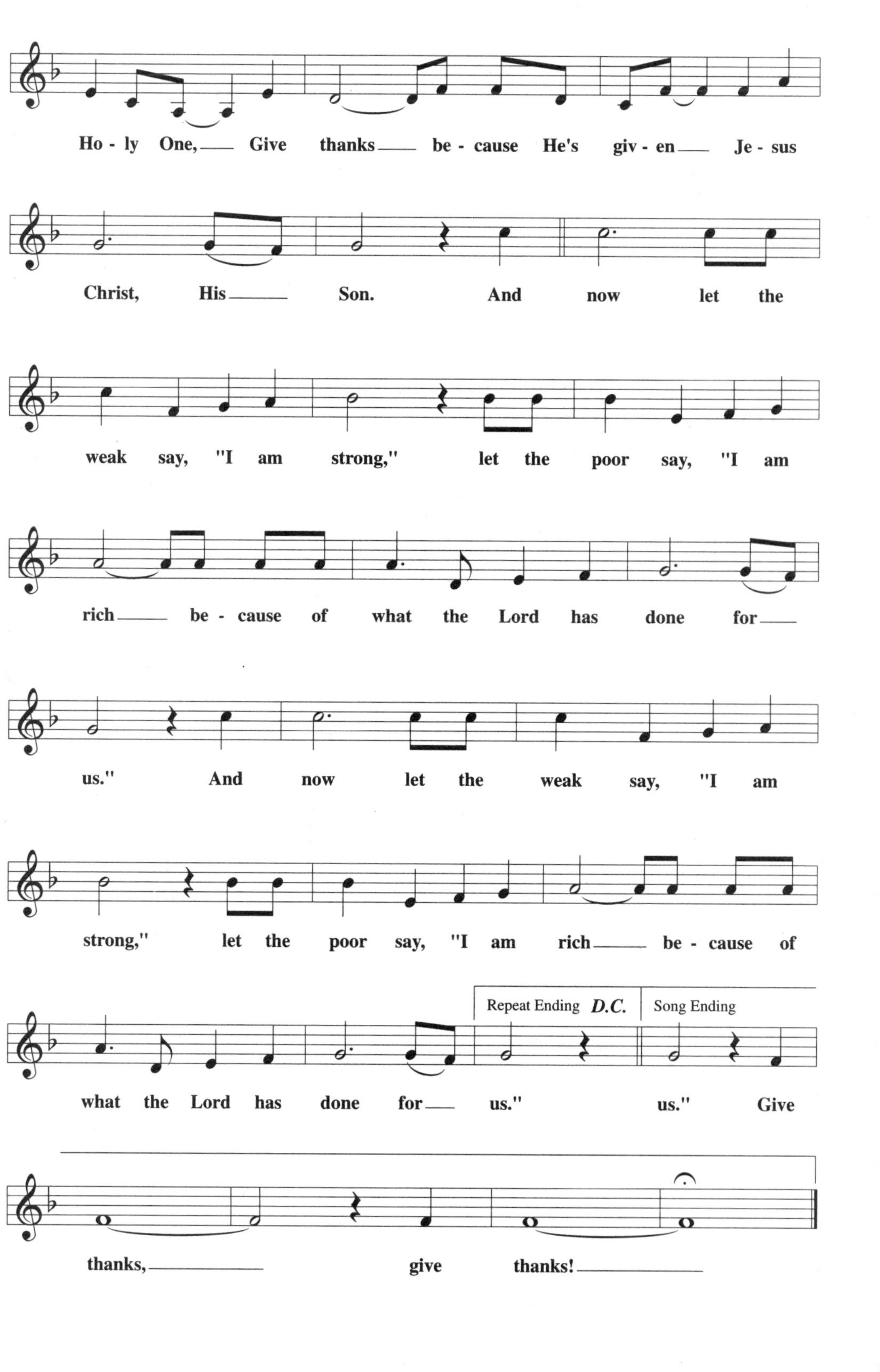
Ho - ly One, Give thanks be - cause He's giv - en Je - sus
Christ, His Son. And now let the
weak say, "I am strong," let the poor say, "I am
rich be - cause of what the Lord has done for
us." And now let the weak say, "I am
strong," let the poor say, "I am rich be - cause of
Repeat Ending D.C.
Song Ending
what the Lord has done for us." us." Give
thanks, give thanks!

171 In All Things Give Him Thanks

Words and Music by
CLAIRE CLONINGER, ANDY CLONINGER and KEN BARKER

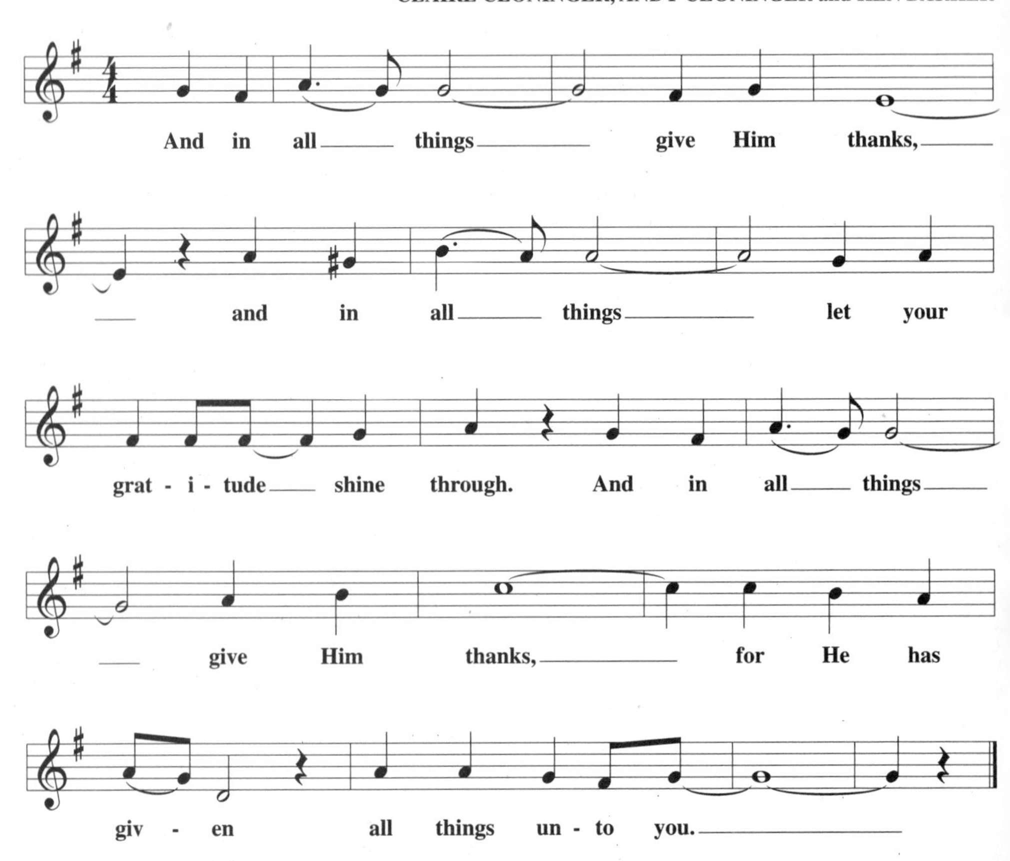

And in all things give Him thanks, and in all things let your grat - i - tude shine through. And in all things give Him thanks, for He has giv - en all things un - to you.

172 Come into His Presence

LYNN BAIRD

LYNN BAIRD

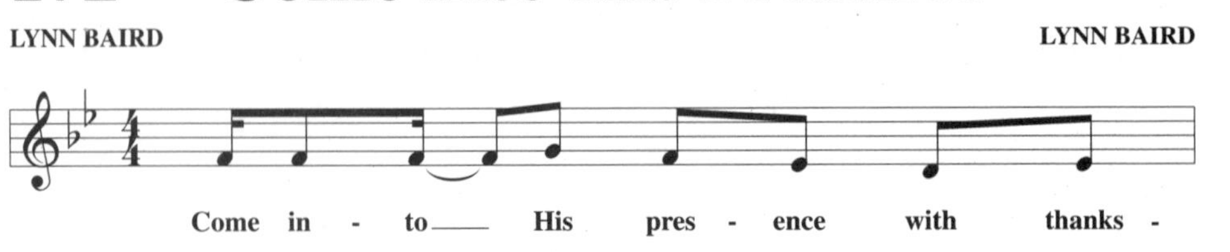

Come in - to His pres - ence with thanks -

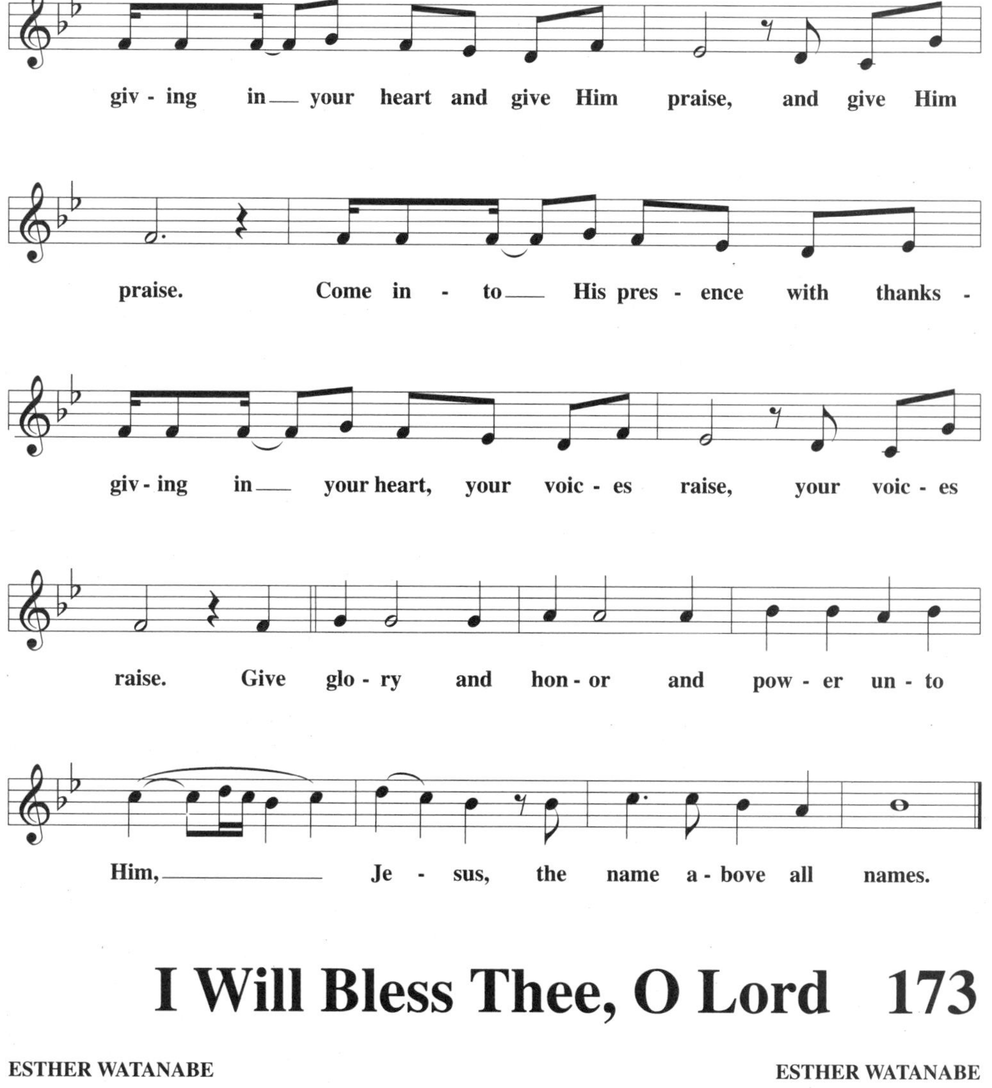

giv- ing in— your heart and give Him praise, and give Him
praise. Come in - to— His pres - ence with thanks -
giv- ing in— your heart, your voic - es raise, your voic - es
raise. Give glo - ry and hon - or and pow - er un - to
Him,———— Je - sus, the name a - bove all names.

I Will Bless Thee, O Lord 173

ESTHER WATANABE   ESTHER WATANABE

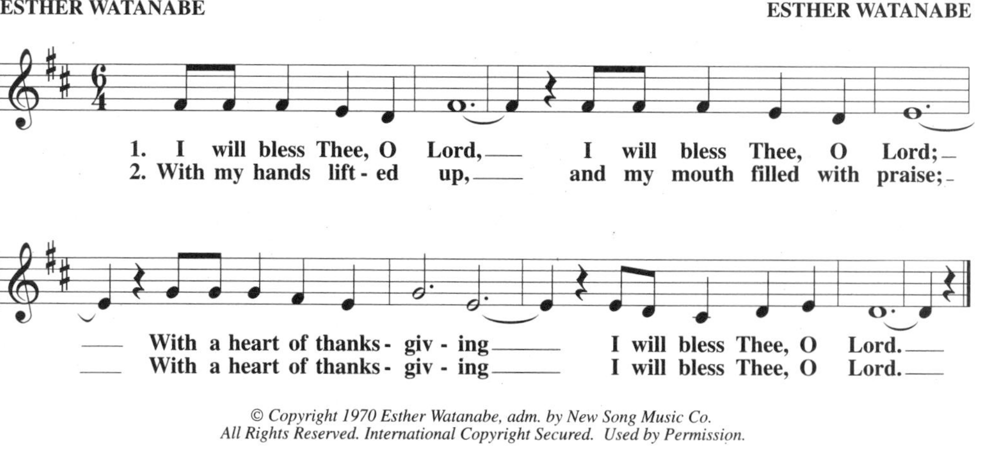

1. I will bless Thee, O Lord,— I will bless Thee, O Lord;—
2. With my hands lift - ed up,— and my mouth filled with praise;—

—— With a heart of thanks- giv - ing———— I will bless Thee, O Lord.——
—— With a heart of thanks- giv - ing———— I will bless Thee, O Lord.——

174 Thank You, Lord!

DENNIS L. JERNIGAN

DENNIS L. JERNIGAN

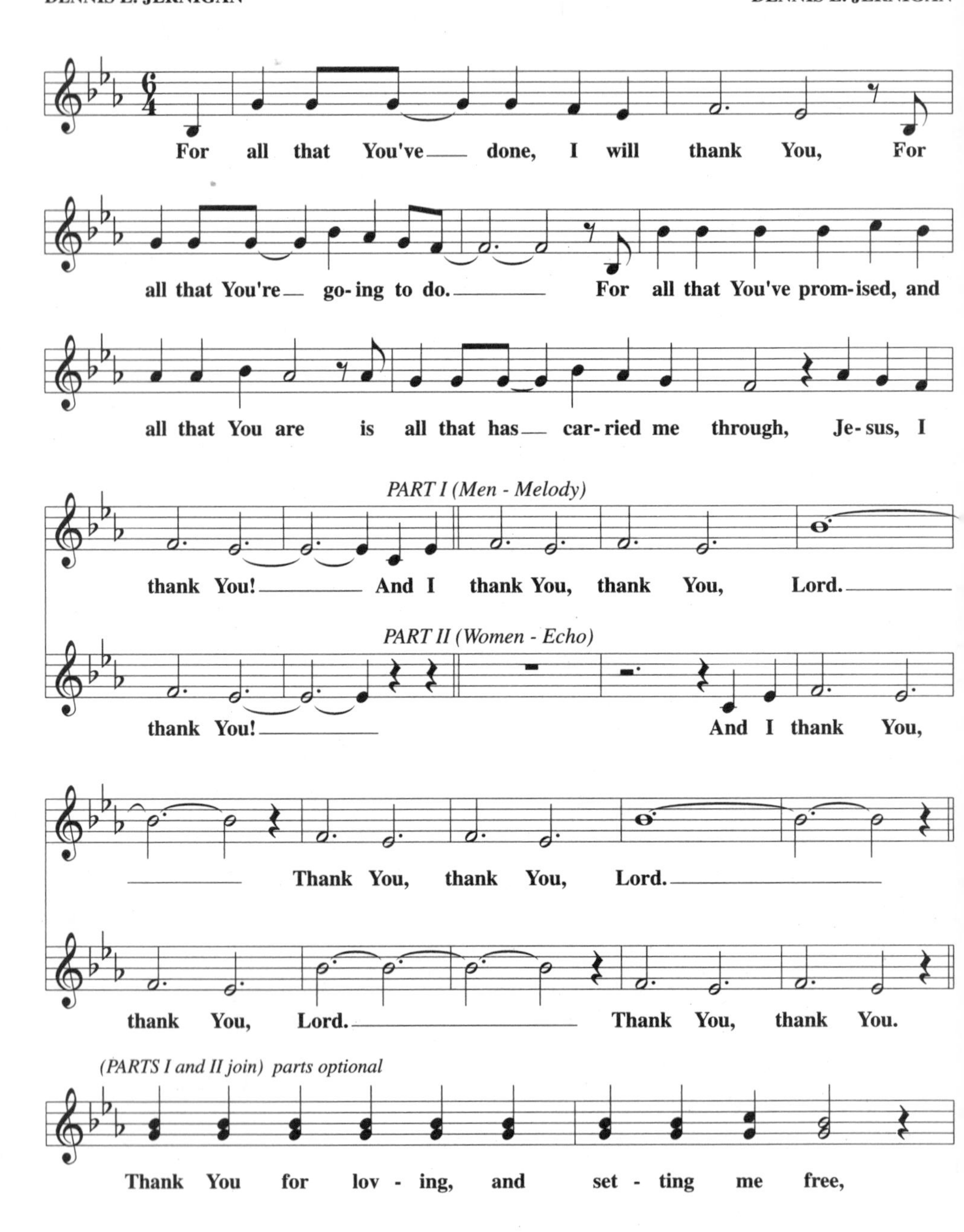

For all that You've done, I will thank You, For
all that You're going to do. For all that You've prom-ised, and
all that You are is all that has carried me through, Je-sus, I

PART I (Men - Melody)

thank You! And I thank You, thank You, Lord.

PART II (Women - Echo)

thank You! And I thank You,

Thank You, thank You, Lord.

thank You, Lord. Thank You, thank You.

(PARTS I and II join) parts optional

Thank You for lov-ing, and set-ting me free,

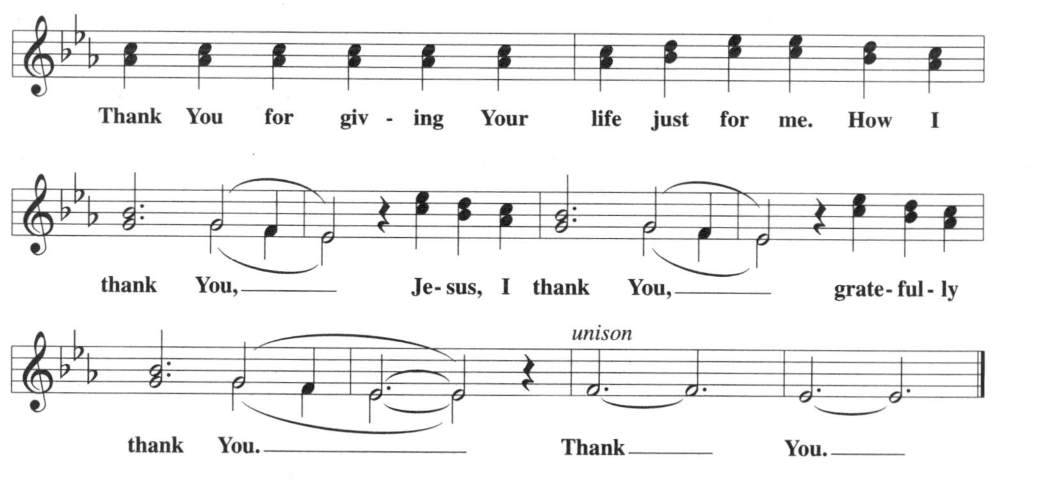

Thank You for giv-ing Your life just for me. How I
thank You,_____ Je-sus, I thank You,_____ grate-ful-ly
thank You._____ Thank_____ You._____

unison

Come Let Us Offer 175

MARLENE BIGLEY   MARLENE BIGLEY

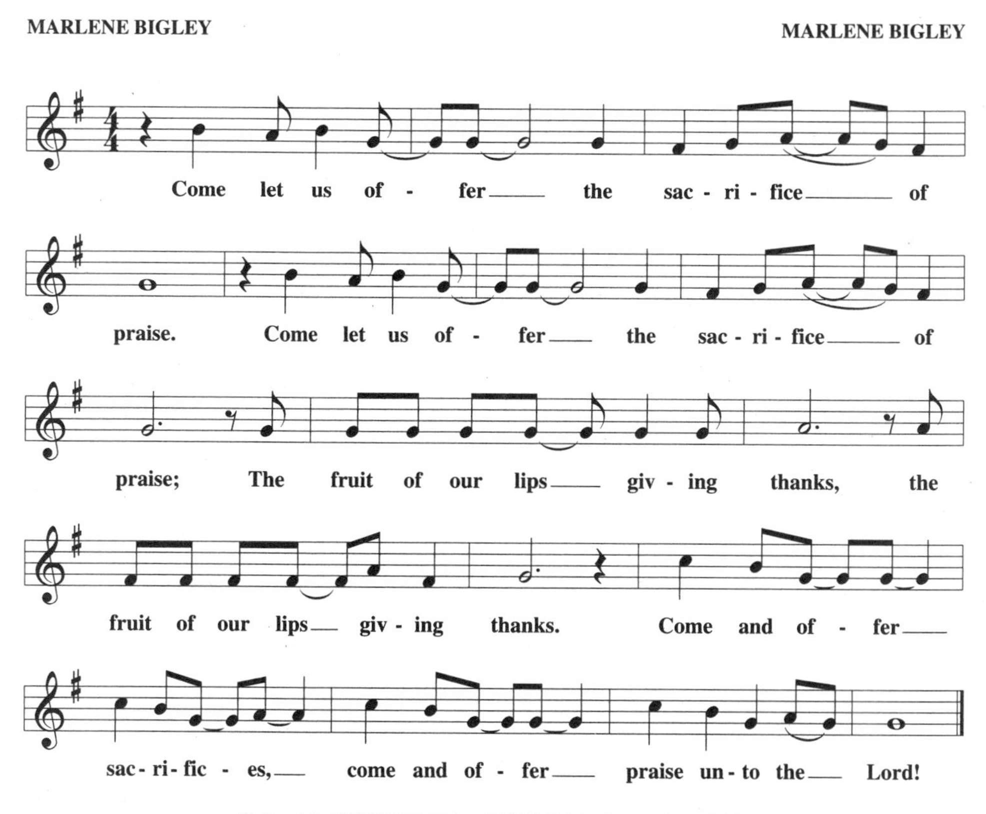

Come let us of-fer_____ the sac-ri-fice_____ of
praise. Come let us of-fer_____ the sac-ri-fice_____ of
praise; The fruit of our lips_____ giv-ing thanks, the
fruit of our lips_____ giv-ing thanks. Come and of-fer_____
sac-ri-fic-es,_____ come and of-fer_____ praise un-to the_____ Lord!

176   Arise Shine

Words and Music by
STEVEN URSPRINGER and JAY ROBINSON

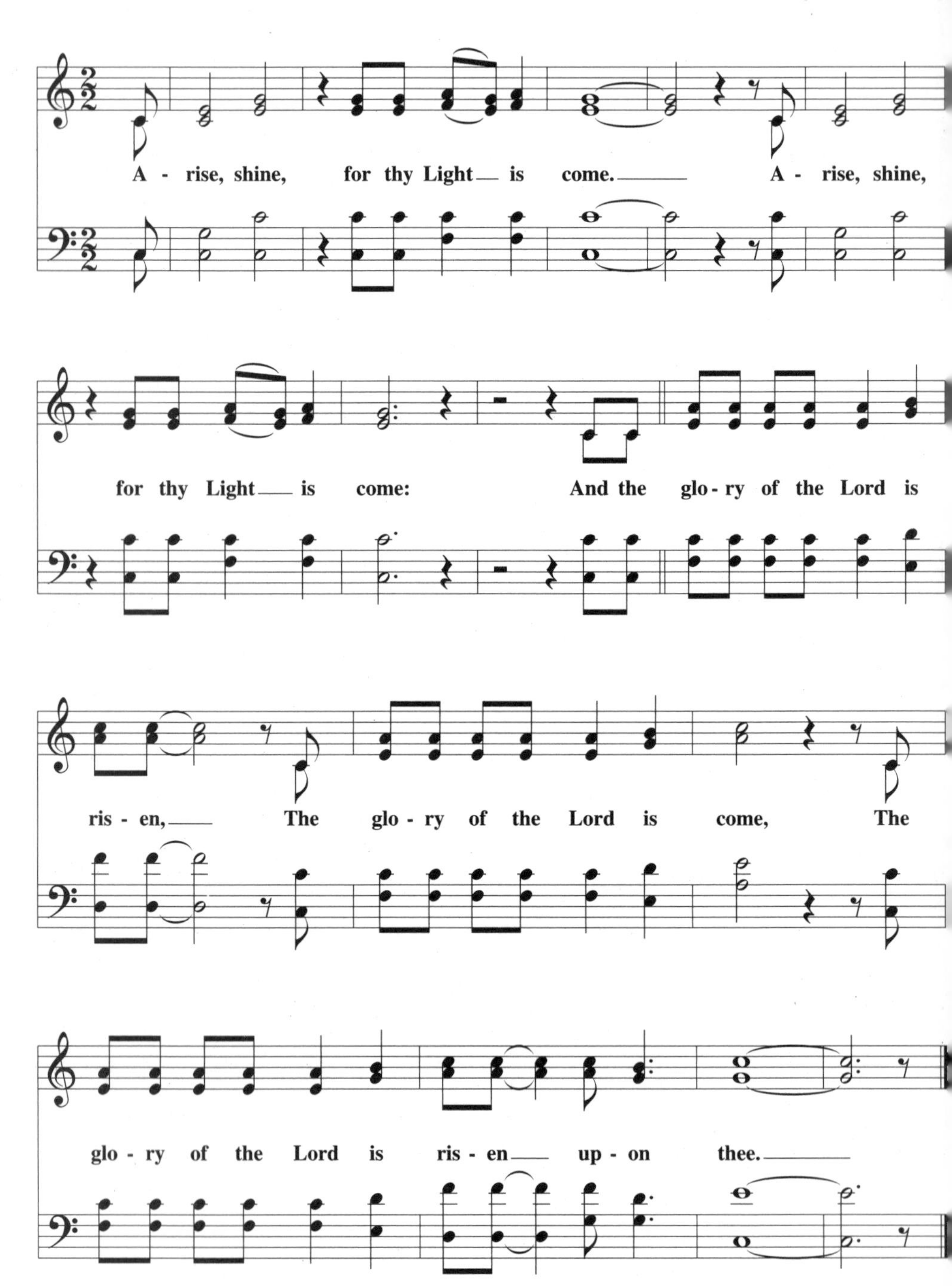

Cornerstone 177

LEON PATILLO
Based on Isaiah 9:6; 28:16

LEON PATILLO

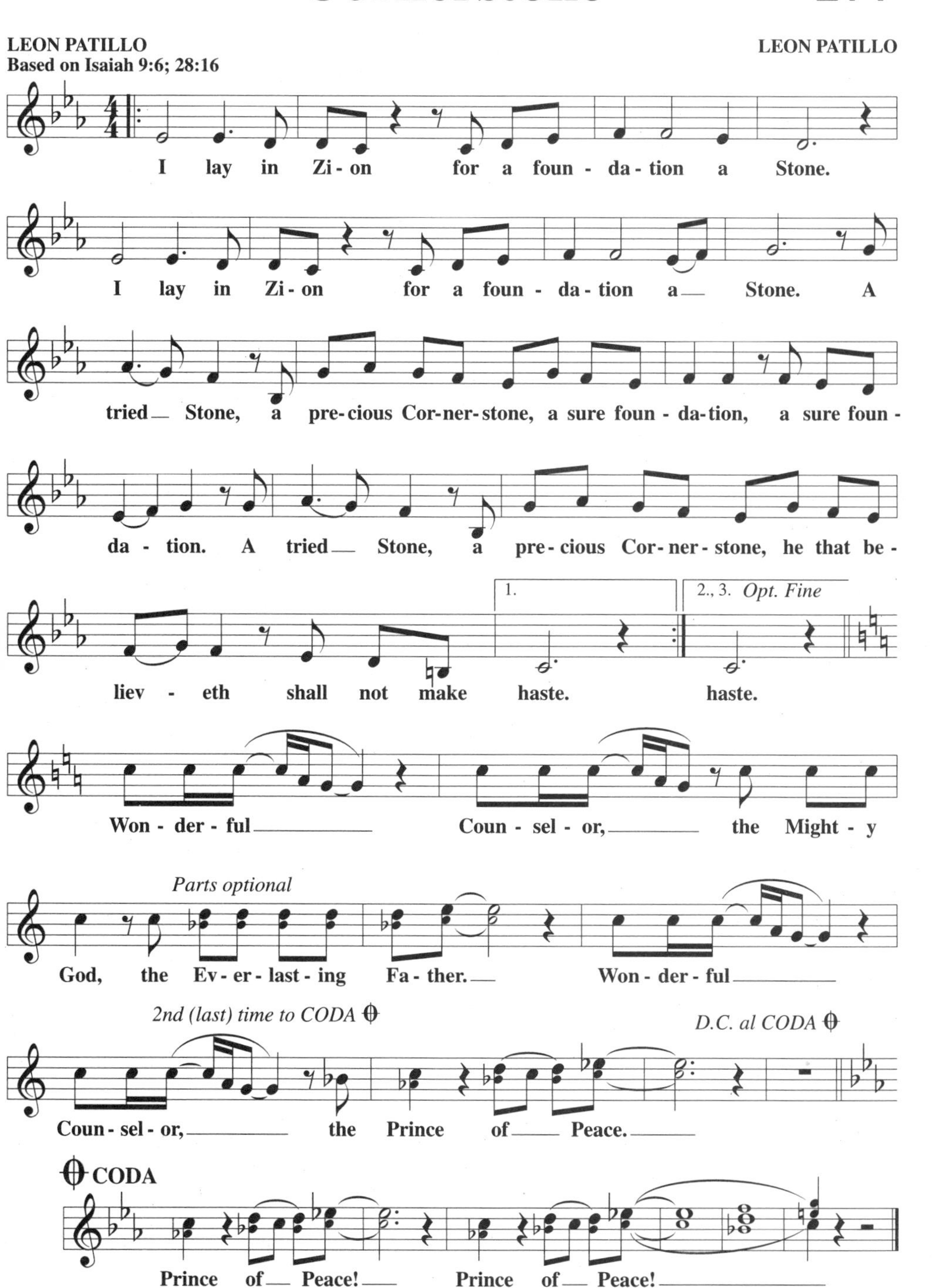

I lay in Zi-on for a foun-da-tion a Stone.

I lay in Zi-on for a foun-da-tion a— Stone. A

tried— Stone, a pre-cious Cor-ner-stone, a sure foun-da-tion, a sure foun-

da-tion. A tried— Stone, a pre-cious Cor-ner-stone, he that be-

1.
2., 3. *Opt. Fine*

liev-eth shall not make haste. haste.

Won-der-ful_____ Coun-sel-or,_____ the Might-y

Parts optional

God, the Ev-er-last-ing Fa-ther.— Won-der-ful_____

2nd (last) time to CODA ✛   *D.C. al CODA* ✛

Coun-sel-or,_____ the Prince of— Peace.

✛ **CODA**

Prince of— Peace! — Prince of— Peace! _____

178 O Lord, You're Beautiful

KEITH GREEN

KEITH GREEN

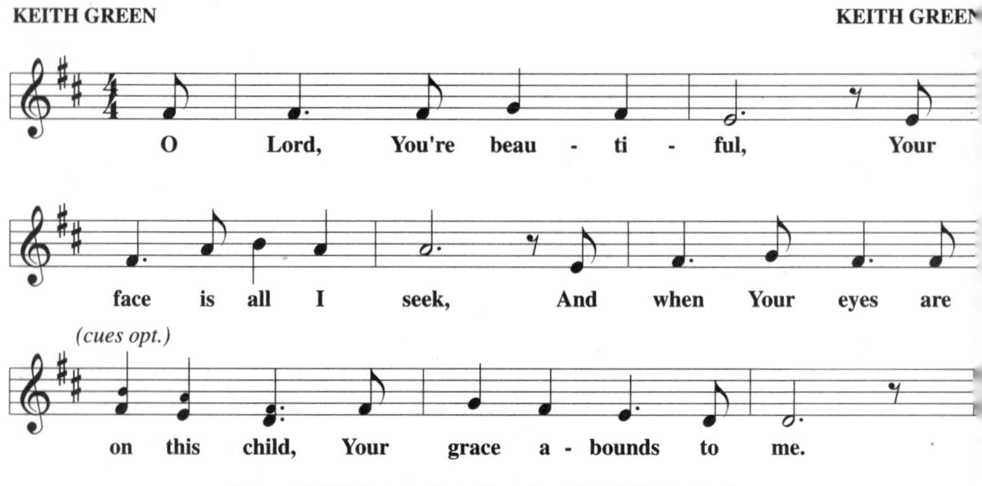

O Lord, You're beau - ti - ful, Your face is all I seek, And when Your eyes are on this child, Your grace a - bounds to me.

(cues opt.)

179 Chosen Generation

Words and Music by
JEANNIE CLATTENBURG and RICK POWELL

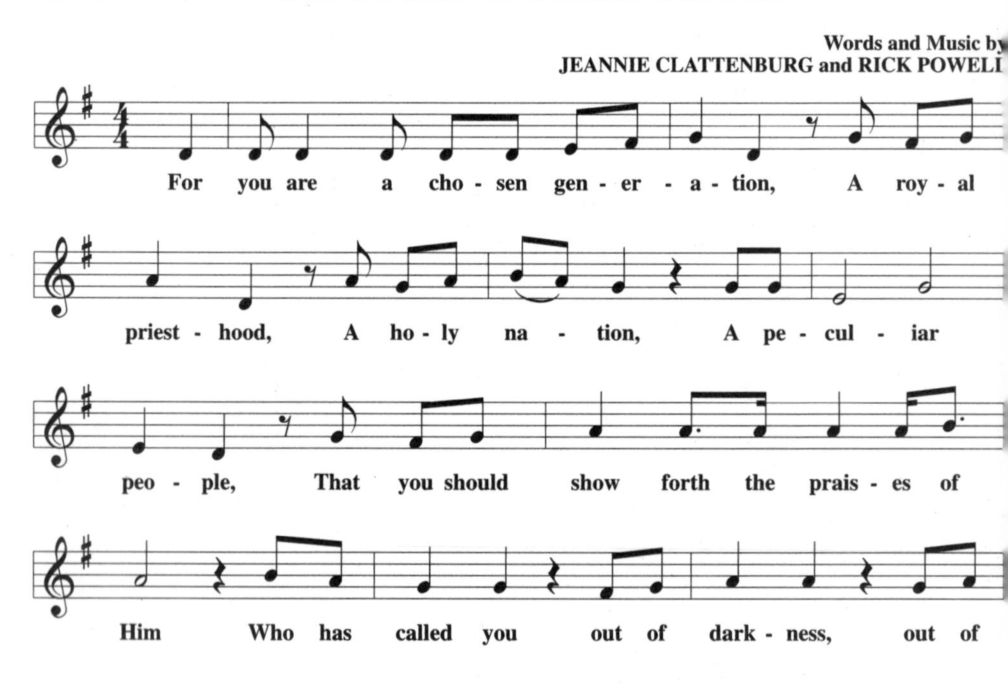

For you are a cho - sen gen - er - a - tion, A roy - al priest - hood, A ho - ly na - tion, A pe - cul - iar peo - ple, That you should show forth the prais - es of Him Who has called you out of dark - ness, out of

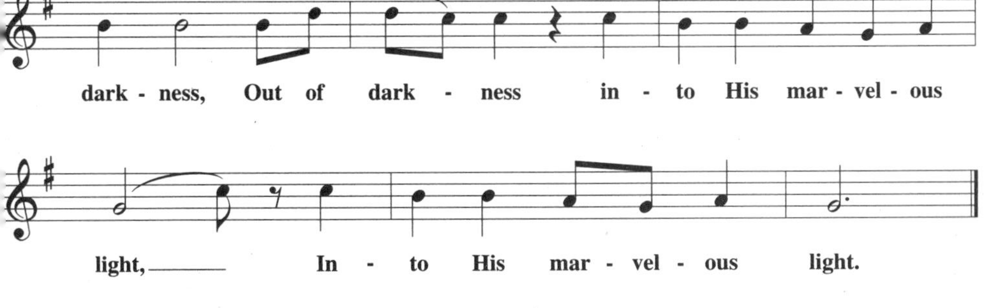

dark - ness, Out of dark - ness in - to His mar - vel - ous

light,_____ In - to His mar - vel - ous light.

He Who Began a Good Work in You

180

JON MOHR
Based on Philippians 1:6

JON MOHR

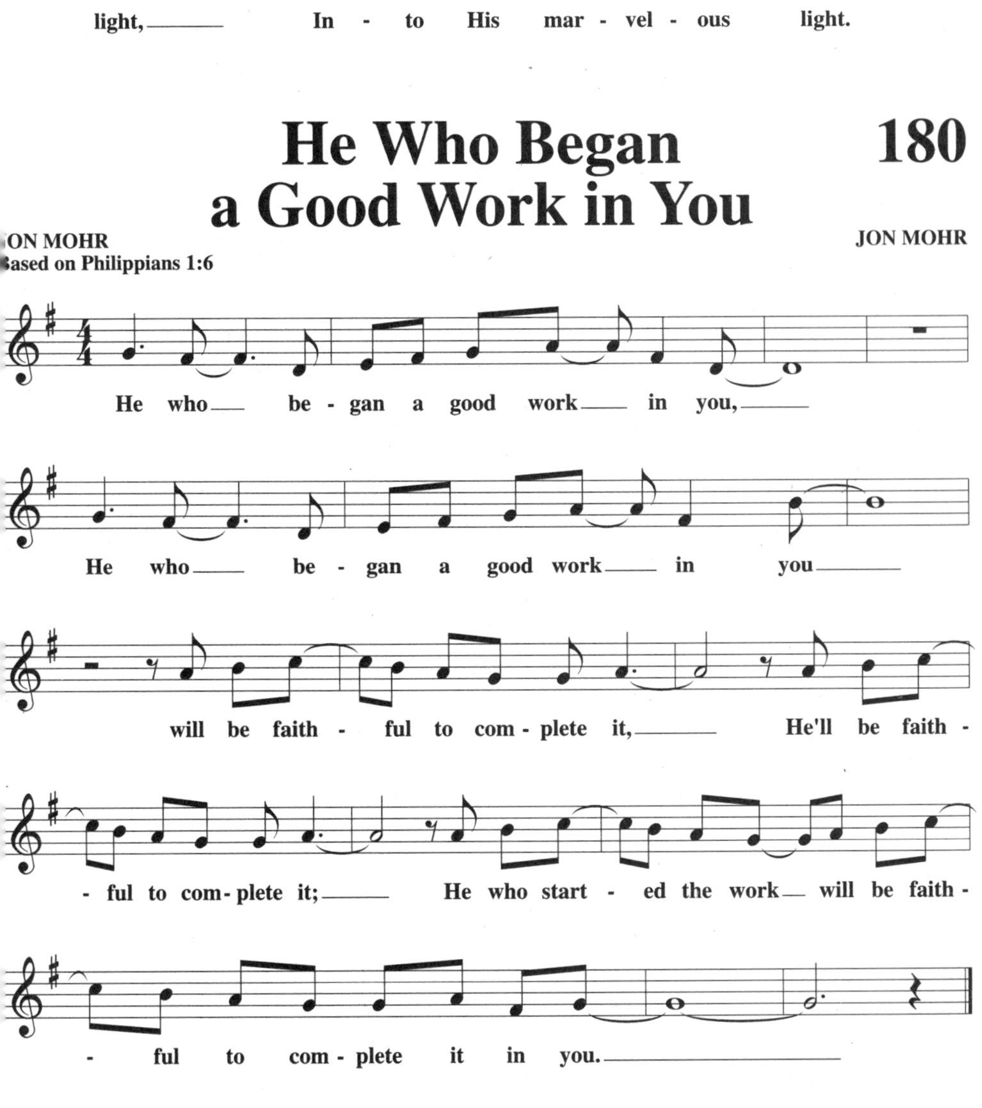

He who___ be - gan a good work___ in you, _____

He who___ be - gan a good work___ in you _____

will be faith - ful to com - plete it, _____ He'll be faith -

- ful to com - plete it; _____ He who start - ed the work___ will be faith -

- ful to com - plete it in you. _____

181 God Is the Strength of My Heart

EUGENE GRECO

EUGENE GRECO

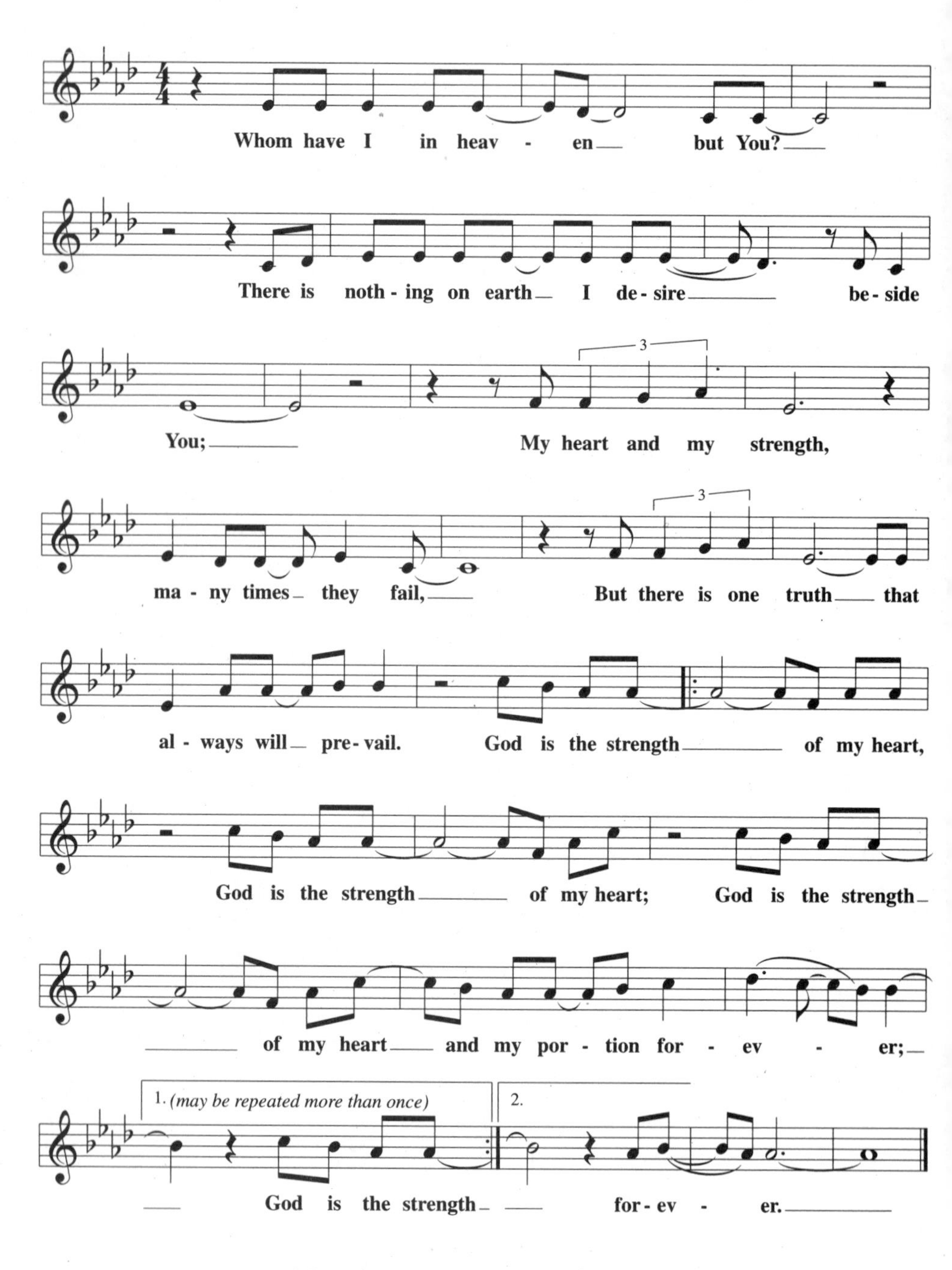

KAREN LAFFERTY
Based on Matt. 6:33; 7:7

KAREN LAFFERTY

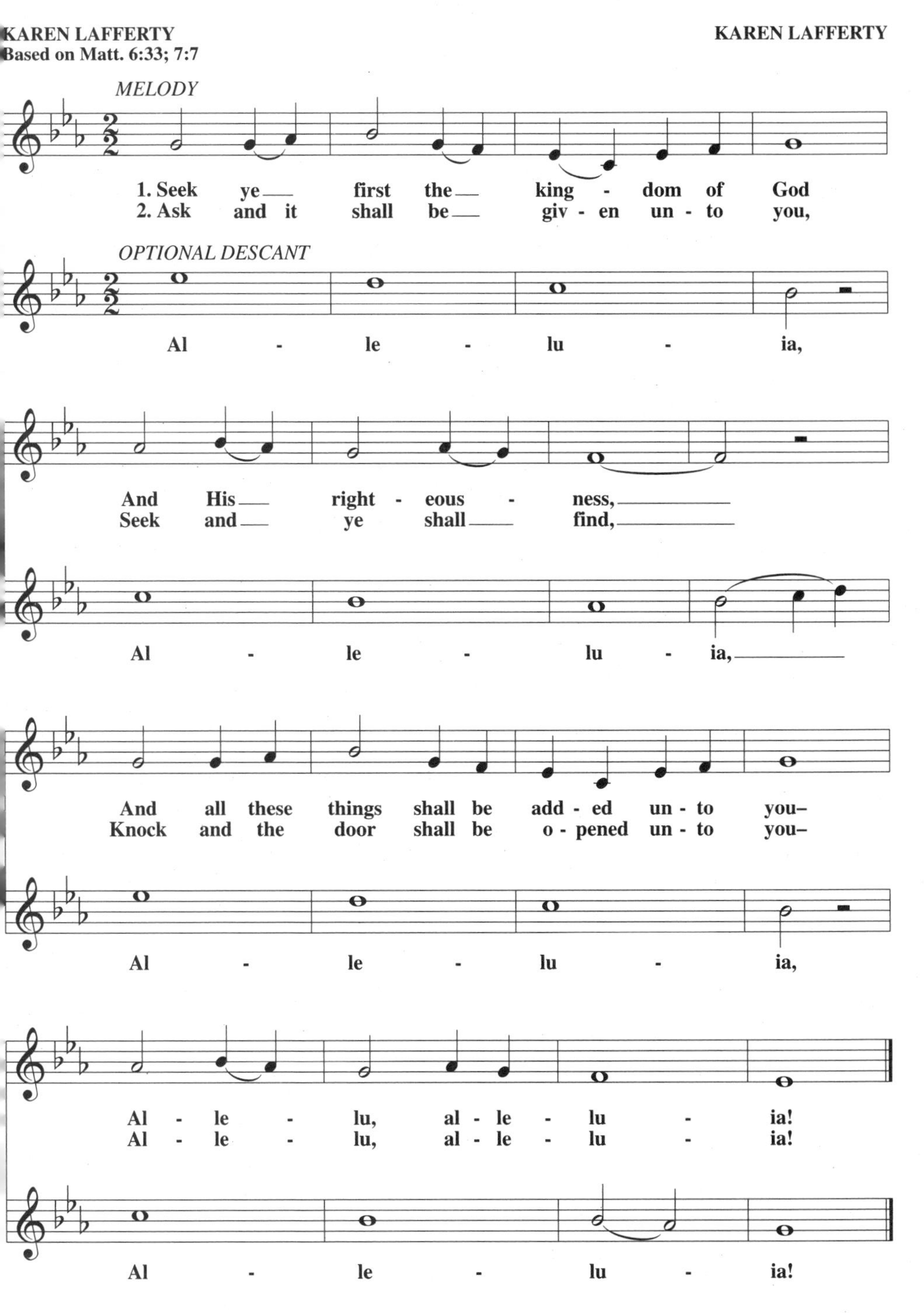

MELODY

1. Seek ye first the king - dom of God
2. Ask and it shall be giv - en un - to you,

OPTIONAL DESCANT

Al - le - lu - ia,

And His right - eous - ness,
Seek and ye shall find,

Al - le - lu - ia,

And all these things shall be add - ed un - to you–
Knock and the door shall be o - pened un - to you–

Al - le - lu - ia,

Al - le - lu, al - le - lu - ia!
Al - le - lu, al - le - lu - ia!

Al - le - lu - ia!

183 Thy Word

AMY GRANT
Based on Psalm 119:105

MICHAEL W. SMITH

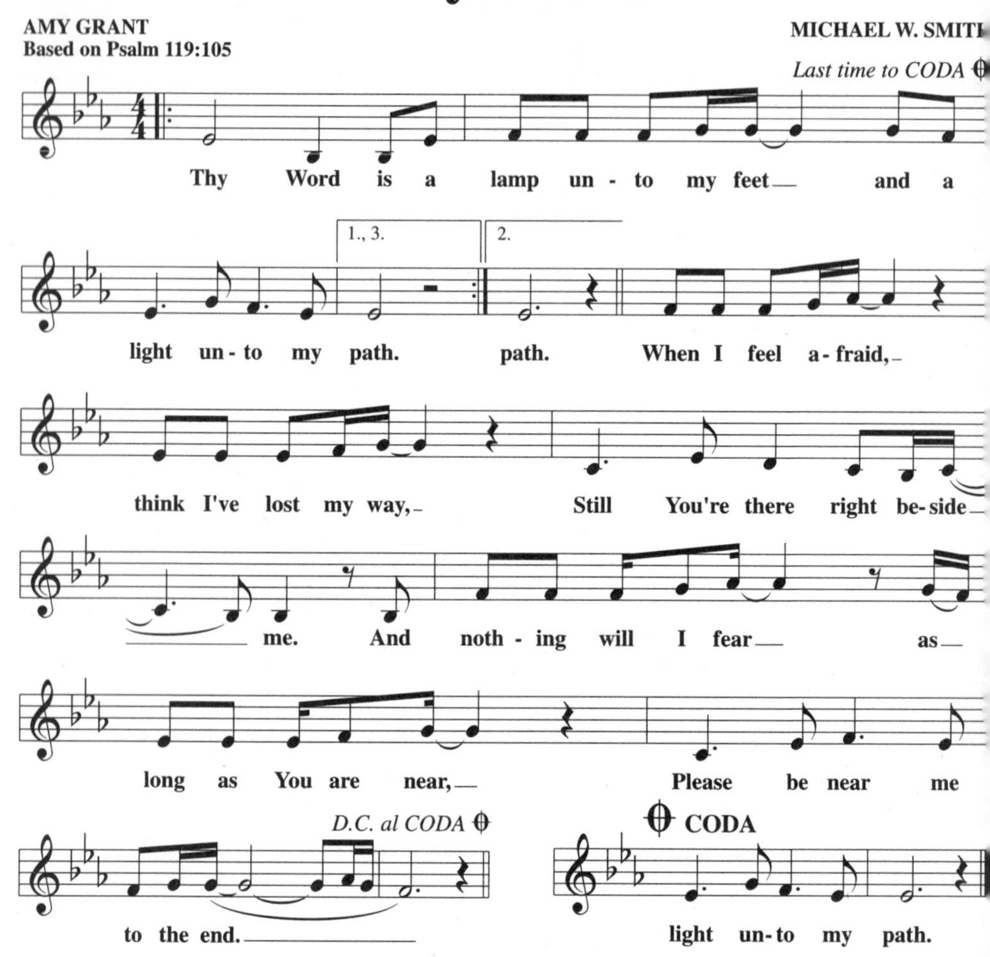

184 Unto Thee, O Lord

Ps. 25:1-6, adapted by CHARLES F. MONROE

CHARLES F. MONROE

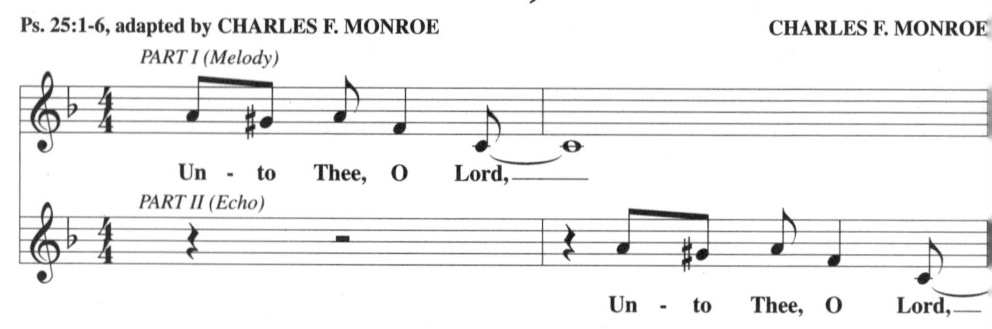

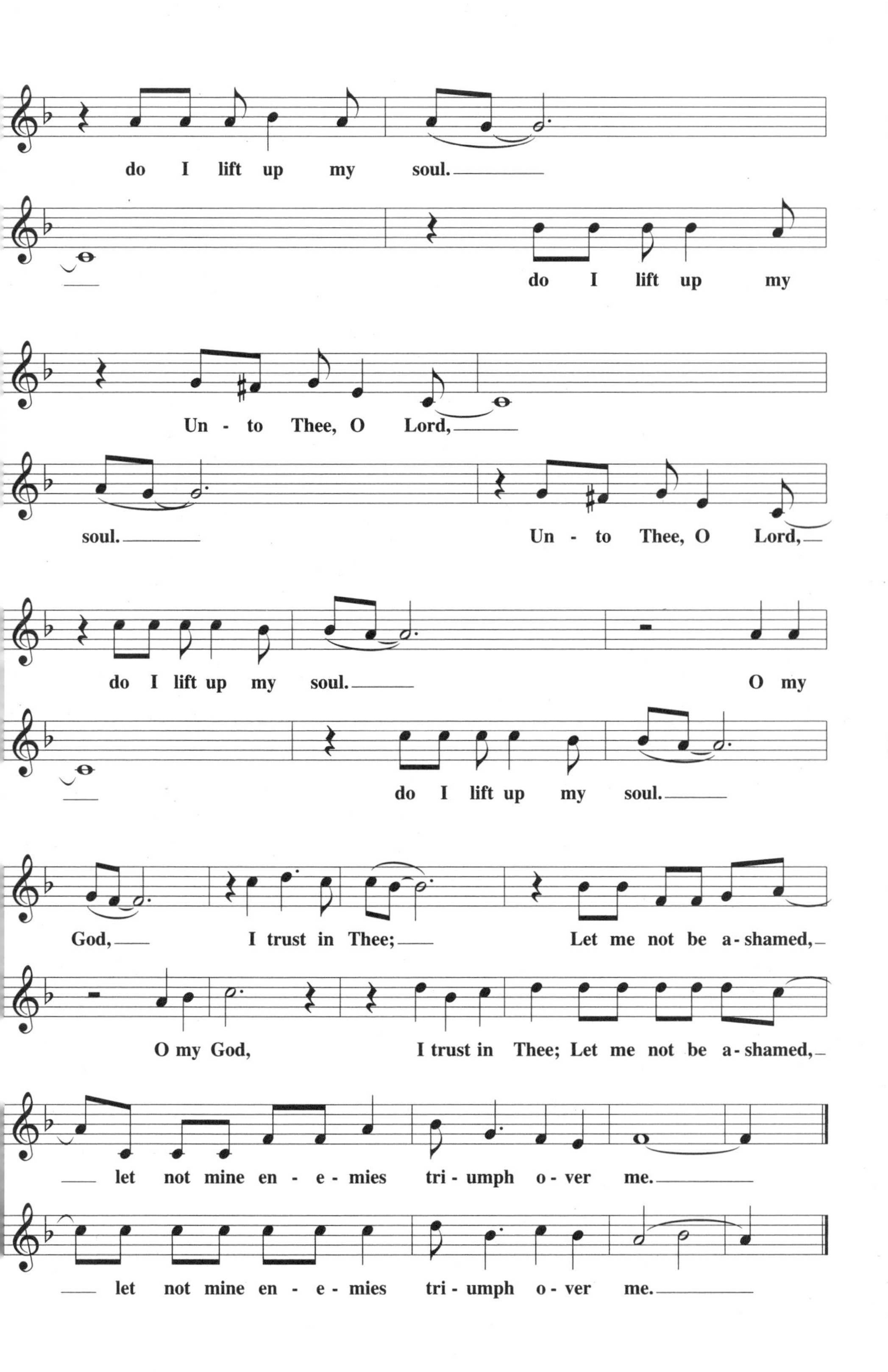

do I lift up my soul.
do I lift up my
Un - to Thee, O Lord,
soul.
Un - to Thee, O Lord,
do I lift up my soul.
O my
do I lift up my soul.
God,
I trust in Thee;
Let me not be a - shamed,
O my God,
I trust in Thee; Let me not be a - shamed,
let not mine en - e - mies tri - umph o - ver me.
let not mine en - e - mies tri - umph o - ver me.

185

The Steadfast Love
of the Lord

Lamentations 3:22-23

EDITH McNEILL

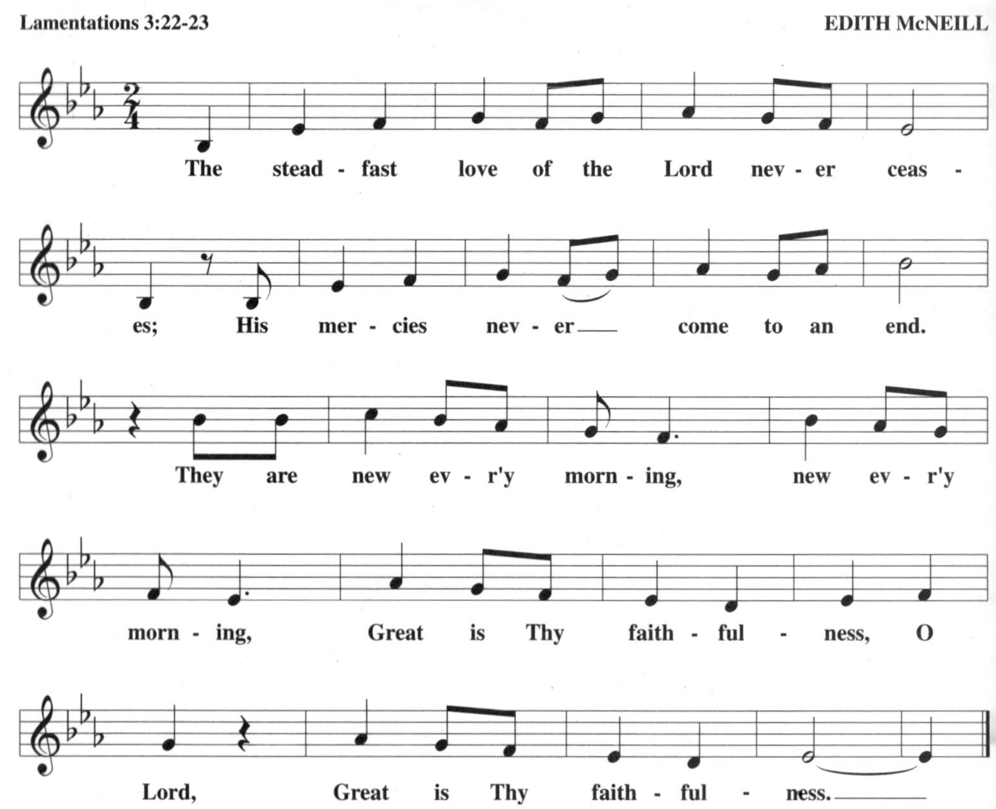

The stead-fast love of the Lord nev-er ceas-es; His mer-cies nev-er—— come to an end. They are new ev-r'y morn-ing, new ev-r'y morn-ing, Great is Thy faith-ful-ness, O Lord, Great is Thy faith-ful-ness.——

186 We Are an Offering

DWIGHT LILES   DWIGHT LILES

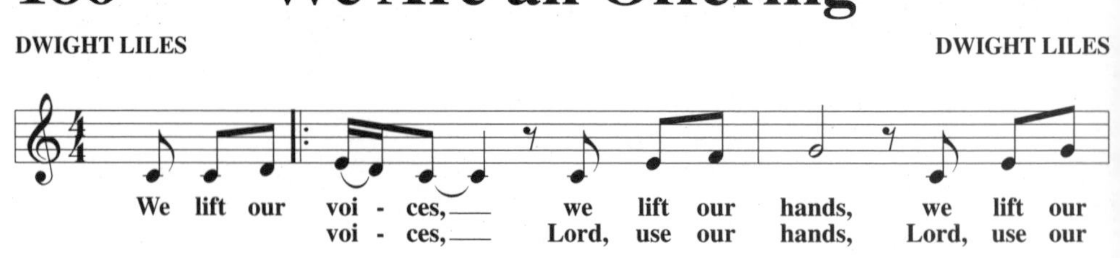

We lift our voi-ces,—— we lift our hands, we lift our
voi-ces,—— Lord, use our hands, Lord, use our

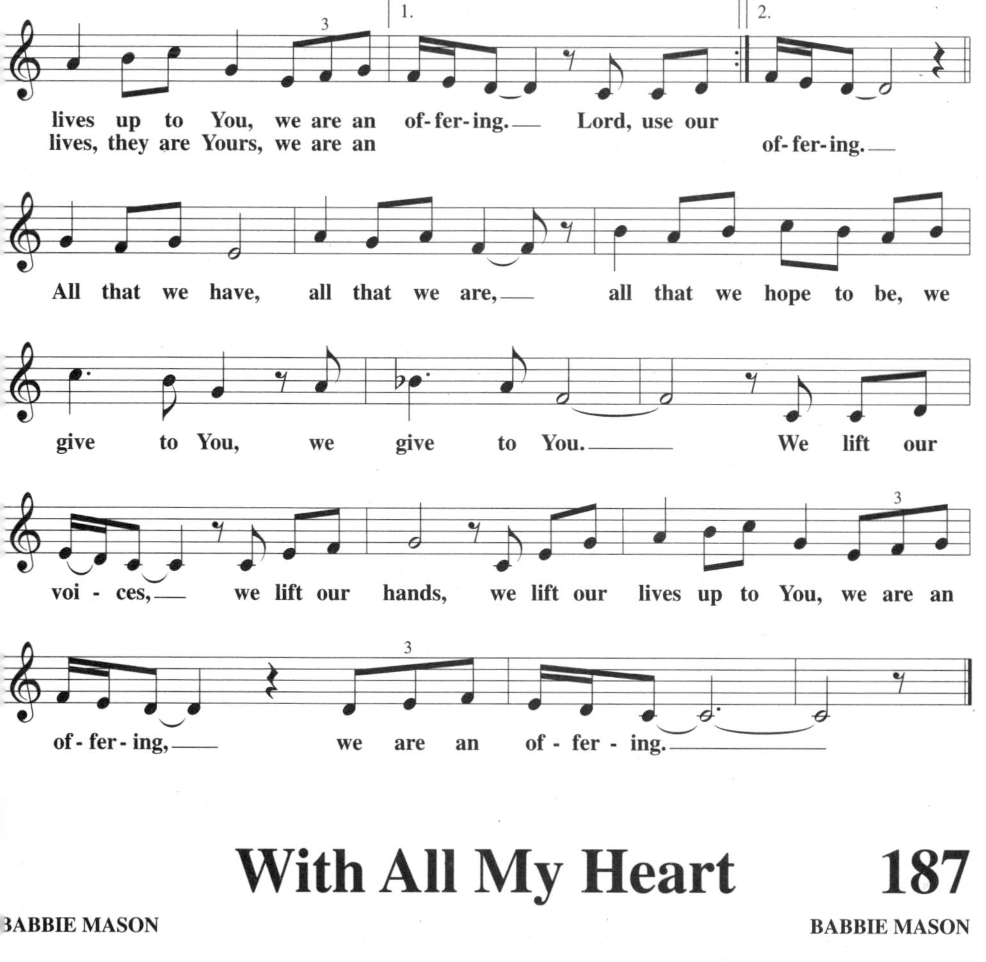

lives up to You, we are an of-fer-ing. —— Lord, use our
lives, they are Yours, we are an of-fer-ing. ——

All that we have, all that we are, —— all that we hope to be, we

give to You, we give to You. —— We lift our

voi - ces, —— we lift our hands, we lift our lives up to You, we are an

of - fer - ing, —— we are an of - fer - ing. ——

With All My Heart   187

BABBIE MASON

BABBIE MASON

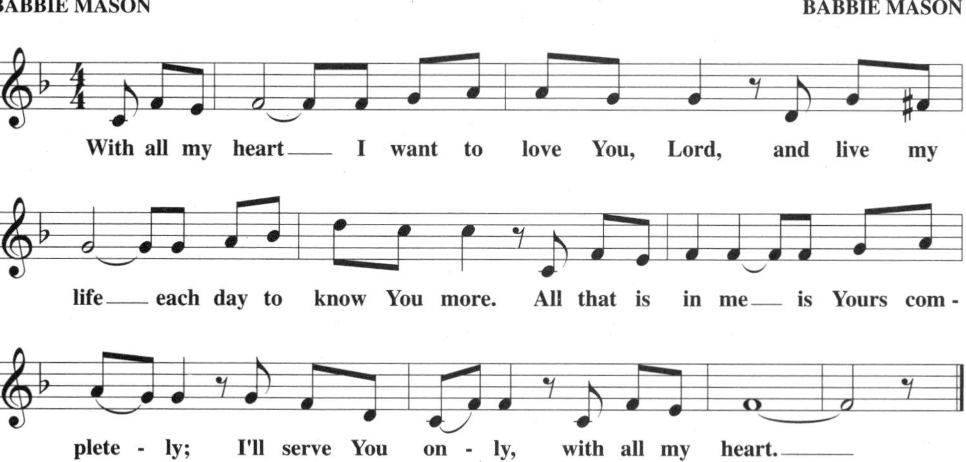

With all my heart —— I want to love You, Lord, and live my

life —— each day to know You more. All that is in me —— is Yours com-

plete - ly; I'll serve You on - ly, with all my heart. ——

188 Take Me In

DAVE BROWNING

DAVE BROWNING

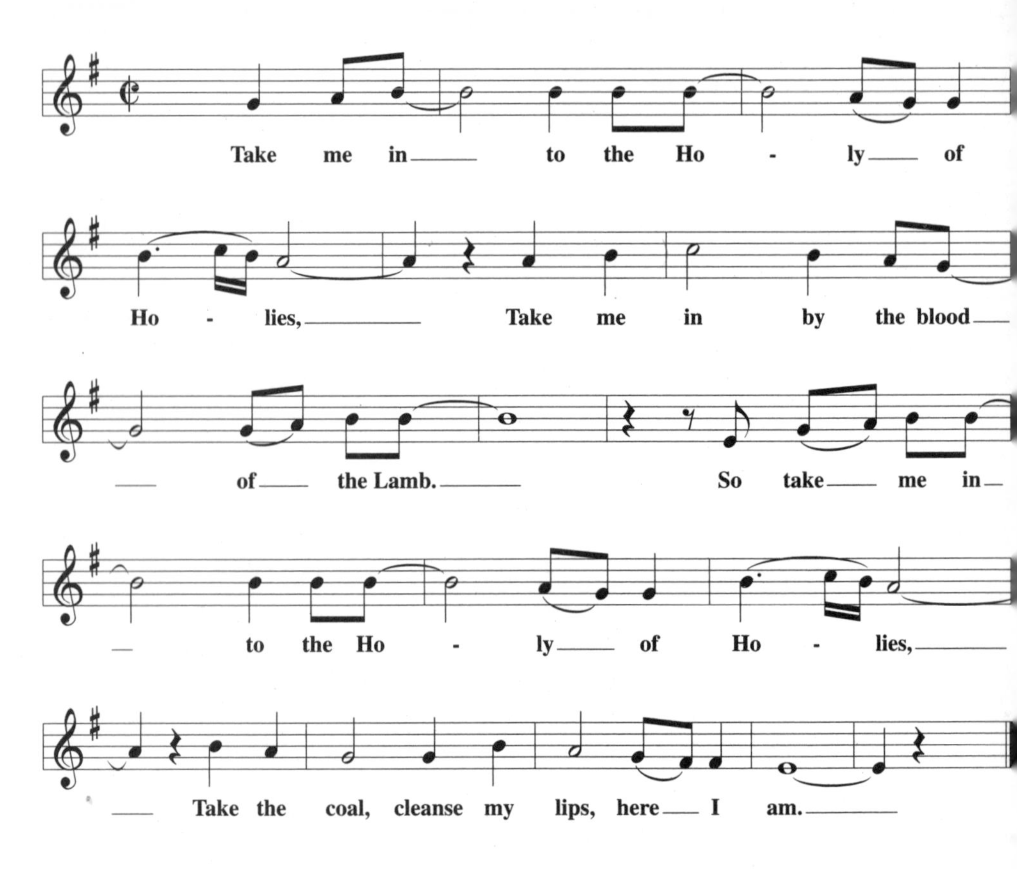

Take me in to the Ho - ly of
Ho - lies, Take me in by the blood
of the Lamb. So take me in
to the Ho - ly of Ho - lies,
Take the coal, cleanse my lips, here I am.

189 Above All Else

Words and Music by
KEVIN WALKER and BARBARA ROSS

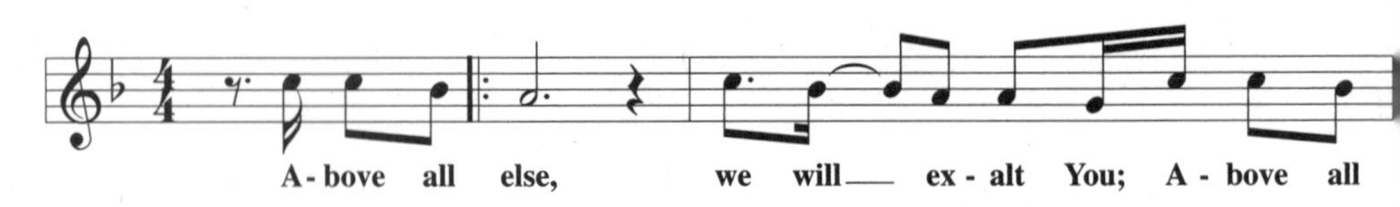

A - bove all else, we will ex - alt You; A - bove all

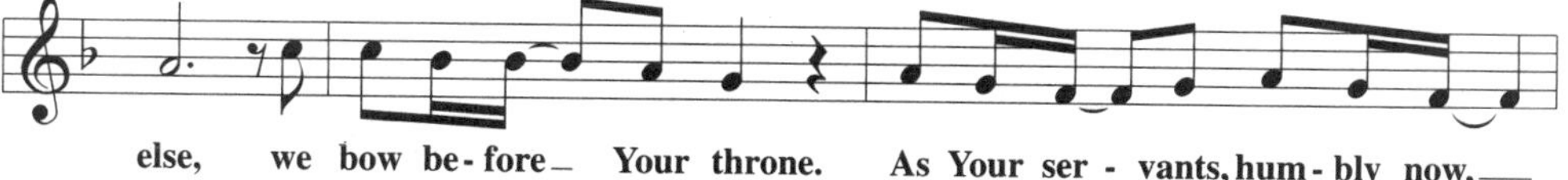

else, we bow be-fore Your throne. As Your ser - vants, hum - bly now,

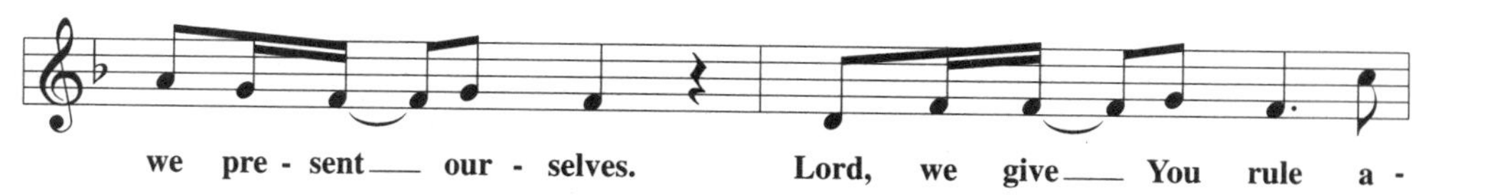

we pre - sent our - selves. Lord, we give You rule a -

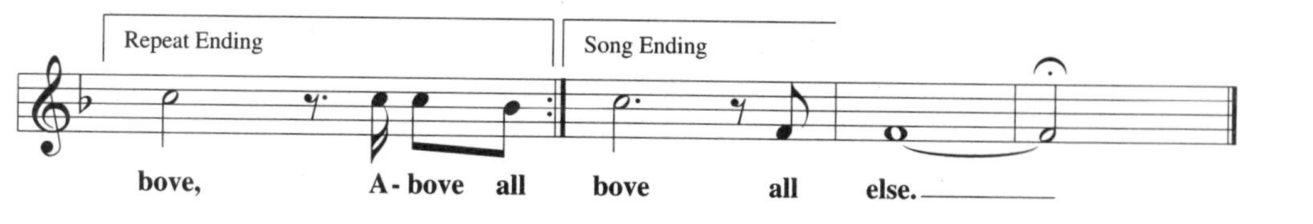

bove, A - bove all bove all else.

Here I Am

190

CHRIS A. BOWATER

CHRIS A. BOWATER
Arranged by Ken Barker

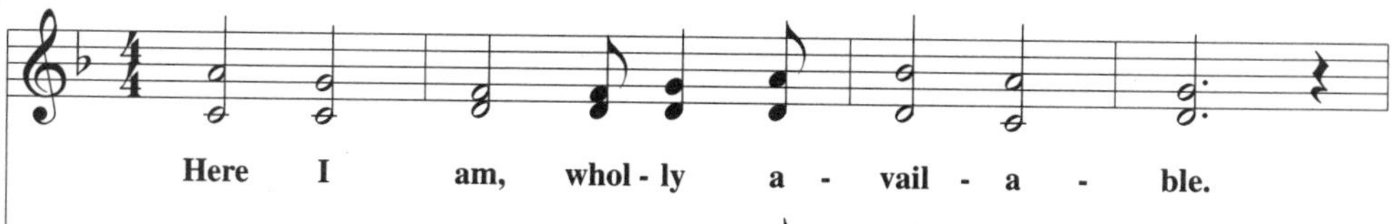

Here I am, whol - ly a - vail - a - ble.

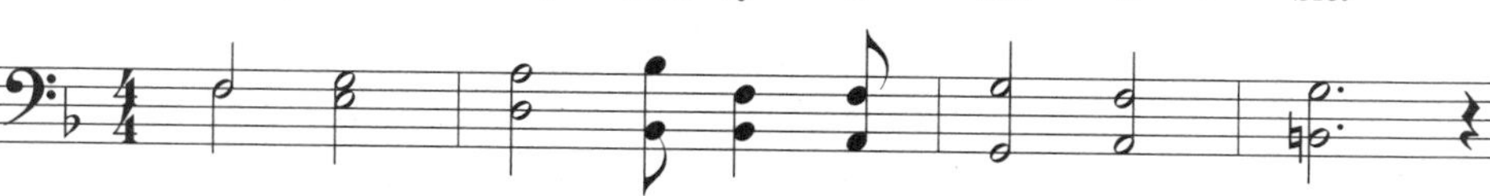

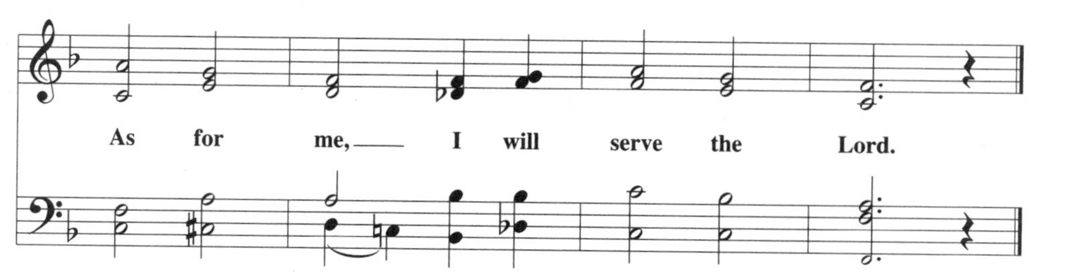

As for me, I will serve the Lord.

191 My Lord, My God

RON MYERS

RON MYERS

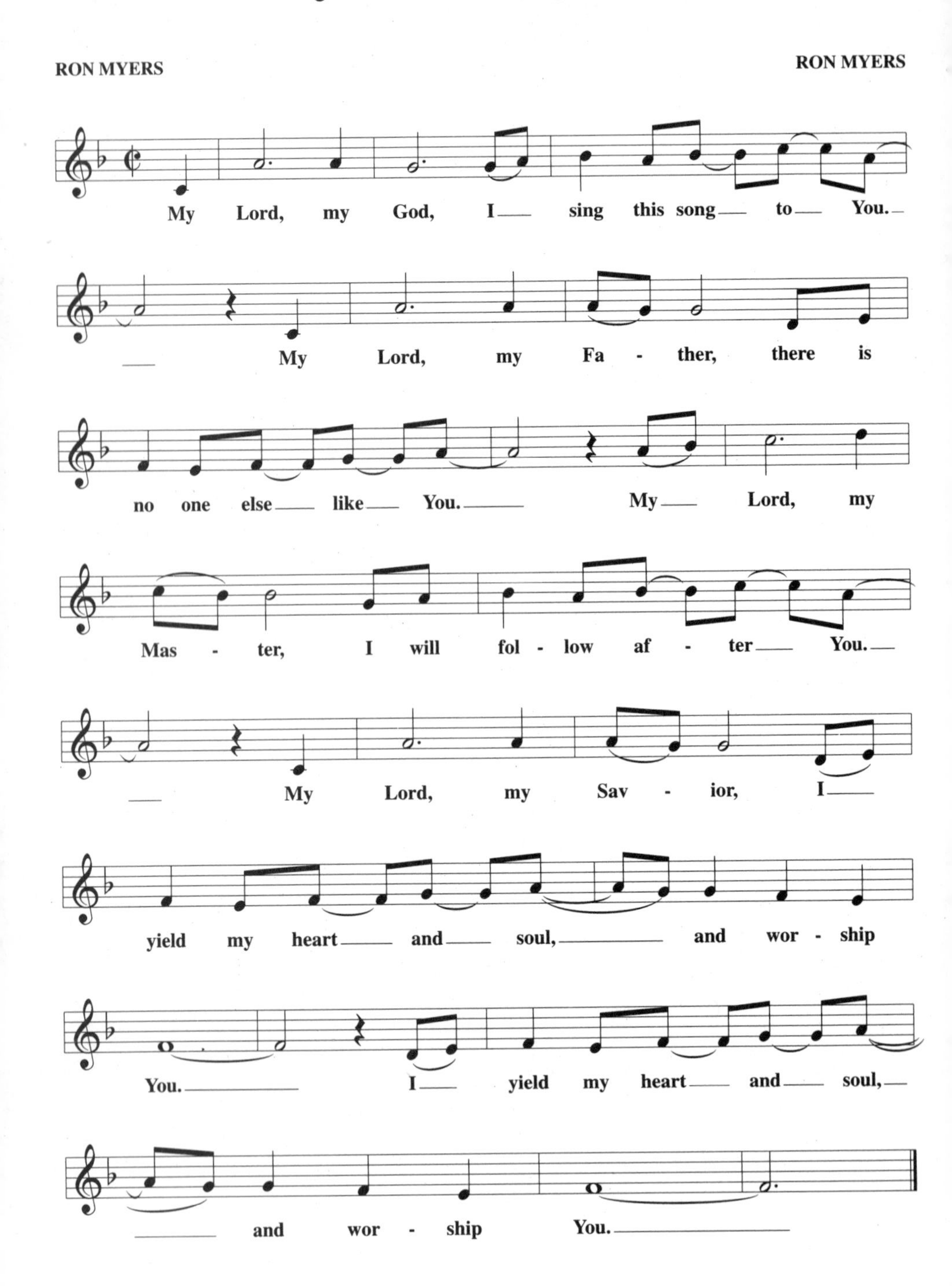

I'm Loving You More Every Day

192

Words and Music by
JIMMY PEARCE, BECKY PEARCE
and C. AARON WILBURN

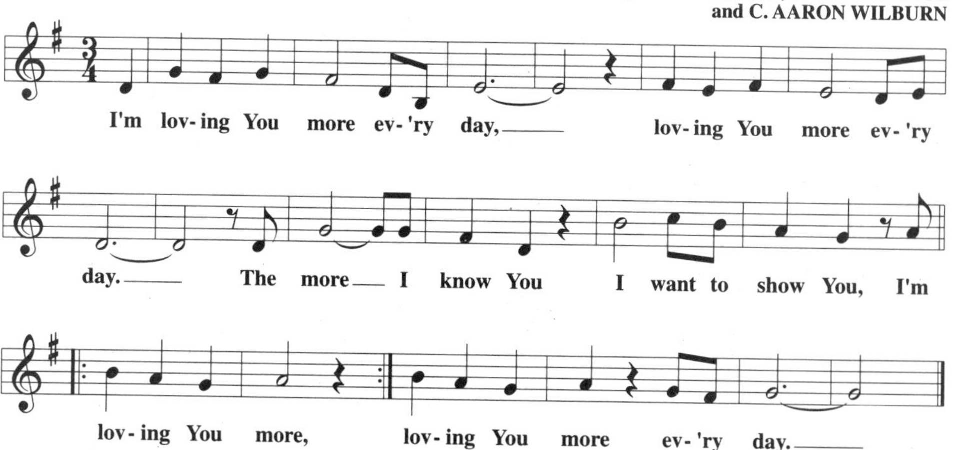

I'm lov-ing You more ev-'ry day,_____ lov-ing You more ev-'ry

day._____ The more_____ I know You I want to show You, I'm

lov-ing You more, lov-ing You more ev-'ry day._____

Make Me a Servant

193

KELLY WILLARD

KELLY WILLARD

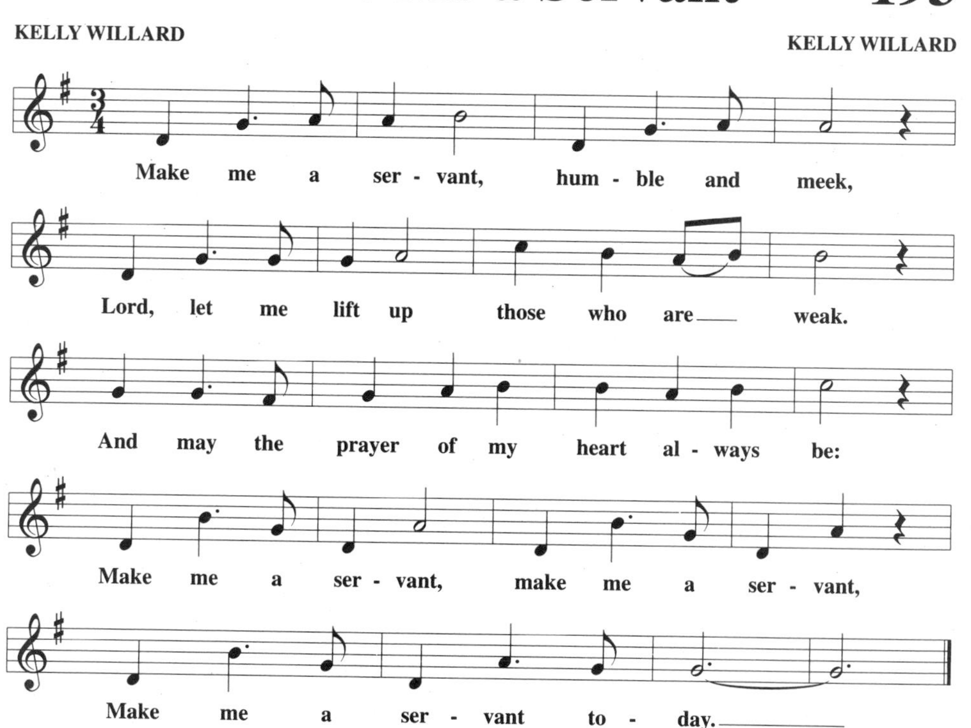

Make me a ser-vant, hum-ble and meek,

Lord, let me lift up those who are_____ weak.

And may the prayer of my heart al-ways be:

Make me a ser-vant, make me a ser-vant,

Make me a ser-vant to-day._____

194 Father, I Adore You

TERRYE COELHO

TERRYE COELHO

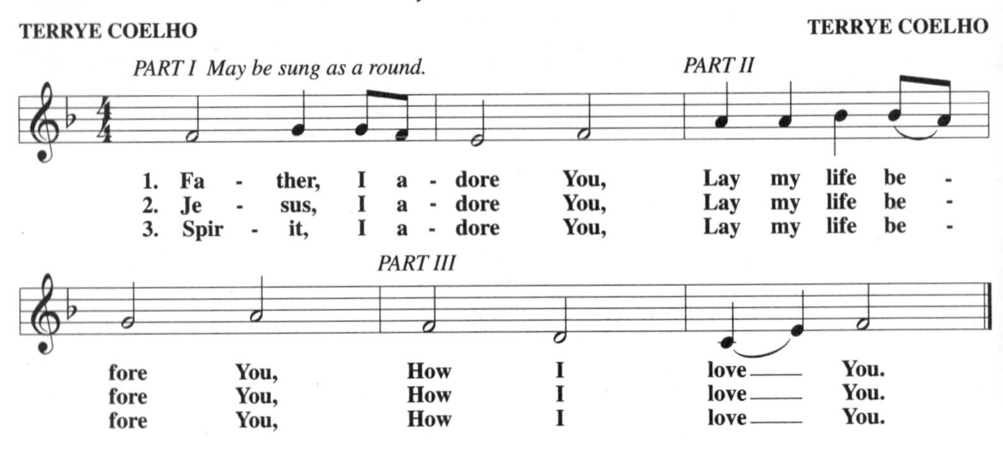

PART I May be sung as a round.

PART II

1. Fa - ther, I a - dore You, Lay my life be -
2. Je - sus, I a - dore You, Lay my life be -
3. Spir - it, I a - dore You, Lay my life be -

PART III

fore You, How I love___ You.
fore You, How I love___ You.
fore You, How I love___ You.

195 Change My Heart, O God

EDDIE ESPINOSA

EDDIE ESPINOSA

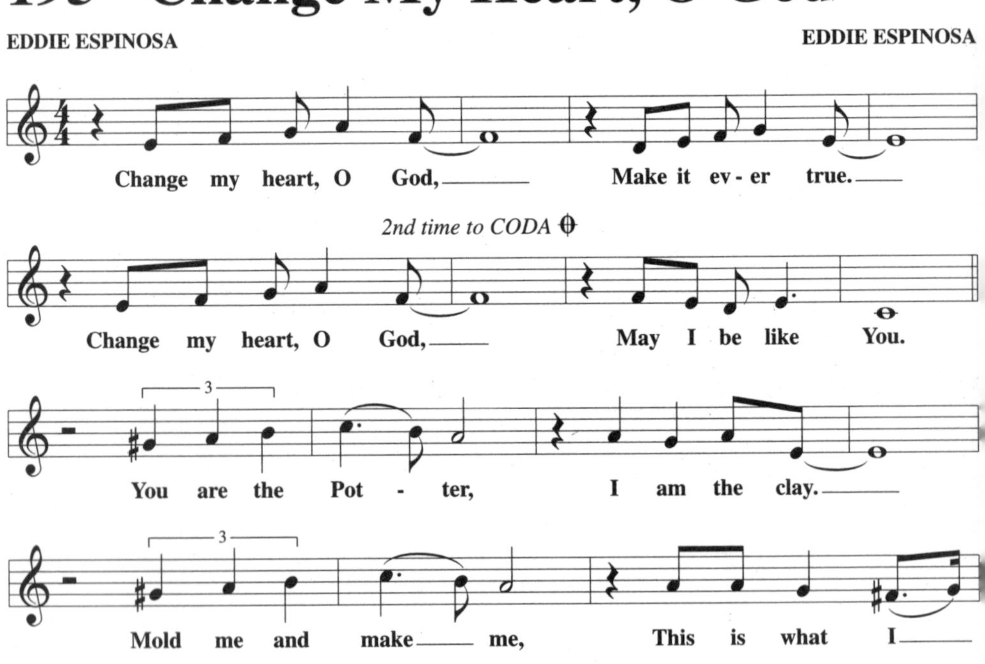

Change my heart, O God,___ Make it ev - er true.___

2nd time to CODA

Change my heart, O God,___ May I be like You.

You are the Pot - ter, I am the clay.___

Mold me and make___ me, This is what I

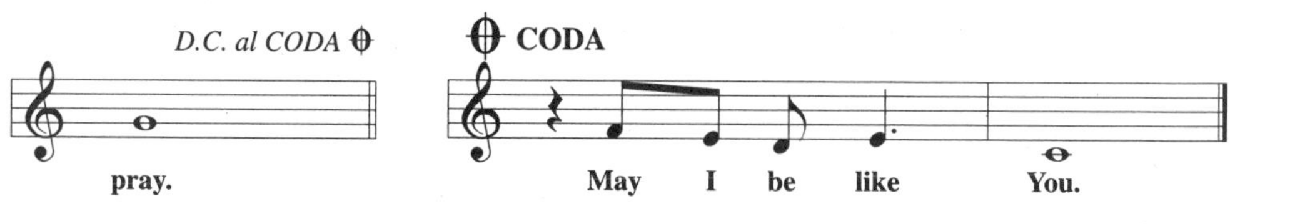

In My Life, Lord, Be Glorified

196

BOB KILPATRICK

BOB KILPATRICK

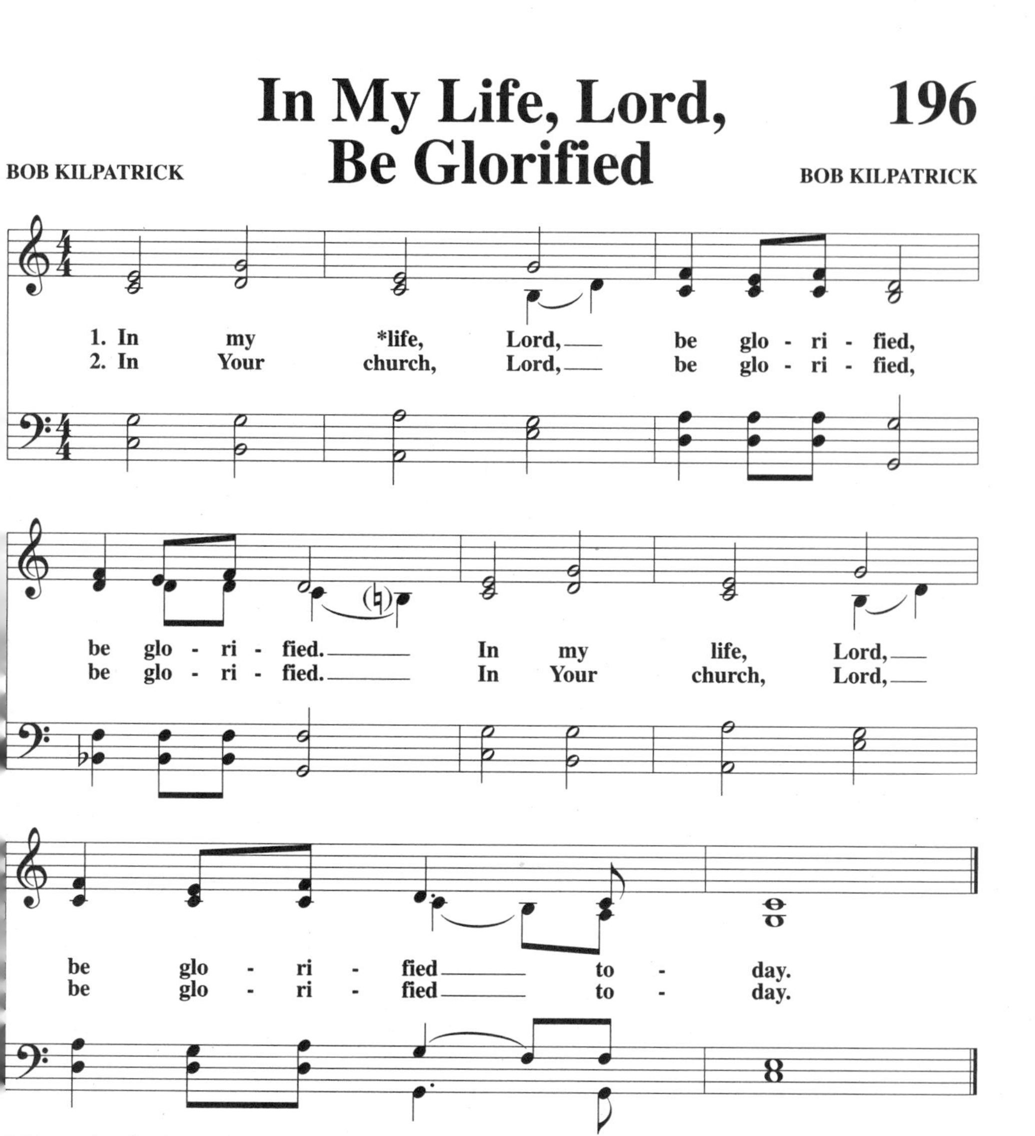

1. In my *life, Lord,—— be glo - ri - fied,
2. In Your church, Lord,—— be glo - ri - fied,

be glo - ri - fied.—— In my life, Lord,——
be glo - ri - fied.—— In Your church, Lord,——

be glo - ri - fied—— to - day.
be glo - ri - fied—— to - day.

D.C. al CODA ⊕   ⊕ CODA

pray.

May I be like You.

* Other words such as "song," "heart," "home," may be used on subsequent verses.

197 All-Consuming Fire

RANDY WRIGHT   RANDY WRIGHT

All-con-sum-ing Fire,_____ You're my heart's de-

sire,_____ And I love You dear-ly, dear-ly

Lord; You're my med-i-ta-tion and my con-so-

la-tion, And I love You dear-ly, dear-ly Lord.____

Glo-ry to the___ Lamb.____ I ex-

alt the great I Am;_____ Reign-ing

on Your glo-rious throne,____

___ You are my e-ter-nal home.____

The Greatest Thing 198

MARK PENDERGRASS

MARK PENDERGRASS

1. The great - est thing_____ in all my life is
2. The great - est thing_____ in all my life is
3. The great - est thing_____ in all my life is

know - ing You._____ The great - est thing_____ in
lov - ing You._____ The great - est thing_____ in
serv - ing You._____ The great - est thing_____ in

all my life is know - ing You._____
all my life is lov - ing You._____
all my life is serv - ing You._____

_____ I want to know You more. I want to
_____ I want to love You more. I want to
_____ I want to serve You more. I want to

know You more. The great - est thing_____ in
love You more. The great - est thing_____ in
serve You more. The great - est thing_____ in

all my life is know - ing You.
all my life is lov - ing You.
all my life is serv - ing You.

199 Open Our Eyes, Lord

ROBERT CULL

ROBERT CULL
Arranged by David Allen

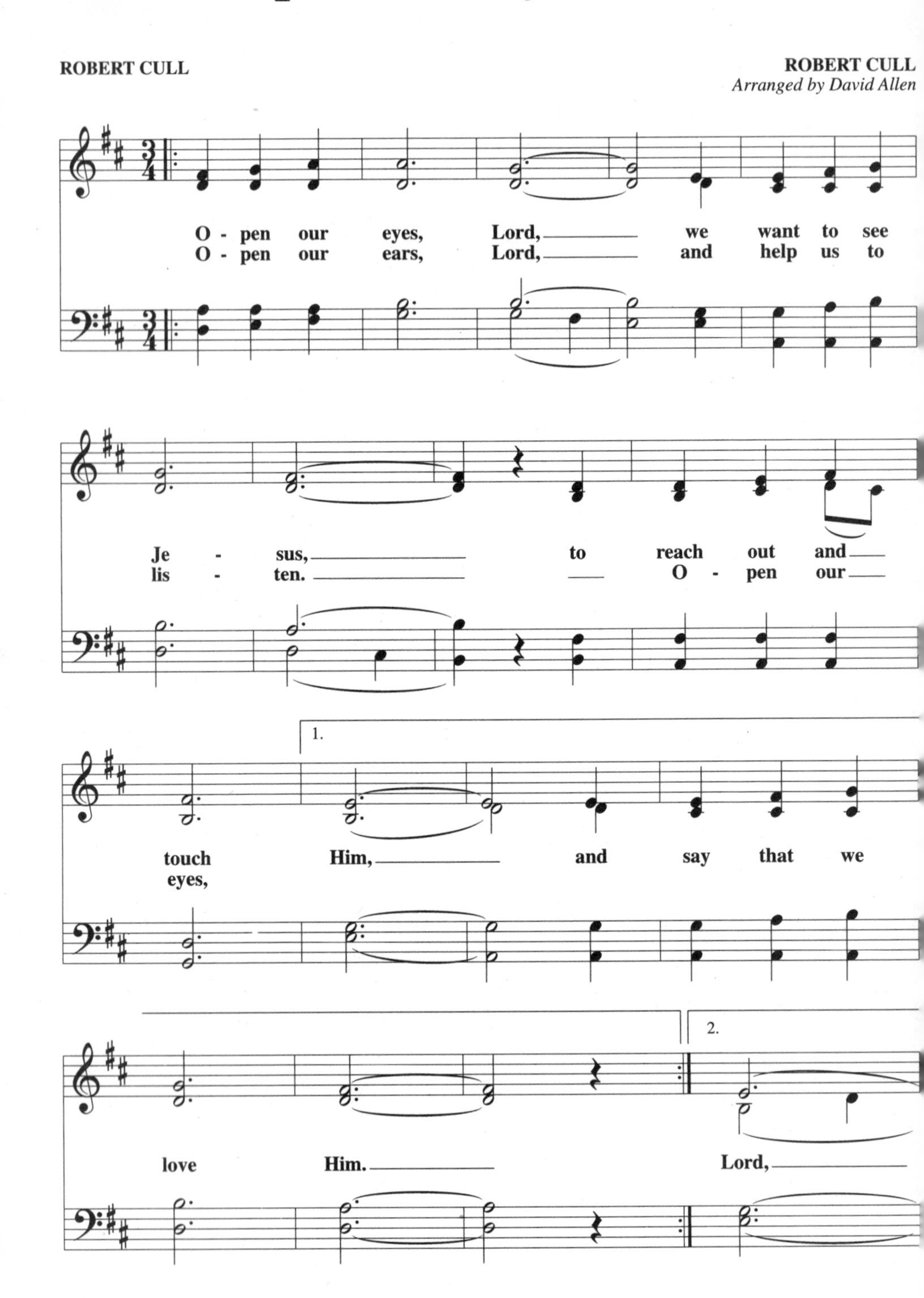

O - pen our eyes, Lord,_____ we want to see
O - pen our ears, Lord,_____ and help us to

Je - sus,_____ to reach out and_____
lis - ten._____ _____ O - pen our_____

1.
touch Him,_____ and say that we
eyes,

2.
love Him._____ Lord,_____

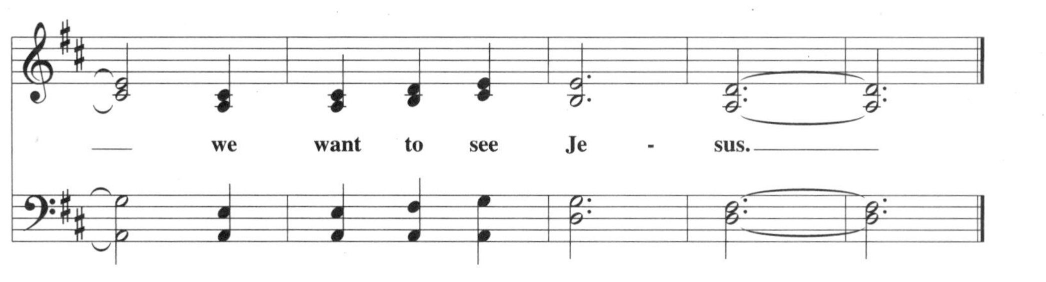

we want to see Je - sus.

As the Deer

200

MARTIN NYSTROM

MARTIN NYSTROM

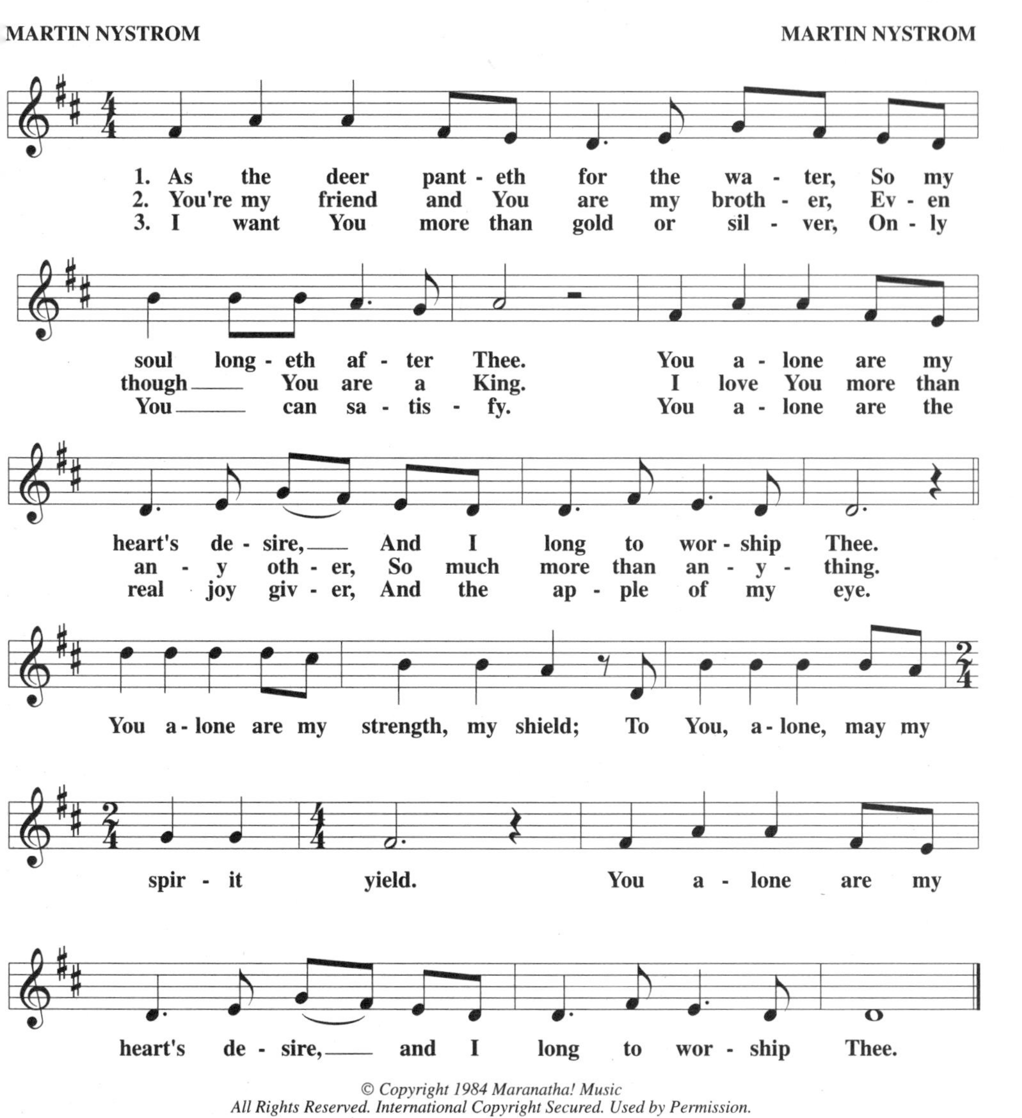

1. As the deer pant - eth for the wa - ter, So my
2. You're my friend and You are my broth - er, Ev - en
3. I want You more than gold or sil - ver, On - ly

soul long - eth af - ter Thee. You a - lone are my
though____ You are a King. I love You more than
You____ can sa - tis - fy. You a - lone are the

heart's de - sire,____ And I long to wor - ship Thee.
an - y oth - er, So much more than an - y - thing.
real joy giv - er, And the ap - ple of my eye.

You a - lone are my strength, my shield; To You, a - lone, may my

spir - it yield. You a - lone are my

heart's de - sire,____ and I long to wor - ship Thee.

201 Let God Be God in Me

KEVIN WALKER, ROBERT TILL,
WARREN WALKER and BARBARA ROSS

KEVIN WALKER and ROBERT TILL

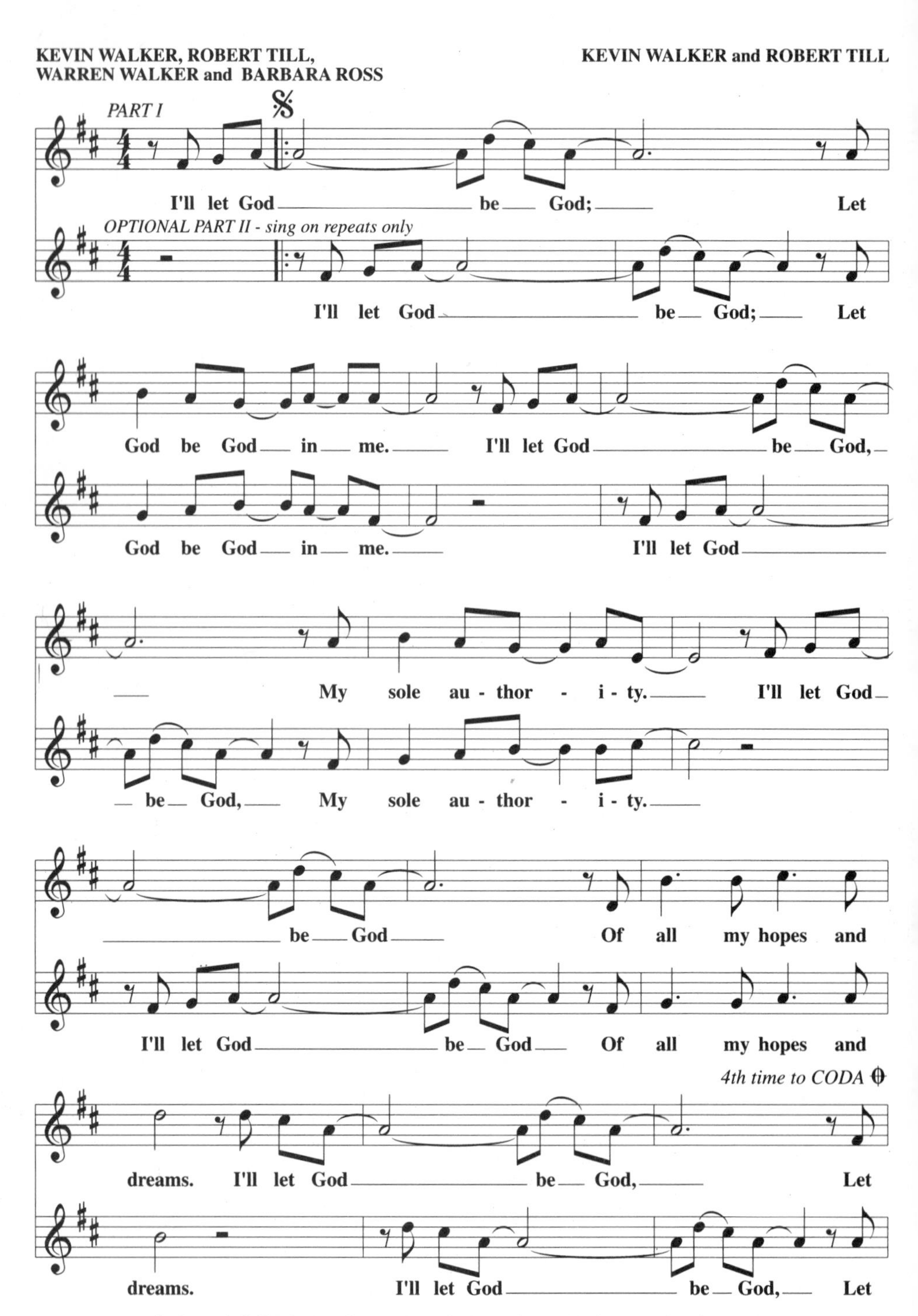

PART I

I'll let God be God; Let God be God in me. I'll let God be God, God be God in me. I'll let God

My sole au - thor - i - ty. I'll let God be God, My sole au - thor - i - ty. I'll let God

be God Of all my hopes and I'll let God be God Of all my hopes and

4th time to CODA

dreams. I'll let God be God, Let dreams. I'll let God be God, Let

OPTIONAL PART II - sing on repeats only

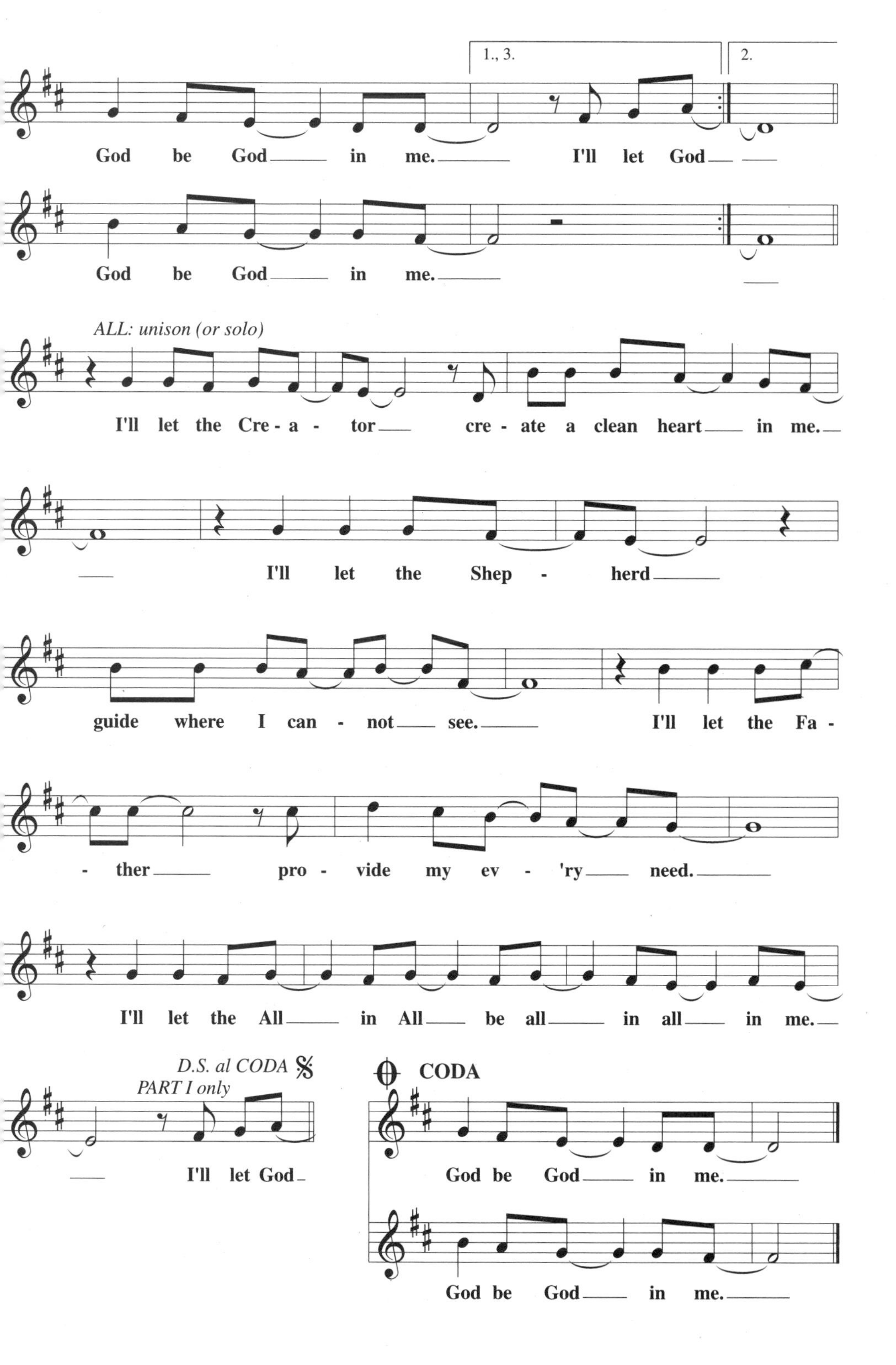
1., 3.
2.
God be God in me. I'll let God
God be God in me.
ALL: unison (or solo)
I'll let the Cre - a - tor cre - ate a clean heart in me.
I'll let the Shep - herd
guide where I can - not see. I'll let the Fa -
- ther pro - vide my ev - 'ry need.
I'll let the All in All be all in all in me.
D.S. al CODA
PART I only
I'll let God
CODA
God be God in me.
God be God in me.

202 Reign in Me

CHRIS BOWATER

CHRIS BOWATER
Arranged by Tom Fettke

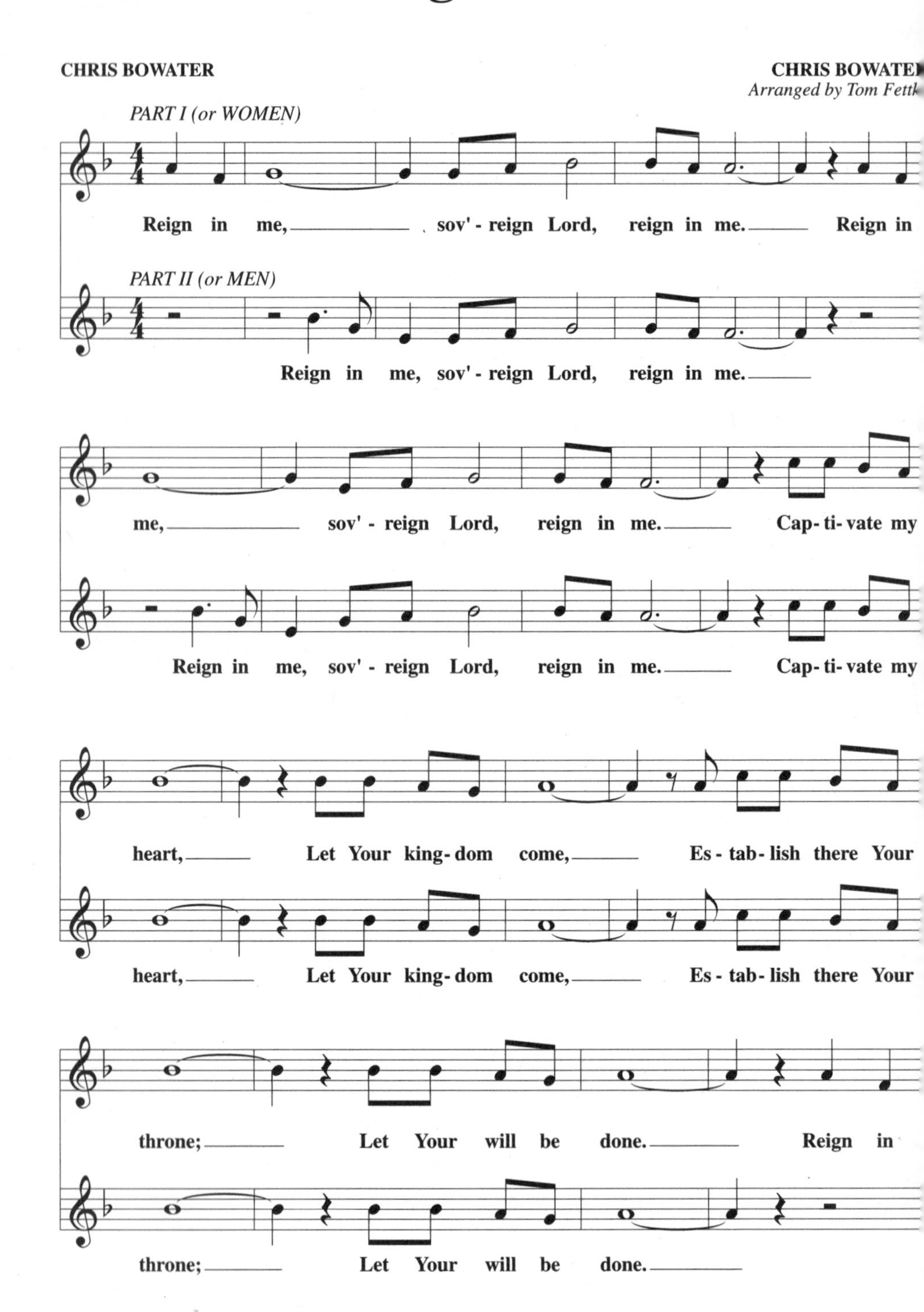

PART I (or WOMEN)

Reign in me, _____ sov' - reign Lord, reign in me. _____ Reign in

PART II (or MEN)

Reign in me, sov' - reign Lord, reign in me. _____

me, _____ sov' - reign Lord, reign in me. _____ Cap - ti - vate my

Reign in me, sov' - reign Lord, reign in me. _____ Cap - ti - vate my

heart, _____ Let Your king - dom come, _____ Es - tab - lish there Your

heart, _____ Let Your king - dom come, _____ Es - tab - lish there Your

throne; _____ Let Your will be done. _____ Reign in

throne; _____ Let Your will be done. _____

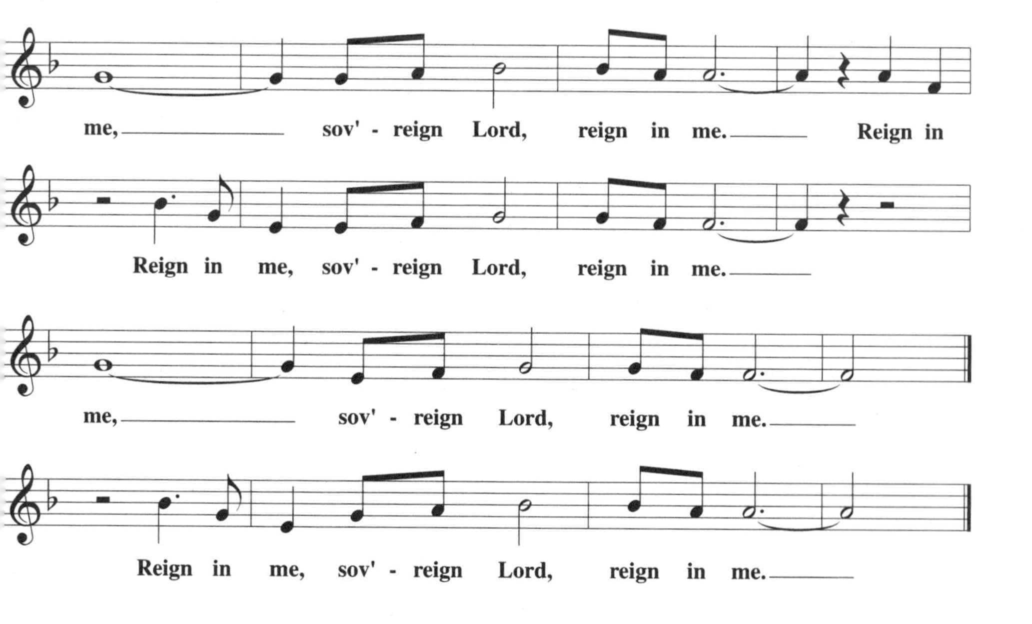

me,_____ sov' - reign Lord, reign in me._____ Reign in

Reign in me, sov' - reign Lord, reign in me._____

me,_____ sov' - reign Lord, reign in me._____

Reign in me, sov' - reign Lord, reign in me._____

In the Name of the Lord 203

ILL McHUGH, GLORIA GAITHER
1 SANDI PATTI HELVERING

SANDI PATTI HELVERING

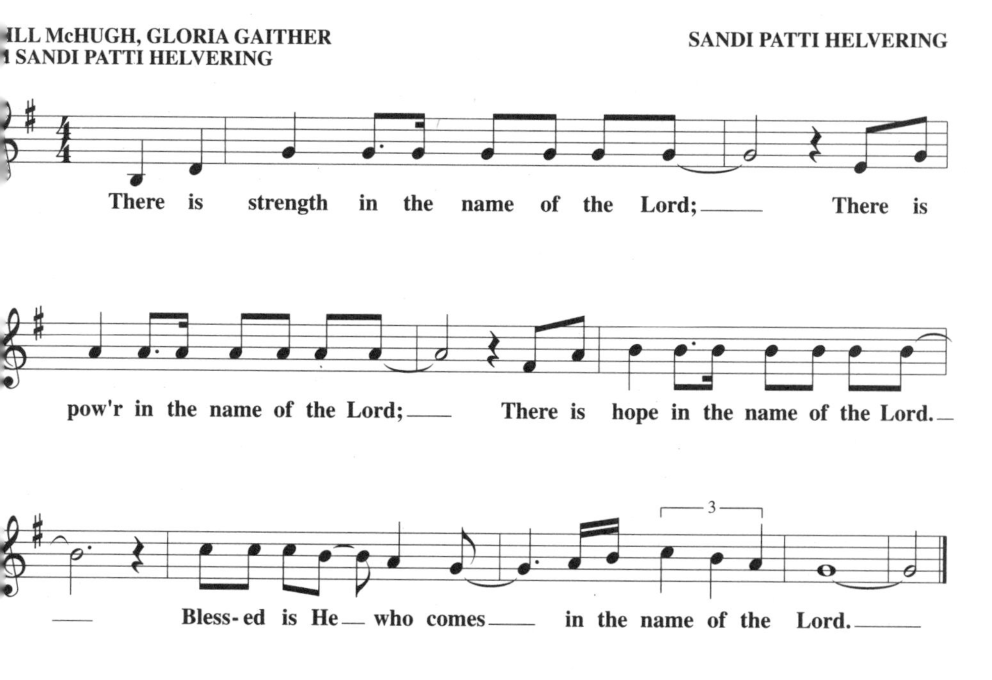

There is strength in the name of the Lord;_____ There is

pow'r in the name of the Lord;____ There is hope in the name of the Lord.____

____ Bless- ed is He__ who comes____ in the name of the Lord.____

204 My Life Is in You, Lord

DANIEL GARDNER

DANIEL GARDNER

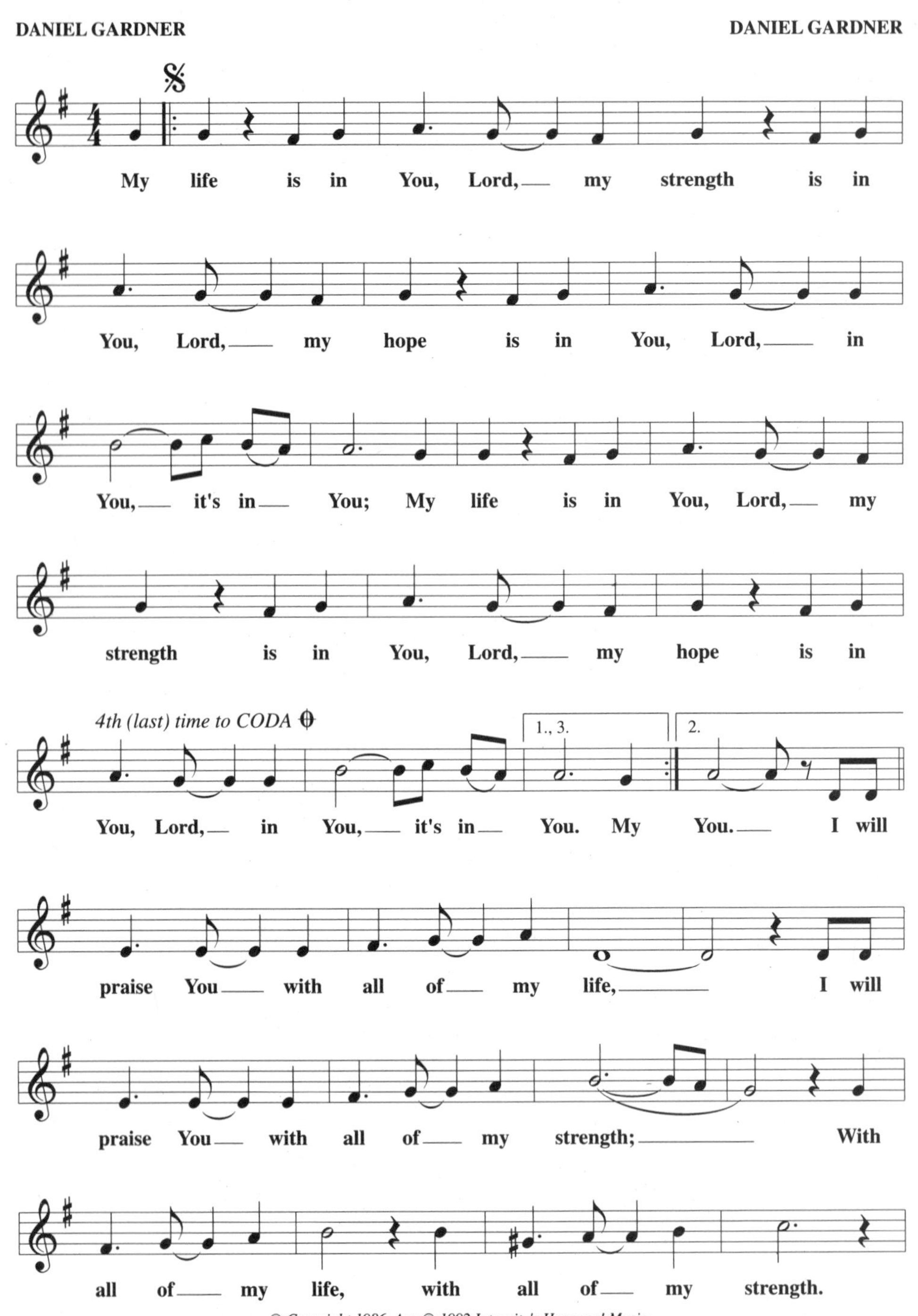

My life is in You, Lord,— my strength is in You, Lord,— my hope is in You, Lord,— in You,— it's in— You; My life is in You, Lord,— my strength is in You, Lord,— my hope is in

4th (last) time to CODA

1., 3. You, Lord,— in You,— it's in— You. My

2. You.— I will

praise You— with all of— my life,— I will praise You— with all of— my strength;— With all of— my life, with all of— my strength.

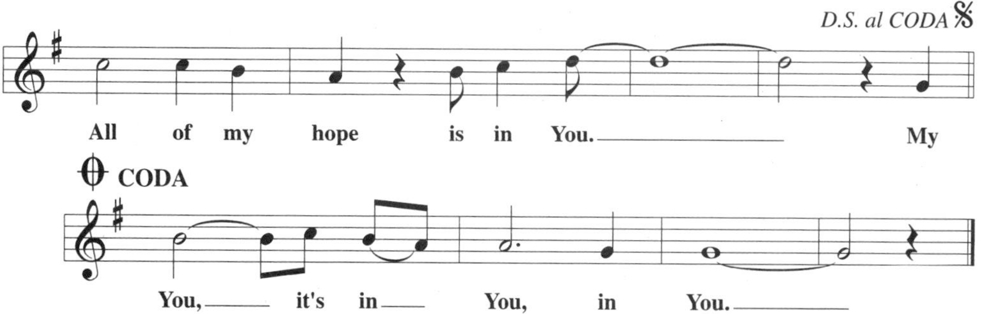

D.S. al CODA %

All of my hope is in You. My

⊕ CODA

You, it's in You, in You.

In Him We Live

205

RANDY SPEIR

RANDY SPEIR

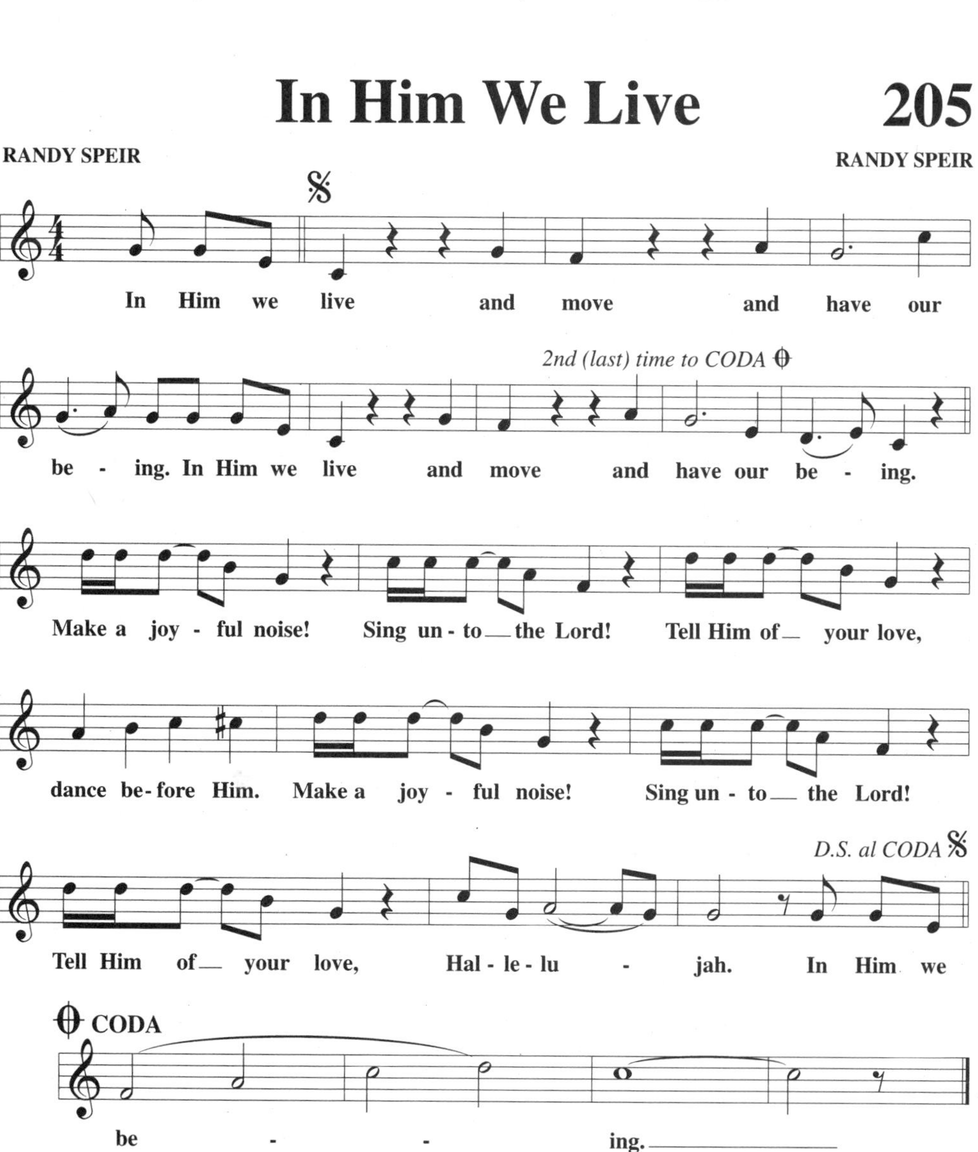

%

In Him we live and move and have our

2nd (last) time to CODA ⊕

be - ing. In Him we live and move and have our be - ing.

Make a joy - ful noise! Sing un - to the Lord! Tell Him of your love,

dance be - fore Him. Make a joy - ful noise! Sing un - to the Lord!

D.S. al CODA %

Tell Him of your love, Hal - le - lu - jah. In Him we

⊕ CODA

be - ing.

206 Jesus Is King

WENDY CHURCHILL

WENDY CHURCHILL
Arranged by Tom Fettke

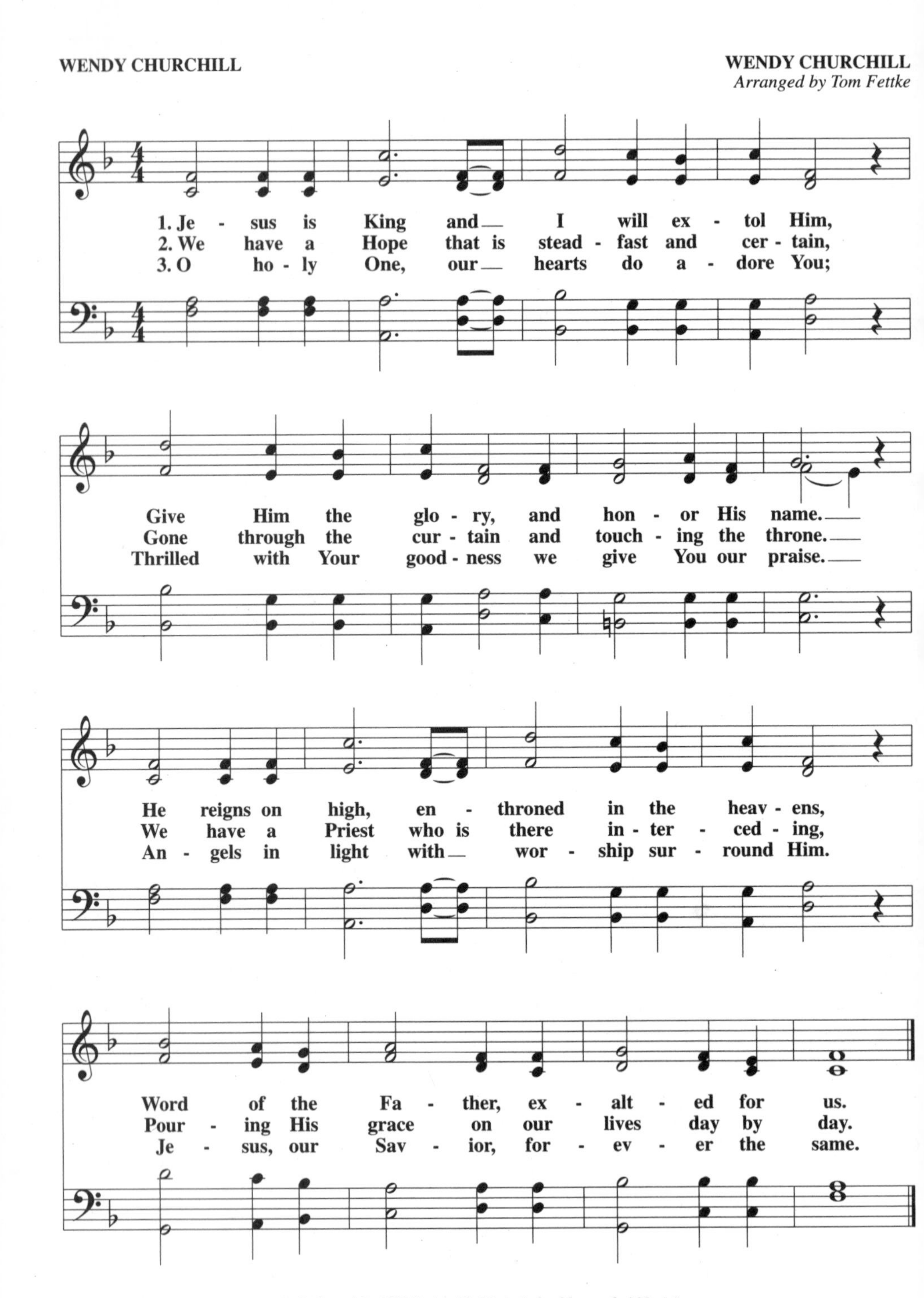

1. Je - sus is King and— I will ex - tol Him,
2. We have a Hope that is stead - fast and cer - tain,
3. O ho - ly One, our— hearts do a - dore You;

Give Him the glo - ry, and hon - or His name.—
Gone through the cur - tain and touch - ing the throne.—
Thrilled with Your good - ness we give You our praise.—

He reigns on high, en - throned in the heav - ens,
We have a Priest who is there in - ter - ced - ing,
An - gels in light with— wor - ship sur - round Him.

Word of the Fa - ther, ex - alt - ed for us.
Pour - ing His grace on our lives day by day.
Je - sus, our Sav - ior, for - ev - er the same.

Be Bold, Be Strong

207

MORRIS CHAPMAN

MORRIS CHAPMAN

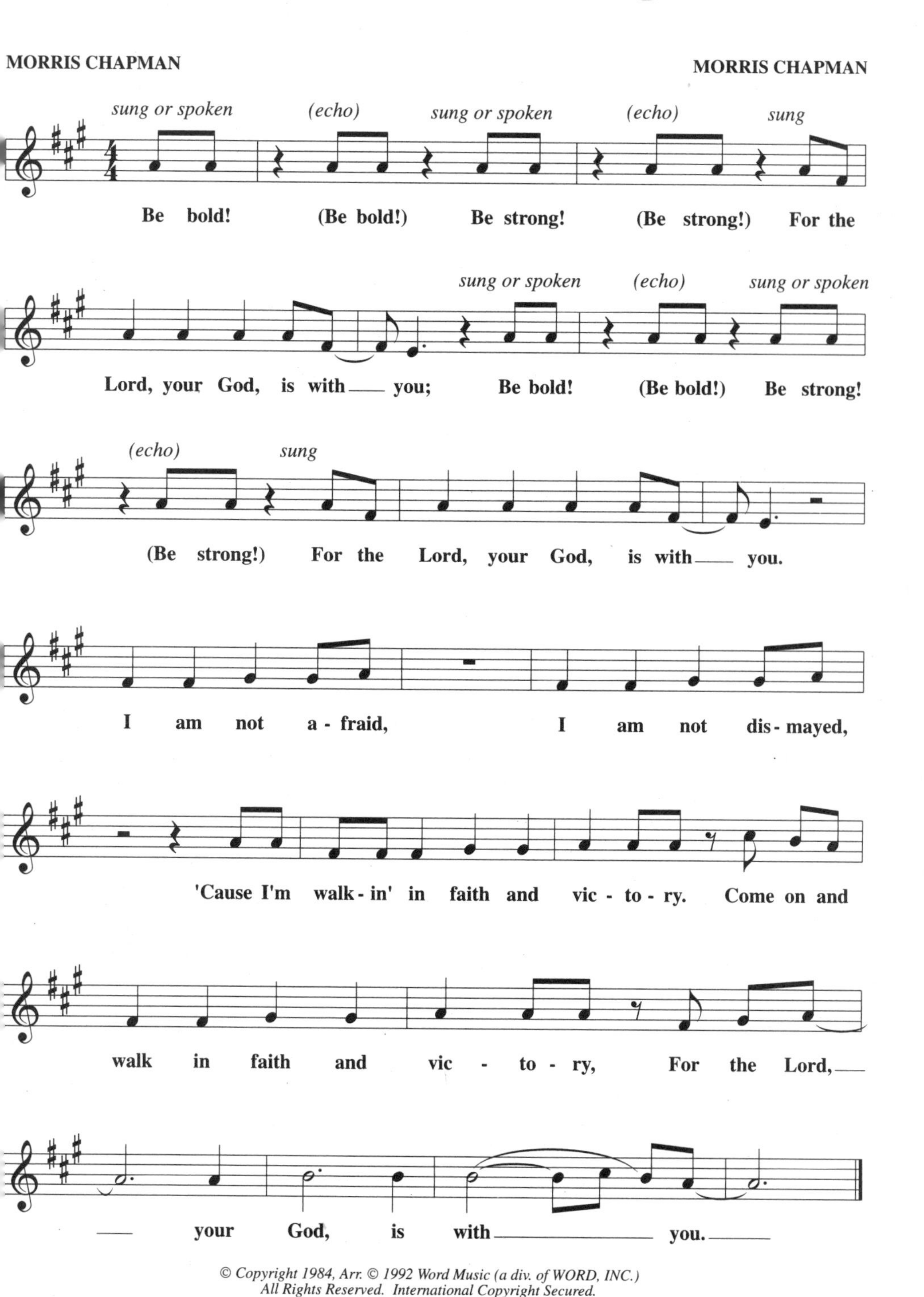

Be bold! (Be bold!) Be strong! (Be strong!) For the

Lord, your God, is with you; Be bold! (Be bold!) Be strong!

(Be strong!) For the Lord, your God, is with you.

I am not a-fraid, I am not dis-mayed,

'Cause I'm walk-in' in faith and vic-to-ry. Come on and

walk in faith and vic - to - ry, For the Lord,

your God, is with you.

208 I Am Crucified with Christ

JOHN G. ELLIOTT
Based on Galatians 2:20

JOHN G. ELLIOTT

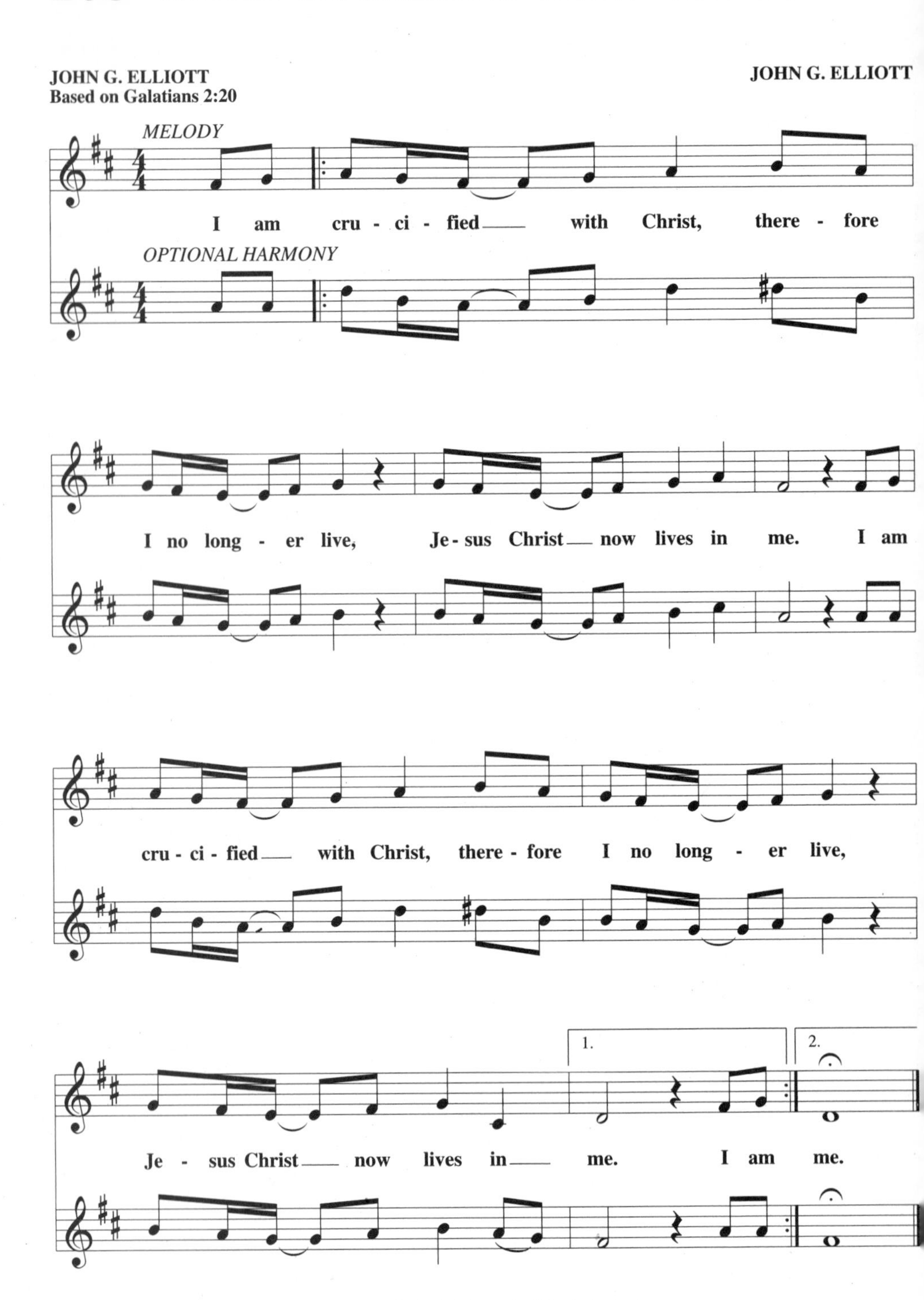

MELODY

I am cru - ci - fied___ with Christ, there - fore

OPTIONAL HARMONY

I no long - er live, Je - sus Christ___ now lives in me. I am

cru - ci - fied___ with Christ, there - fore I no long - er live,

Je - sus Christ___ now lives in___ me. I am me.

The Lord Is My Light

JEFF NELSON
Based on Psalm 27:1

209

JEFF NELSON

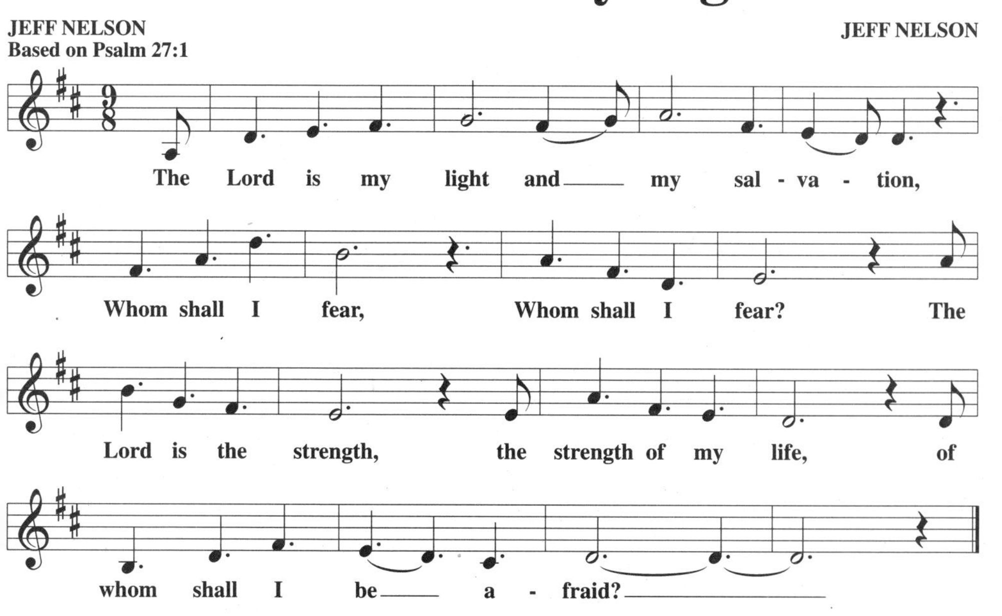

The Lord is my light and my sal-va-tion, Whom shall I fear, Whom shall I fear? The Lord is the strength, the strength of my life, of whom shall I be a-fraid?

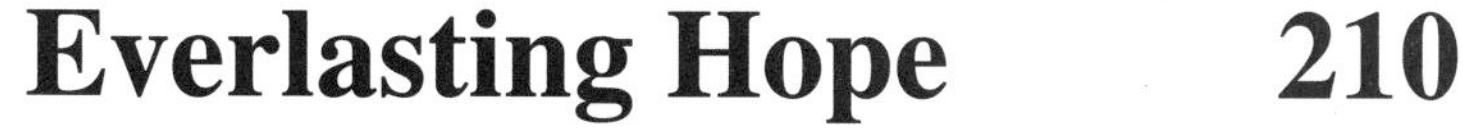

Everlasting Hope

210

CHRISSY CYMBALA

CHRISSY CYMBALA

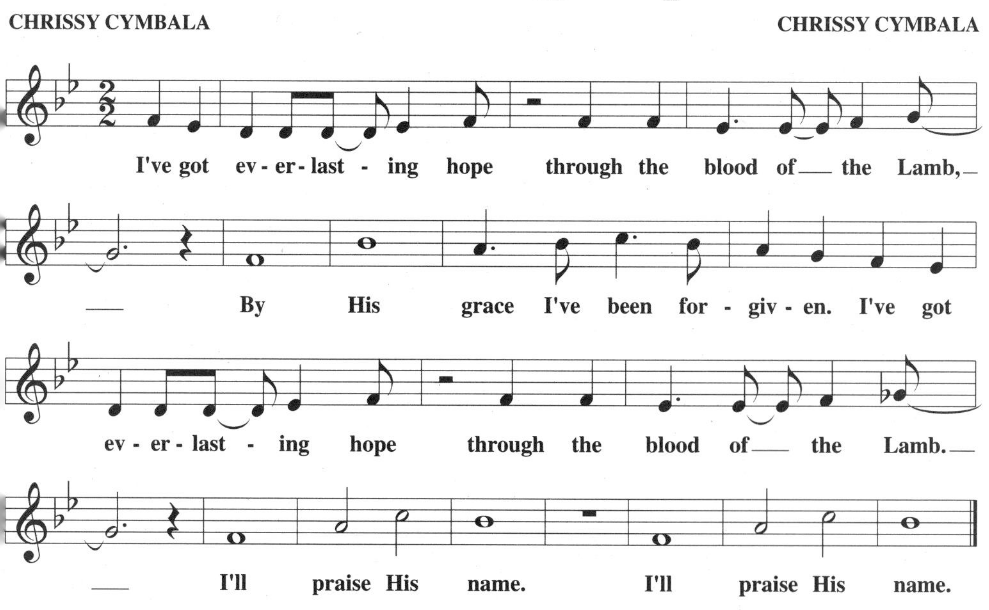

I've got ev-er-last-ing hope through the blood of the Lamb, By His grace I've been for-giv-en. I've got ev-er-last-ing hope through the blood of the Lamb. I'll praise His name. I'll praise His name.

211   The Sweetest Name of All

TOM COOMES   TOM COOMES

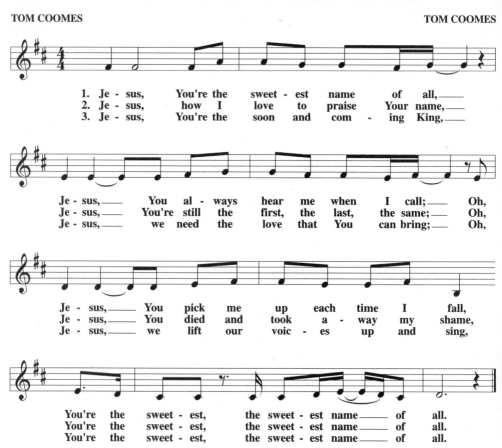

1. Je - sus, You're the sweet - est name of all,——
2. Je - sus, how I love to praise Your name,——
3. Je - sus, You're the soon and com - ing King,——

Je - sus,—— You al - ways hear me when I call;—— Oh,
Je - sus,—— You're still the first, the last, the same;—— Oh,
Je - sus,—— we need the love that You can bring;—— Oh,

Je - sus,—— You pick me up each time I fall,
Je - sus,—— You died and took a - way my shame,
Je - sus,—— we lift our voic - es up and sing,

You're the sweet - est, the sweet - est name —— of all.
You're the sweet - est, the sweet - est name —— of all.
You're the sweet - est, the sweet - est name —— of all.

212   Joy of My Desire

JENNIFER RANDOLPH   JENNIFER RANDOLPH

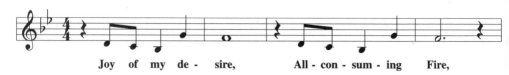

Joy of my de - sire, All - con - sum - ing Fire,

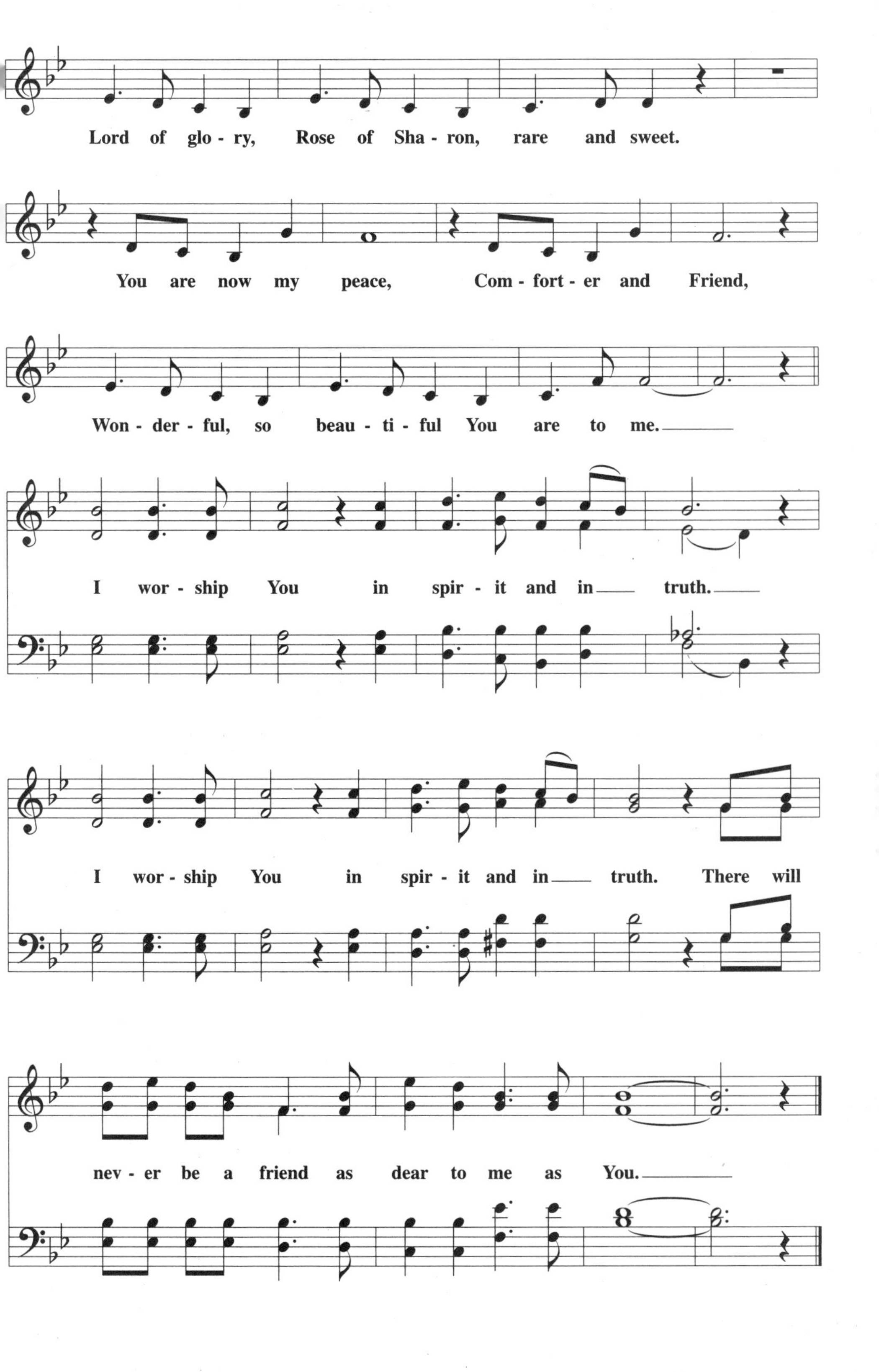

Lord of glo - ry, Rose of Sha - ron, rare and sweet.

You are now my peace, Com - fort - er and Friend,

Won - der - ful, so beau - ti - ful You are to me.____

I wor - ship You in spir - it and in____ truth.____

I wor - ship You in spir - it and in____ truth. There will

nev - er be a friend as dear to me as You.____

213   He Is Our Peace

KANDELA GROVES
Based on Eph. 2:14 and I Pet. 5:7

KANDELA GROVES

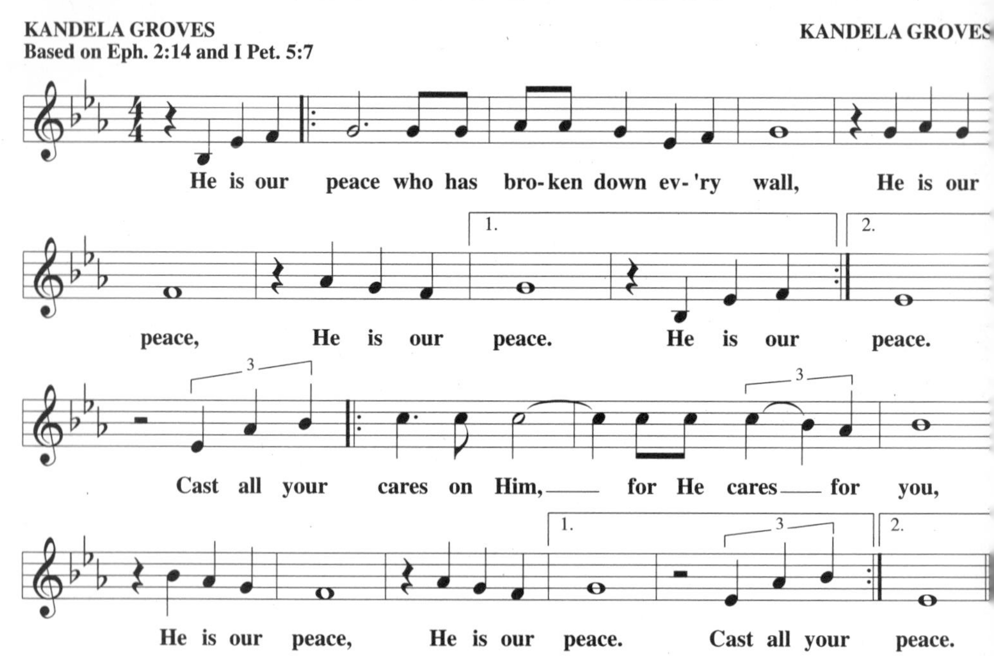

He is our peace who has bro-ken down ev-'ry wall, He is our

peace, He is our peace. He is our peace.

Cast all your cares on Him, for He cares for you,

He is our peace, He is our peace. Cast all your peace.

214 Wonderful, Merciful Savior

Words and Music by
DAWN RODGERS and ERIC WYSE
Arranged by Ken Barker and David Maddux

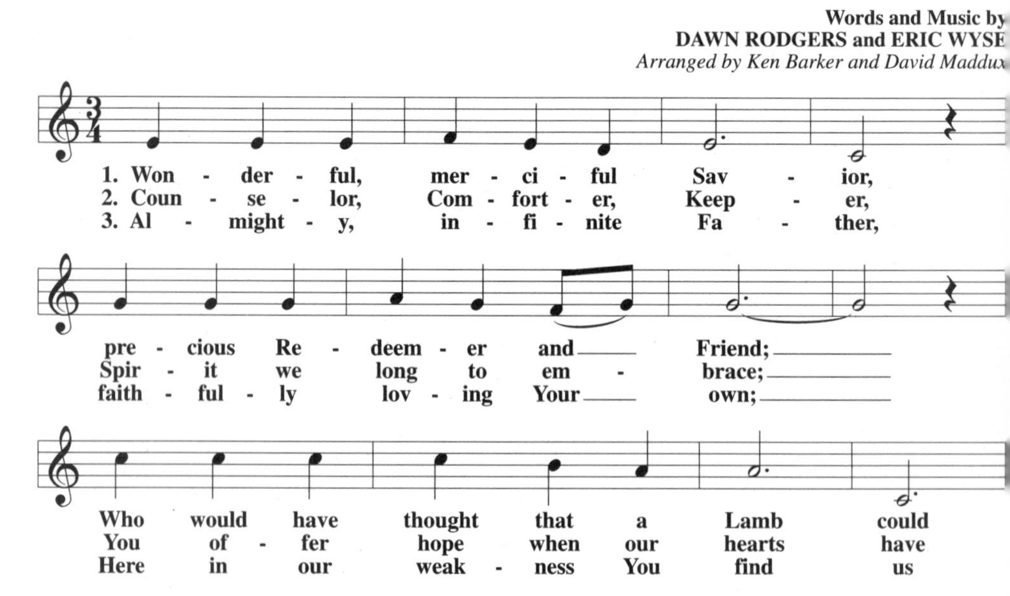

1. Won - der - ful, mer - ci - ful Sav - ior,
2. Coun - se - lor, Com - fort - er, Keep - er,
3. Al - might - y, in - fi - nite Fa - ther,

pre - cious Re - deem - er and Friend;
Spir - it we long to em - brace;
faith - ful - ly lov - ing Your own;

Who would have thought that a Lamb could
You of - fer hope when our hearts have
Here in our weak - ness You find us

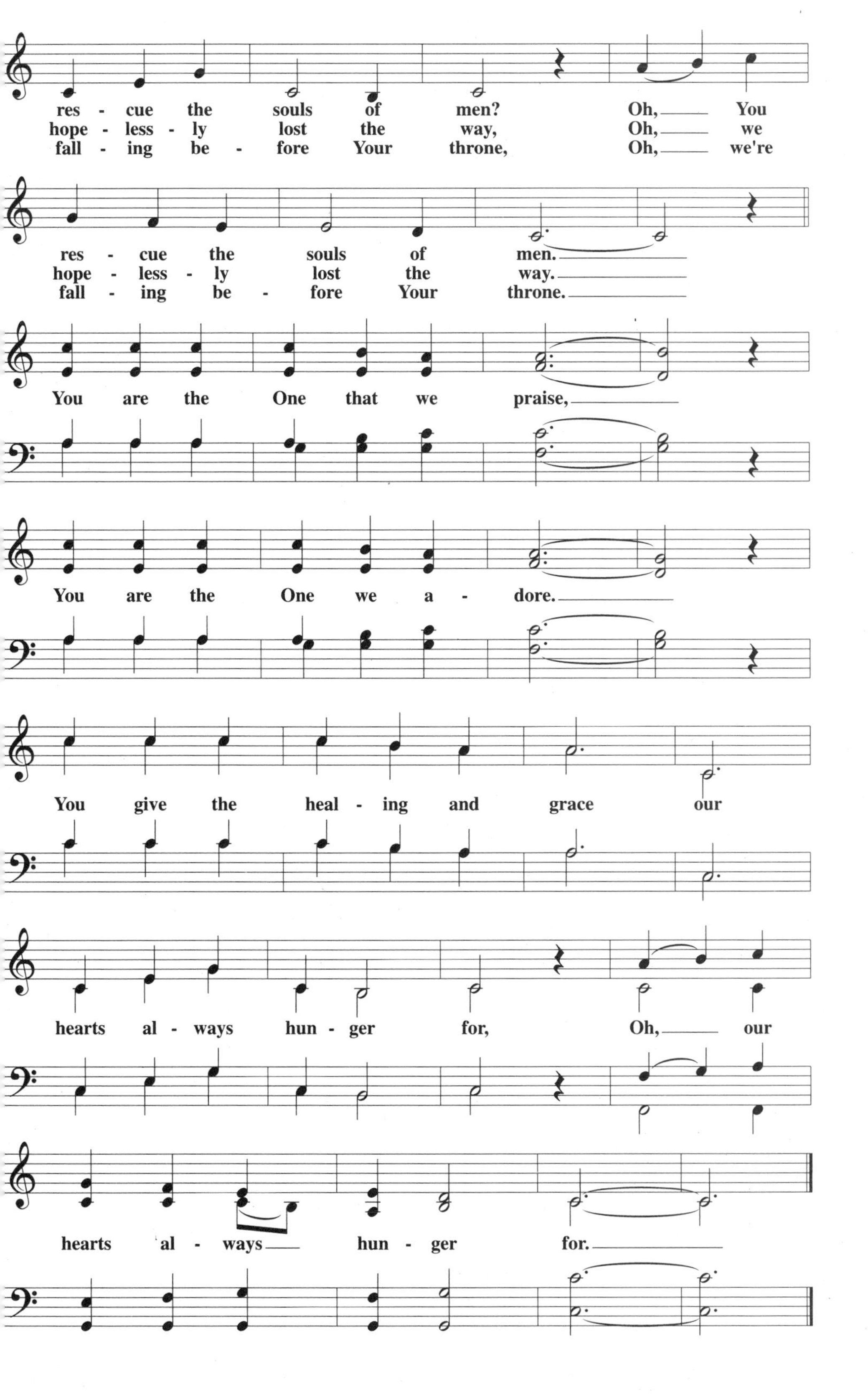

res - cue the souls of men? Oh, You
hope - less - ly lost the way, Oh, we
fall - ing be - fore Your throne, Oh, we're
res - cue the souls of men.
hope - less - ly lost the way.
fall - ing be - fore Your throne.
You are the One that we praise,
You are the One we a - dore.
You give the heal - ing and grace our
hearts al - ways hun - ger for, Oh, our
hearts al - ways hun - ger for.

215 My All in All

Words and Music by
FRANK HERNANDEZ and SHERRY SAUNDERS

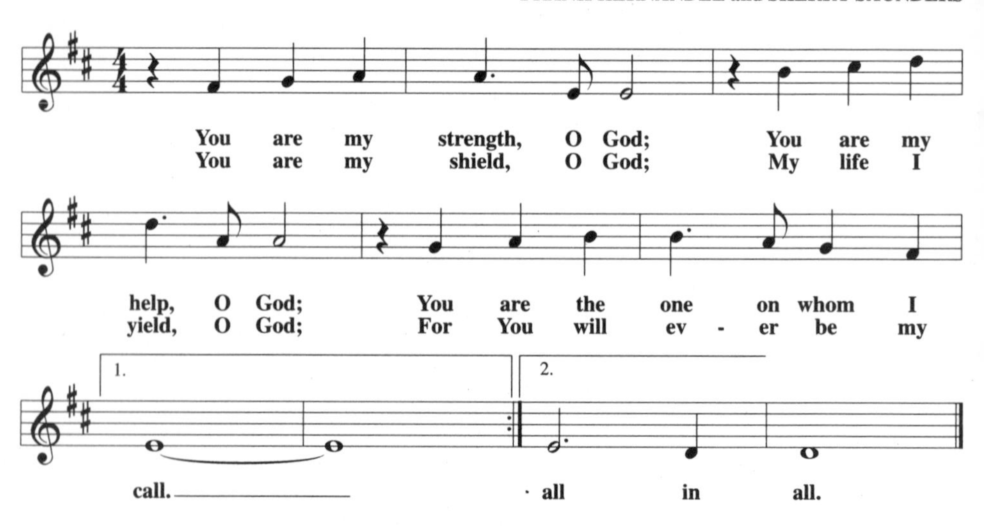

You are my strength, O God; You are my
You are my shield, O God; My life I

help, O God; You are the one on whom I
yield, O God; For You will ev - er be my

1.
call.

2.
· all in all.

216 Abba Father

STEVE FRY

STEVE FRY

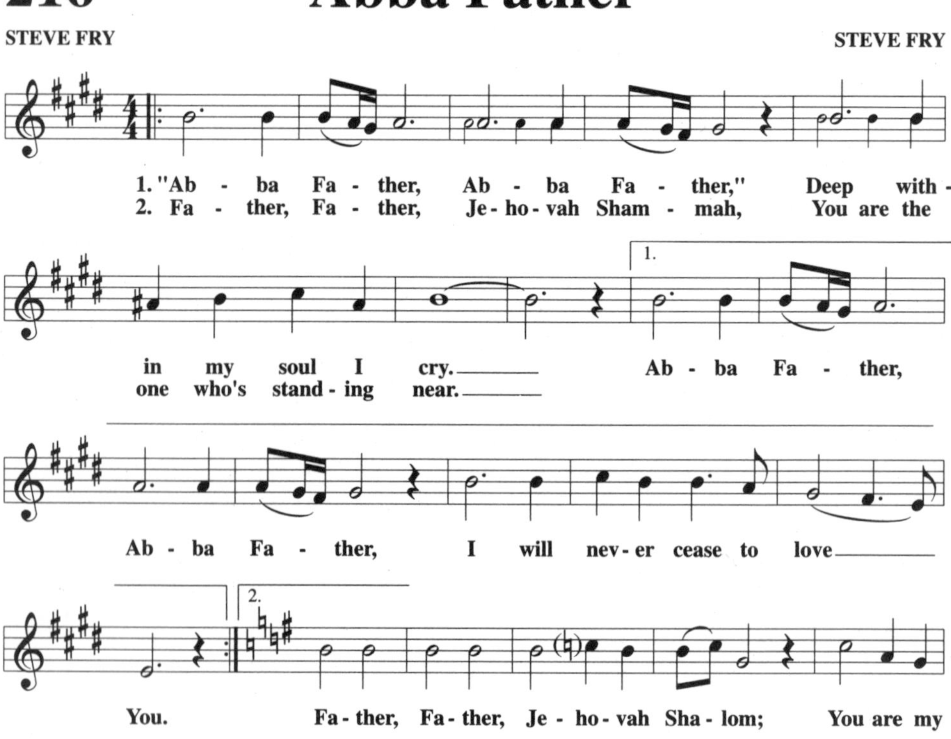

1. "Ab - ba Fa - ther, Ab - ba Fa - ther," Deep with -
2. Fa - ther, Fa - ther, Je - ho - vah Sham - mah, You are the

in my soul I cry. Ab - ba Fa - ther,
one who's stand - ing near.

1.

Ab - ba Fa - ther, I will nev - er cease to love

You.

2.
Fa - ther, Fa - ther, Je - ho - vah Sha - lom; You are my

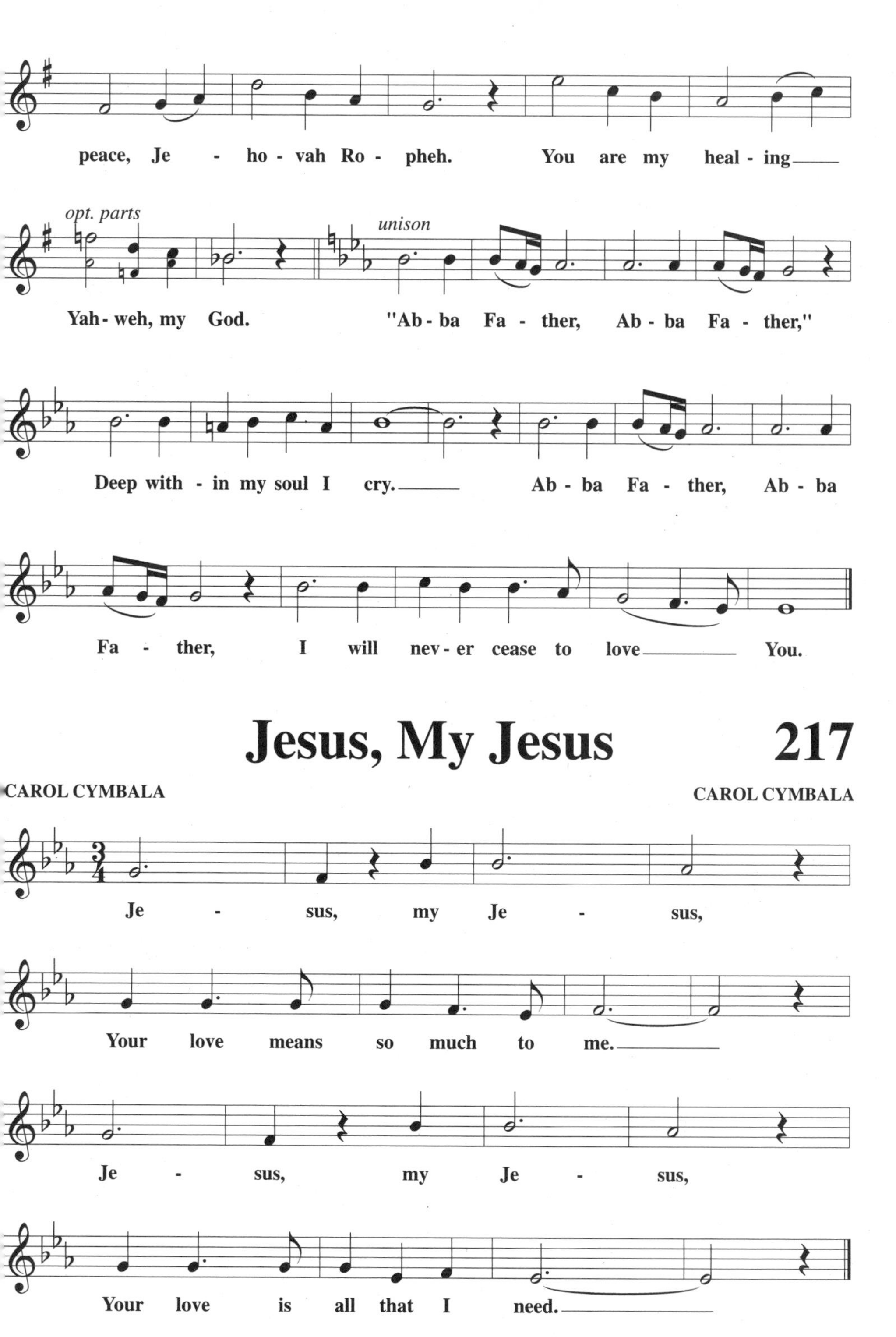

peace, Je - ho - vah Ro - pheh. You are my heal - ing

opt. parts .... *unison*

Yah - weh, my God. "Ab - ba Fa - ther, Ab - ba Fa - ther,"

Deep with - in my soul I cry._____ Ab - ba Fa - ther, Ab - ba

Fa - ther, I will nev - er cease to love_____ You.

Jesus, My Jesus
217

CAROL CYMBALA

CAROL CYMBALA

Je - sus, my Je - sus,

Your love means so much to me._____

Je - sus, my Je - sus,

Your love is all that I need._____

218
Turn Your Eyes
upon Jesus

HELEN H. LEMMEL

HELEN H. LEMMEL

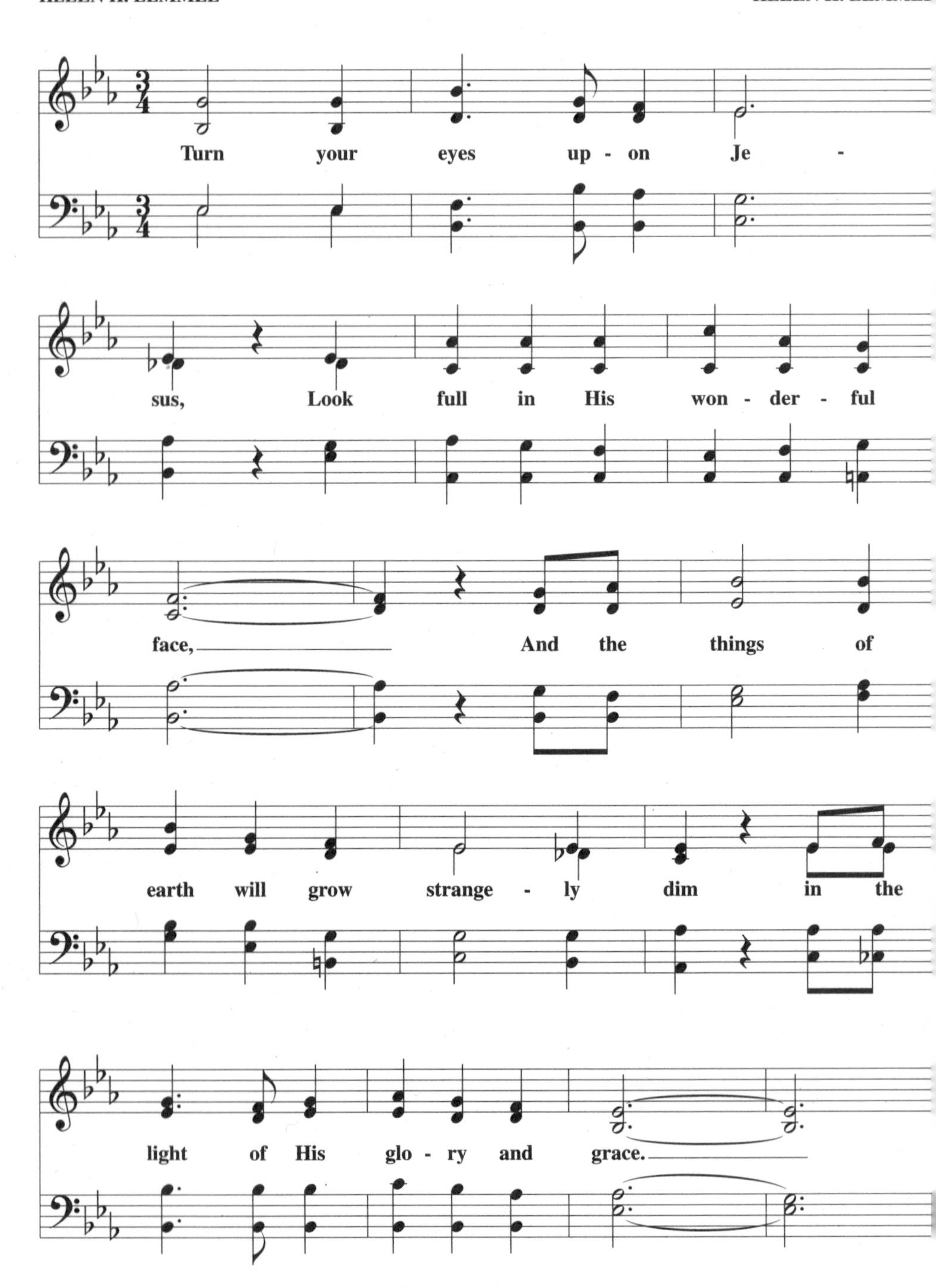

Turn your eyes up-on Je - sus, Look full in His won-der-ful face, And the things of earth will grow strange-ly dim in the light of His glo - ry and grace.

You Who Are Thirsty

219

BARBARA ROSS

BARBARA ROSS

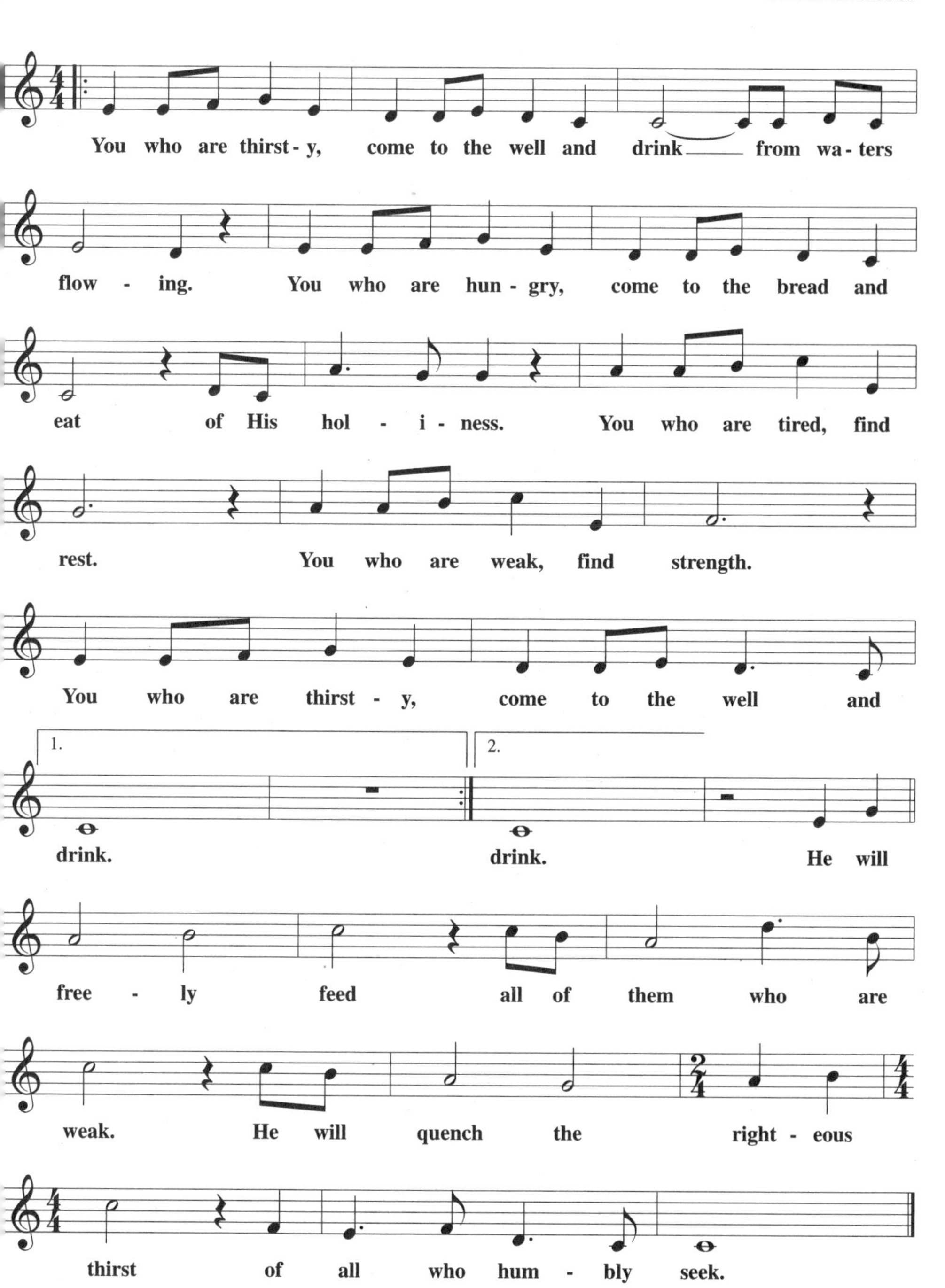

You who are thirst-y, come to the well and drink from wa-ters flow - ing. You who are hun-gry, come to the bread and eat of His hol - i - ness. You who are tired, find rest. You who are weak, find strength. You who are thirst - y, come to the well and

1. drink.

2. drink. He will free - ly feed all of them who are weak. He will quench the right - eous thirst of all who hum - bly seek.

220 You Are My All in All

DENNIS L. JERNIGAN

DENNIS L. JERNIGAN

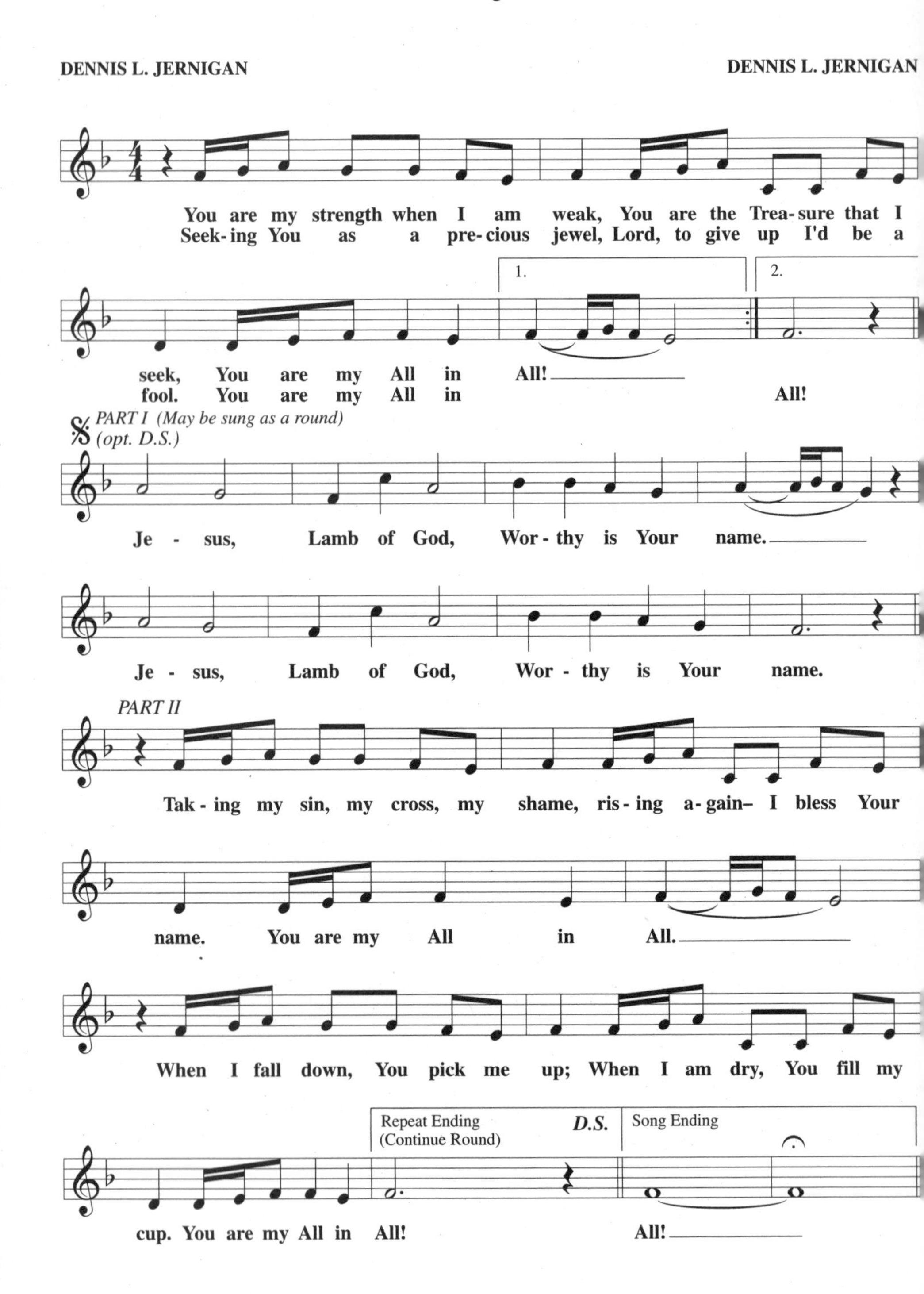

You are my strength when I am weak, You are the Trea-sure that I
Seek-ing You as a pre-cious jewel, Lord, to give up I'd be a

1.
seek, You are my All in All! ——
fool. You are my All in

2.
All!

PART I *(May be sung as a round)*
(opt. D.S.)

Je - sus, Lamb of God, Wor - thy is Your name. ——

Je - sus, Lamb of God, Wor - thy is Your name.

PART II

Tak - ing my sin, my cross, my shame, ris - ing a-gain– I bless Your

name. You are my All in All. ——

When I fall down, You pick me up; When I am dry, You fill my

Repeat Ending (Continue Round) | **D.S.** | **Song Ending**

cup. You are my All in All! | | All! ——

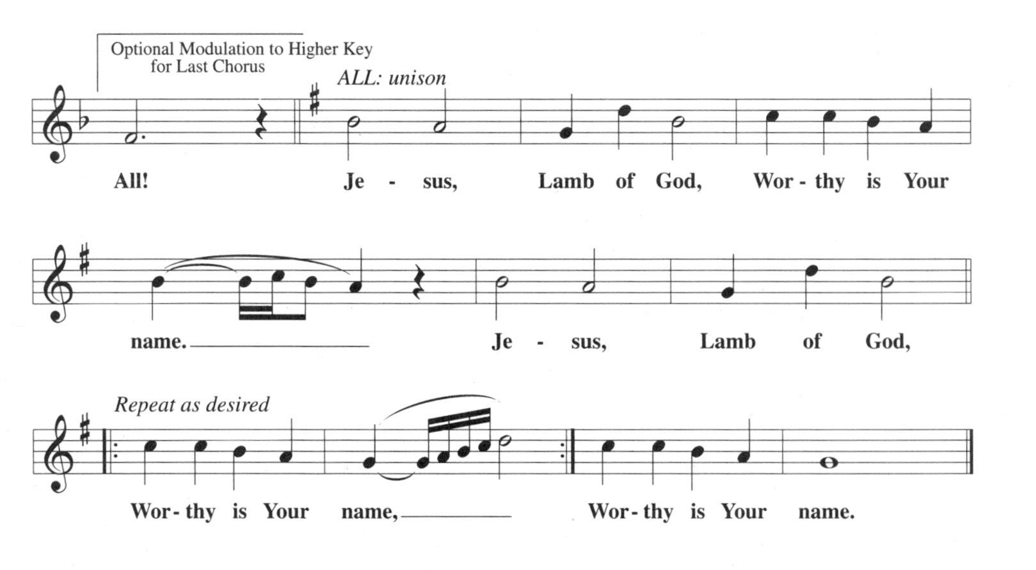

All! Je - sus, Lamb of God, Wor - thy is Your

name. Je - sus, Lamb of God,

Wor- thy is Your name, Wor- thy is Your name.

Cares Chorus

221

KELLY WILLARD

KELLY WILLARD

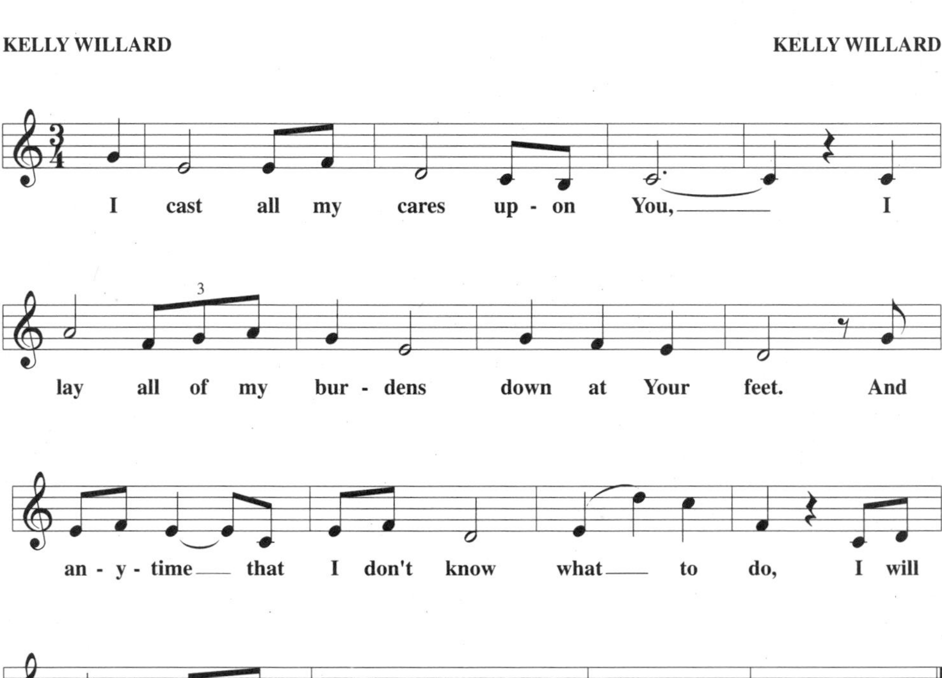

I cast all my cares up - on You, I

lay all of my bur - dens down at Your feet. And

an - y - time that I don't know what to do, I will

cast all my cares up - on You.

222 Thy Loving Kindness

HUGH MITCHELL
Based on Psalm 63:3-4

HUGH MITCHELL

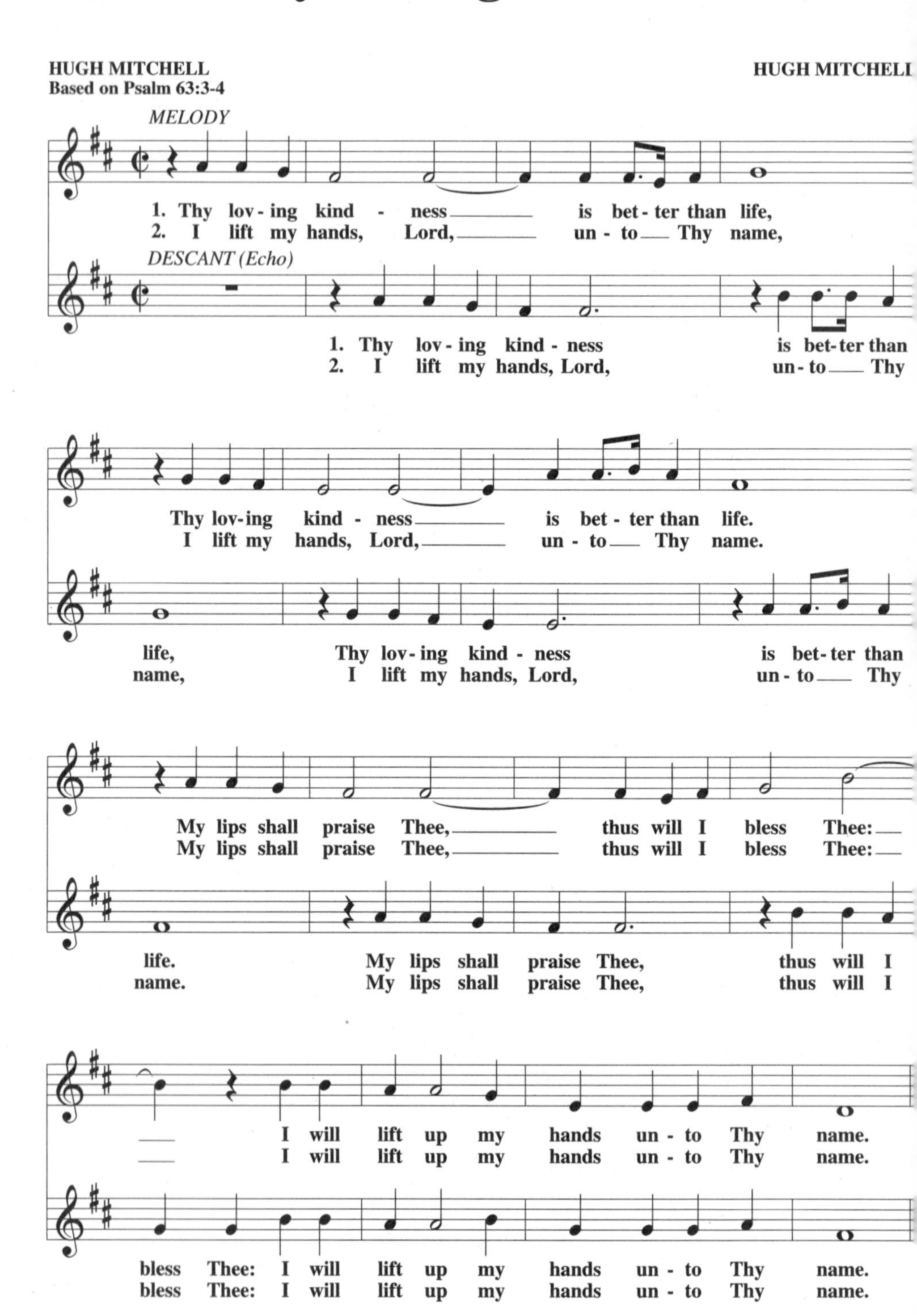

MELODY

1. Thy lov-ing kind - ness_____ is bet-ter than life,
2. I lift my hands, Lord,_____ un - to____ Thy name,

DESCANT (Echo)

1. Thy lov-ing kind - ness is bet-ter than
2. I lift my hands, Lord, un - to____ Thy

Thy lov-ing kind - ness_____ is bet-ter than life.
I lift my hands, Lord,_____ un - to____ Thy name.

life, Thy lov-ing kind - ness is bet-ter than
name, I lift my hands, Lord, un - to____ Thy

My lips shall praise Thee,_____ thus will I bless Thee:____
My lips shall praise Thee,_____ thus will I bless Thee:____

life. My lips shall praise Thee, thus will I
name. My lips shall praise Thee, thus will I

____ I will lift up my hands un - to Thy name.
____ I will lift up my hands un - to Thy name.

bless Thee: I will lift up my hands un - to Thy name.
bless Thee: I will lift up my hands un - to Thy name.

Humble Thyself in the Sight of the Lord

223

BOB HUDSON
Based on I Peter 5:6

BOB HUDSON

PART I (Men)

Hum - ble thy-self in the sight of the Lord.

PART II (Women)

Hum - ble thy-self in the sight of the

Hum - ble thy-self in the sight of the Lord. And

Lord. Hum - ble thy-self in the sight of the Lord,

He will lift you up, high - er and high - er, and

And He will lift you up,

He will lift you up.

And He will lift you up.

224   I Will Call upon the Lord

MICHAEL O'SHIELDS
Based on Psalm 18:3, 46

MICHAEL O'SHIELDS

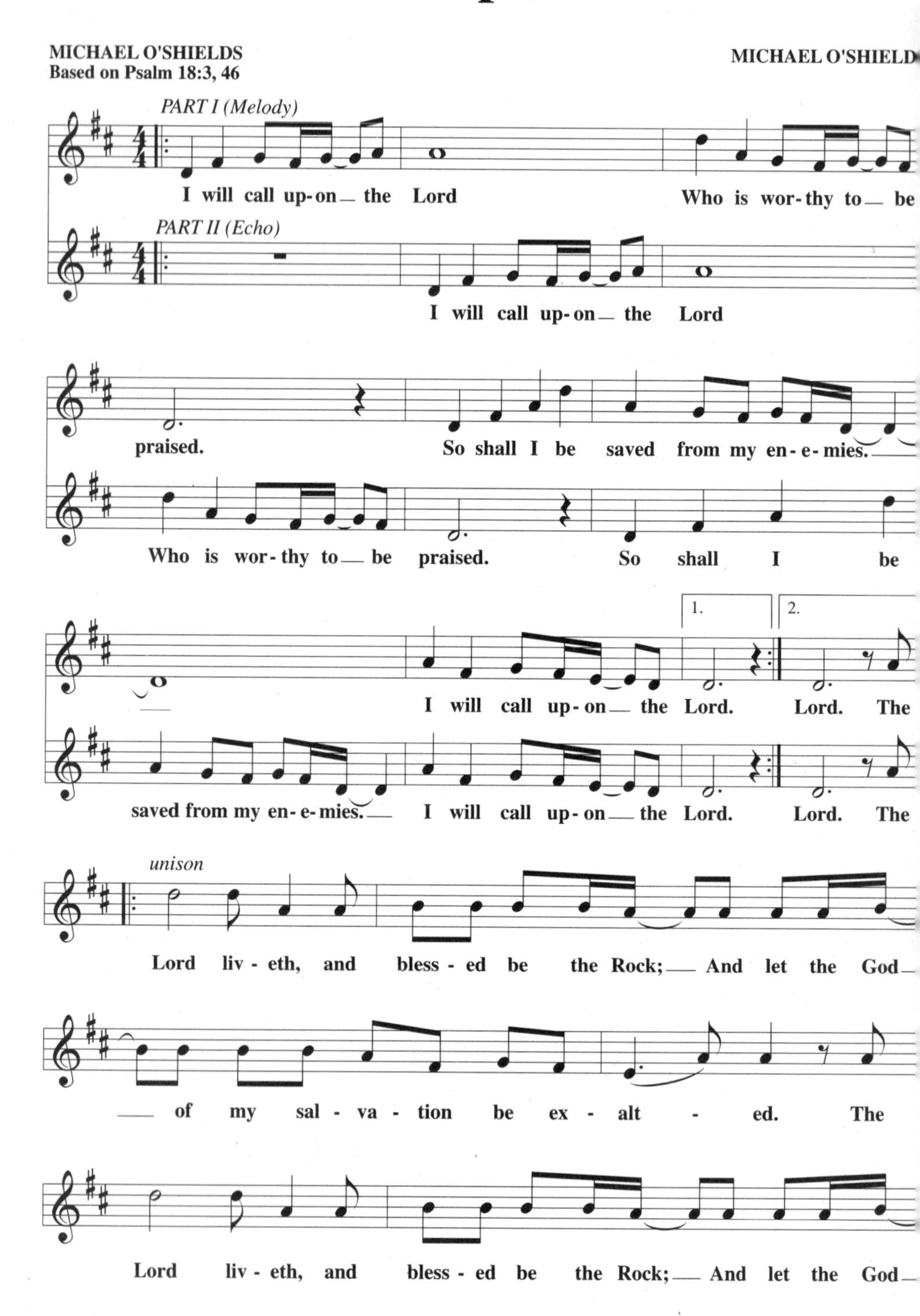

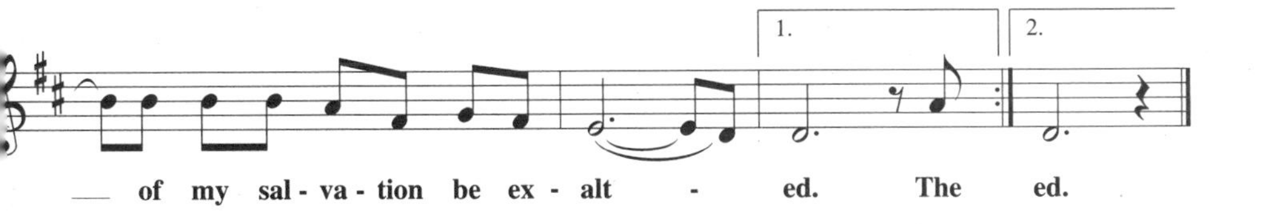

of my sal - va - tion be ex - alt - ed. The ed.

Arise and Sing

225

MEL RAY, JR.

MEL RAY, JR.

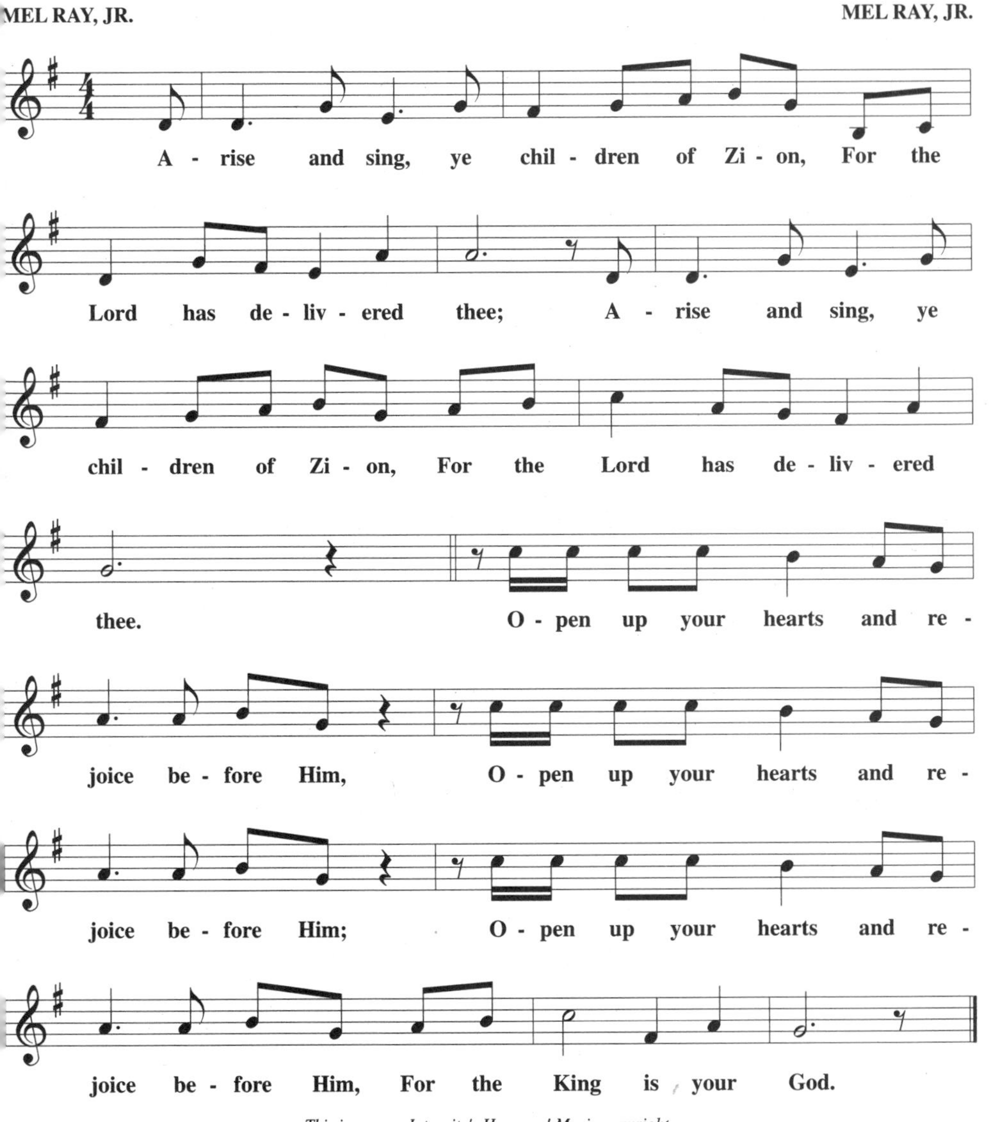

A - rise and sing, ye chil - dren of Zi - on, For the

Lord has de - liv - ered thee; A - rise and sing, ye

chil - dren of Zi - on, For the Lord has de - liv - ered

thee. O - pen up your hearts and re -

joice be - fore Him, O - pen up your hearts and re -

joice be - fore Him; O - pen up your hearts and re -

joice be - fore Him, For the King is your God.

226 He Is the King

Words and Music by
TOM EWING, DON MOEN and JOHN STOCKER

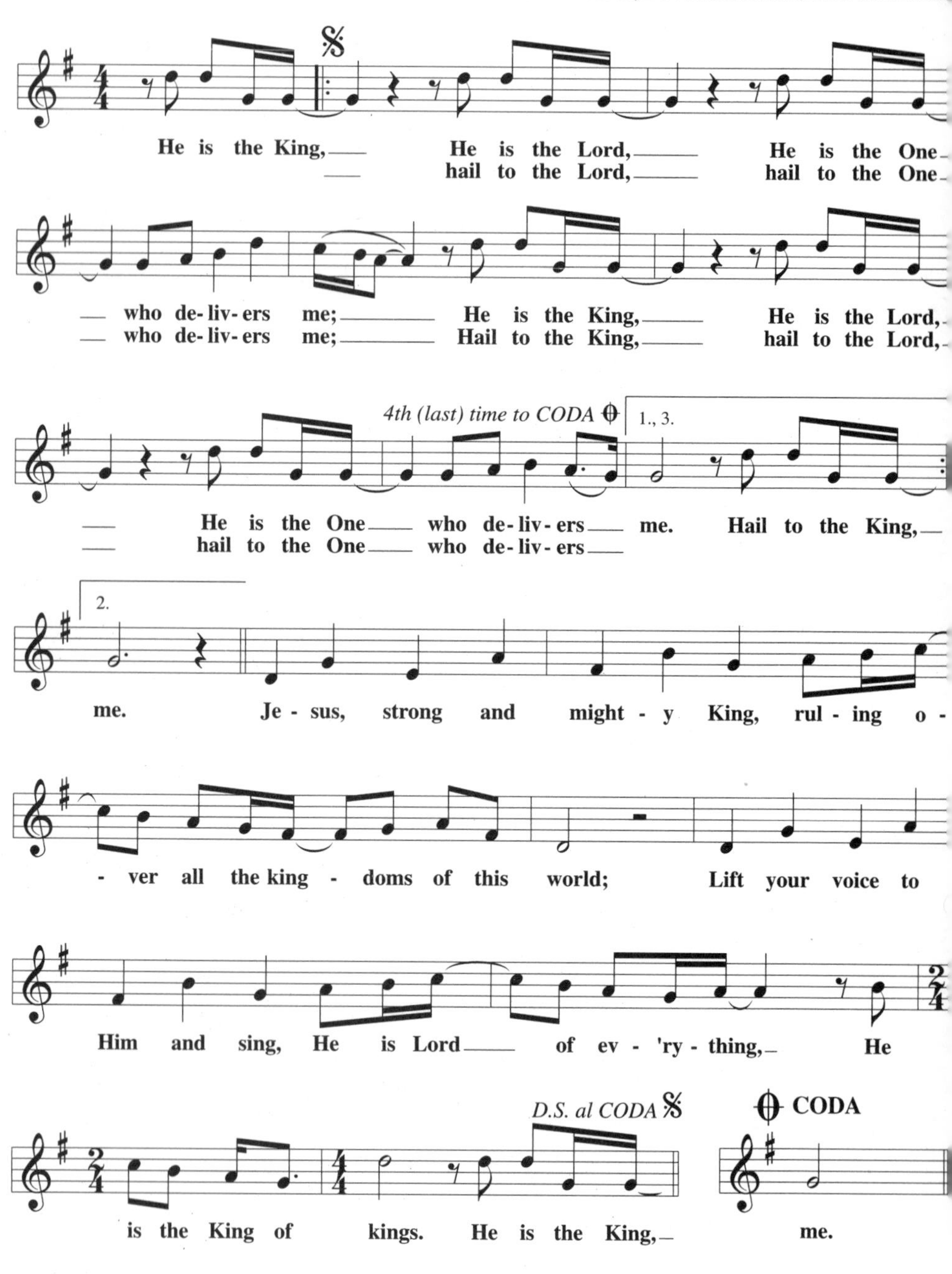

He is the King,____ He is the Lord,____ He is the One____
hail to the Lord,____ hail to the One____

____ who de-liv-ers me;____ He is the King,____ He is the Lord,____
____ who de-liv-ers me;____ Hail to the King,____ hail to the Lord,____

4th (last) time to CODA |1., 3.

____ He is the One____ who de-liv-ers____ me. Hail to the King,
____ hail to the One____ who de-liv-ers____

|2.

me. Je-sus, strong and might-y King, rul-ing o-

-ver all the king-doms of this world; Lift your voice to

Him and sing, He is Lord____ of ev-'ry-thing,____ He

D.S. al CODA ⊕ **CODA**

is the King of kings. He is the King,____ me.

He Is Jehovah

BETTY JEAN ROBINSON

BETTY JEAN ROBINSON

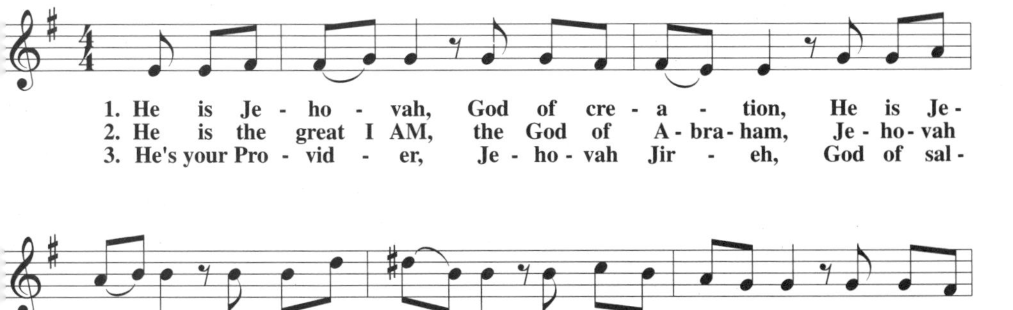

1. He is Je - ho - vah, God of cre - a - tion, He is Je -
2. He is the great I AM, the God of A - bra - ham, Je - ho - vah
3. He's your Pro - vid - er, Je - ho - vah Jir - eh, God of sal -

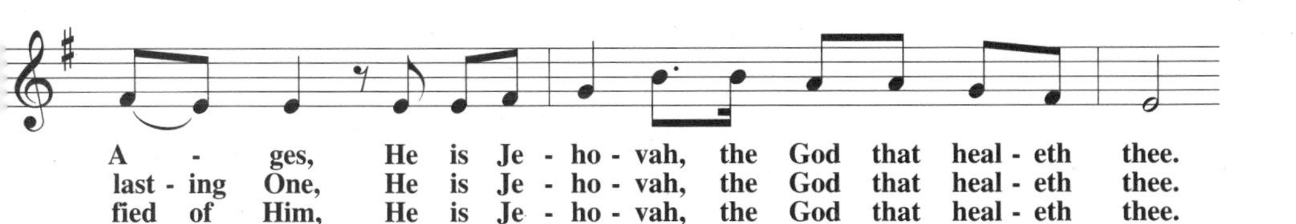

ho - vah, Lord God Al - might - y, The Balm of Gil - e - ad, the Rock of
Sha - lom, The God of peace, I AM. The God of Is - ra - el, the Ev - er -
va - tion, God of Mes - si - ah. The Son He sent to you, He tes - ti -

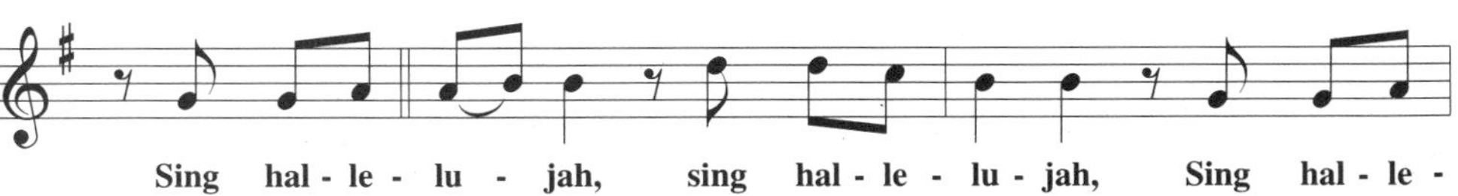

A - ges, He is Je - ho - vah, the God that heal - eth thee.
last - ing One, He is Je - ho - vah, the God that heal - eth thee.
fied of Him, He is Je - ho - vah, the God that heal - eth thee.

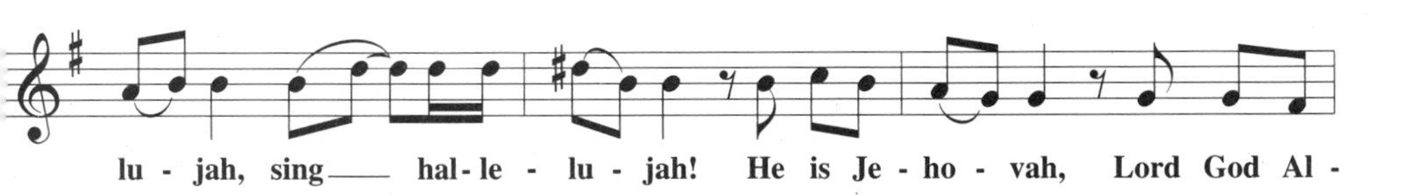

Sing hal - le - lu - jah, sing hal - le - lu - jah, Sing hal - le -

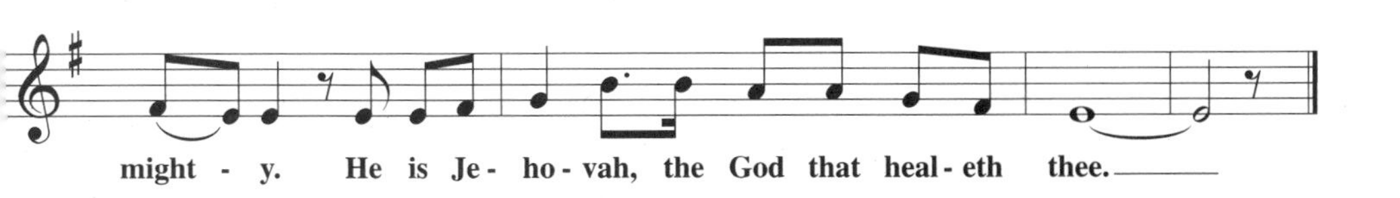

lu - jah, sing—— hal - le - lu - jah! He is Je - ho - vah, Lord God Al -

might - y. He is Je - ho - vah, the God that heal - eth thee.——

228 Jehovah - Jireh

MERLA WATSON

MERLA WATSON

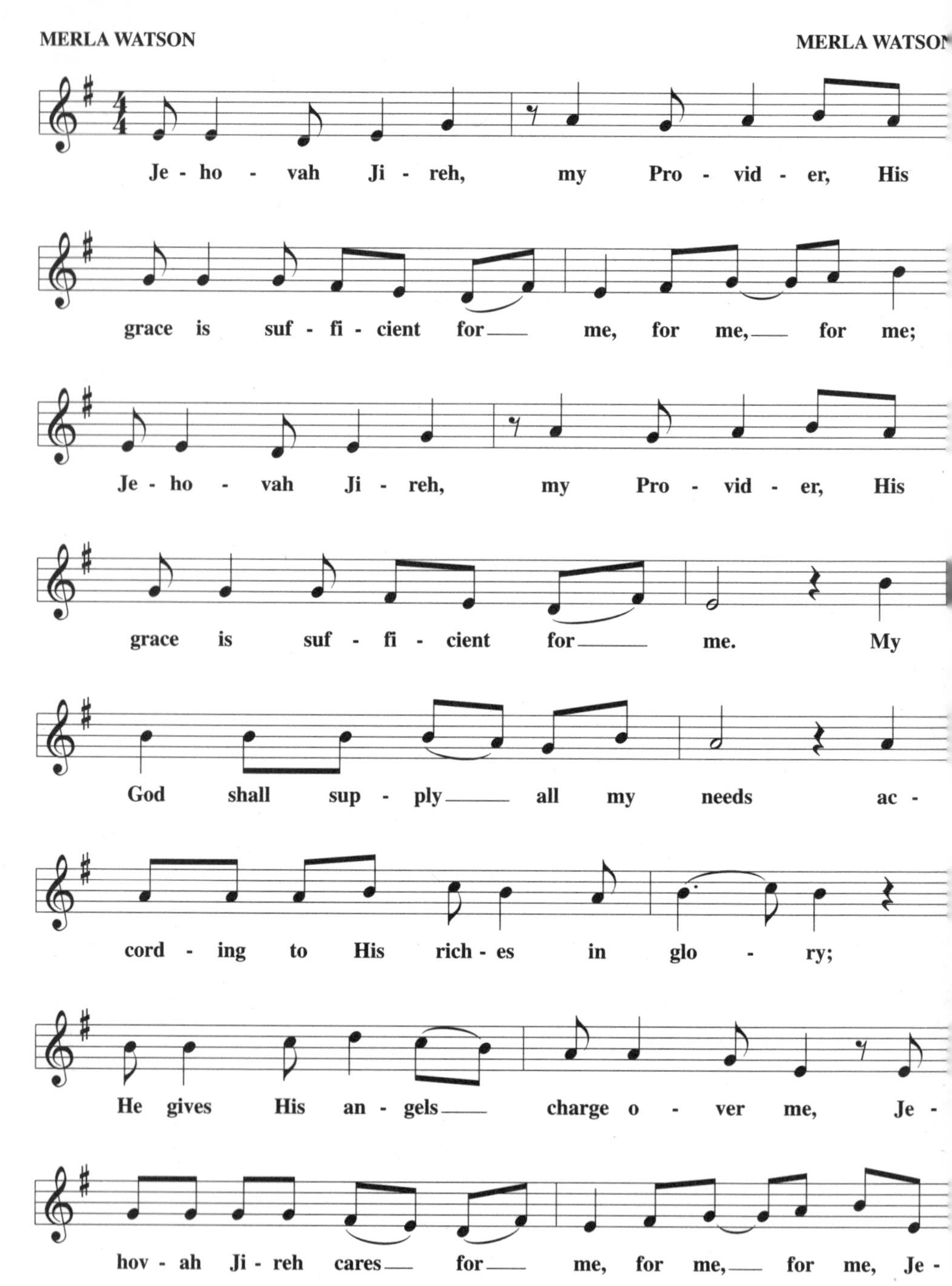

Je - ho - vah Ji - reh, my Pro - vid - er, His grace is suf - fi - cient for me, for me, for me; Je - ho - vah Ji - reh, my Pro - vid - er, His grace is suf - fi - cient for me. My God shall sup - ply all my needs ac - cord - ing to His rich - es in glo - ry; He gives His an - gels charge o - ver me, Je - hov - ah Ji - reh cares for me, for me, for me, Je-

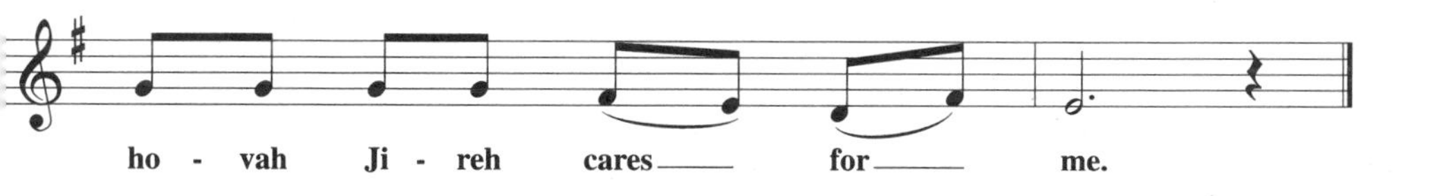

ho - vah Ji - reh cares⎯⎯ for⎯⎯ me.

The Joy of the Lord 229

ALLIENE G. VALE
Based on Nehemiah 8:10

ALLIENE G. VALE

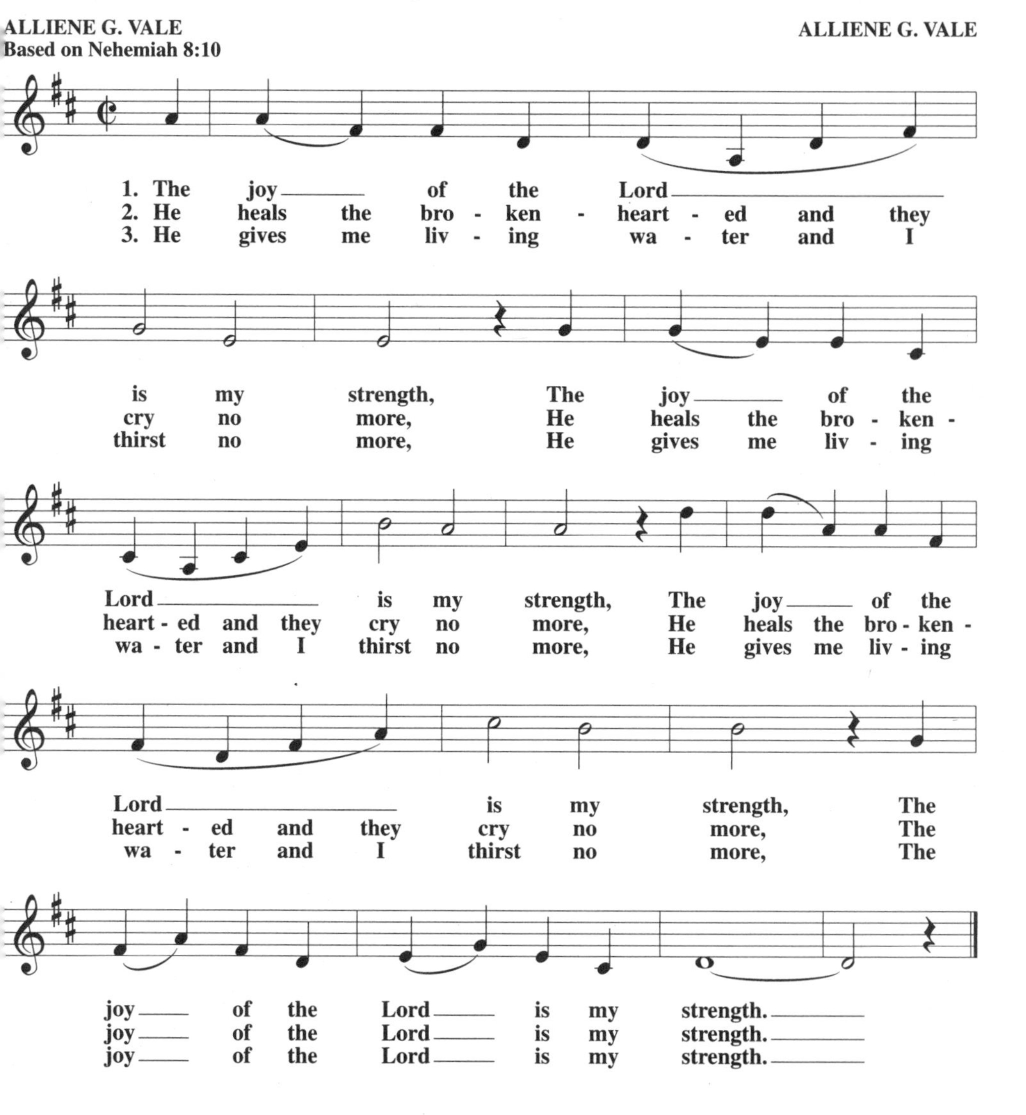

1. The joy⎯⎯ of the Lord⎯⎯
2. He heals the bro - ken - heart - ed and they
3. He gives me liv - ing - wa - ter and I

is my strength, The joy⎯⎯ of the
cry no more, He heals the bro - ken -
thirst no more, He gives me liv - ing

Lord⎯⎯ is my strength, The joy⎯⎯ of the
heart - ed and they cry no more, He heals the bro - ken -
wa - ter and I thirst no more, He gives me liv - ing

Lord⎯⎯ is my strength, The
heart - ed and they cry no more, The
wa - ter and I thirst no more, The

joy⎯⎯ of the Lord⎯⎯ is my strength.⎯⎯
joy⎯⎯ of the Lord⎯⎯ is my strength.⎯⎯
joy⎯⎯ of the Lord⎯⎯ is my strength.⎯⎯

230 You Are My Hiding Place

MICHAEL LEDNER
Based on Psalm 32:7

MICHAEL LEDNER

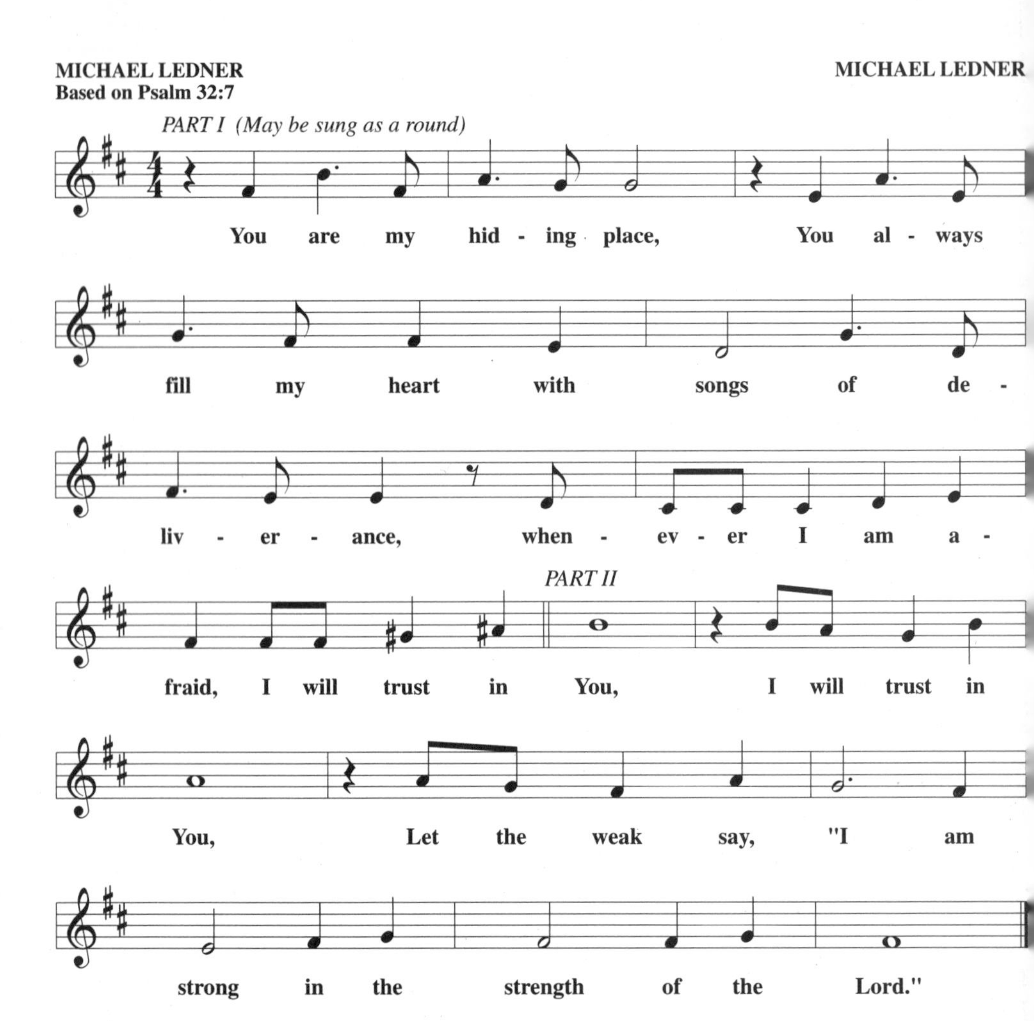

PART I (May be sung as a round)

You are my hid-ing place, You al-ways fill my heart with songs of de-liv-er-ance, when-ev-er I am a-fraid,

PART II

I will trust in You, I will trust in You, Let the weak say, "I am strong in the strength of the Lord."

231 Jehovah to Me

CLAIRE CLONINGER

LYNN KEESECKER

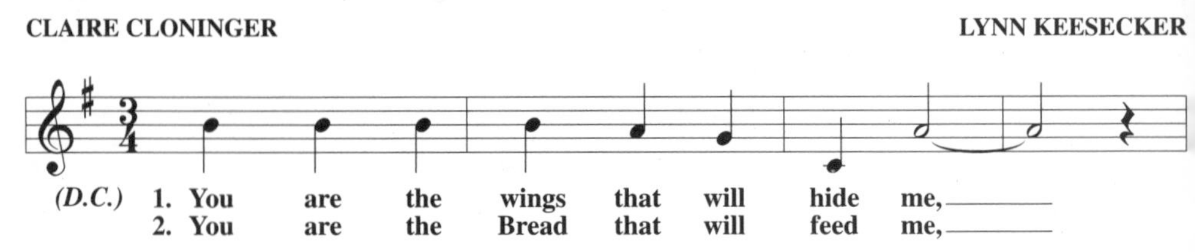

(D.C.) 1. You are the wings that will hide me,_____
2. You are the Bread that will feed me,_____

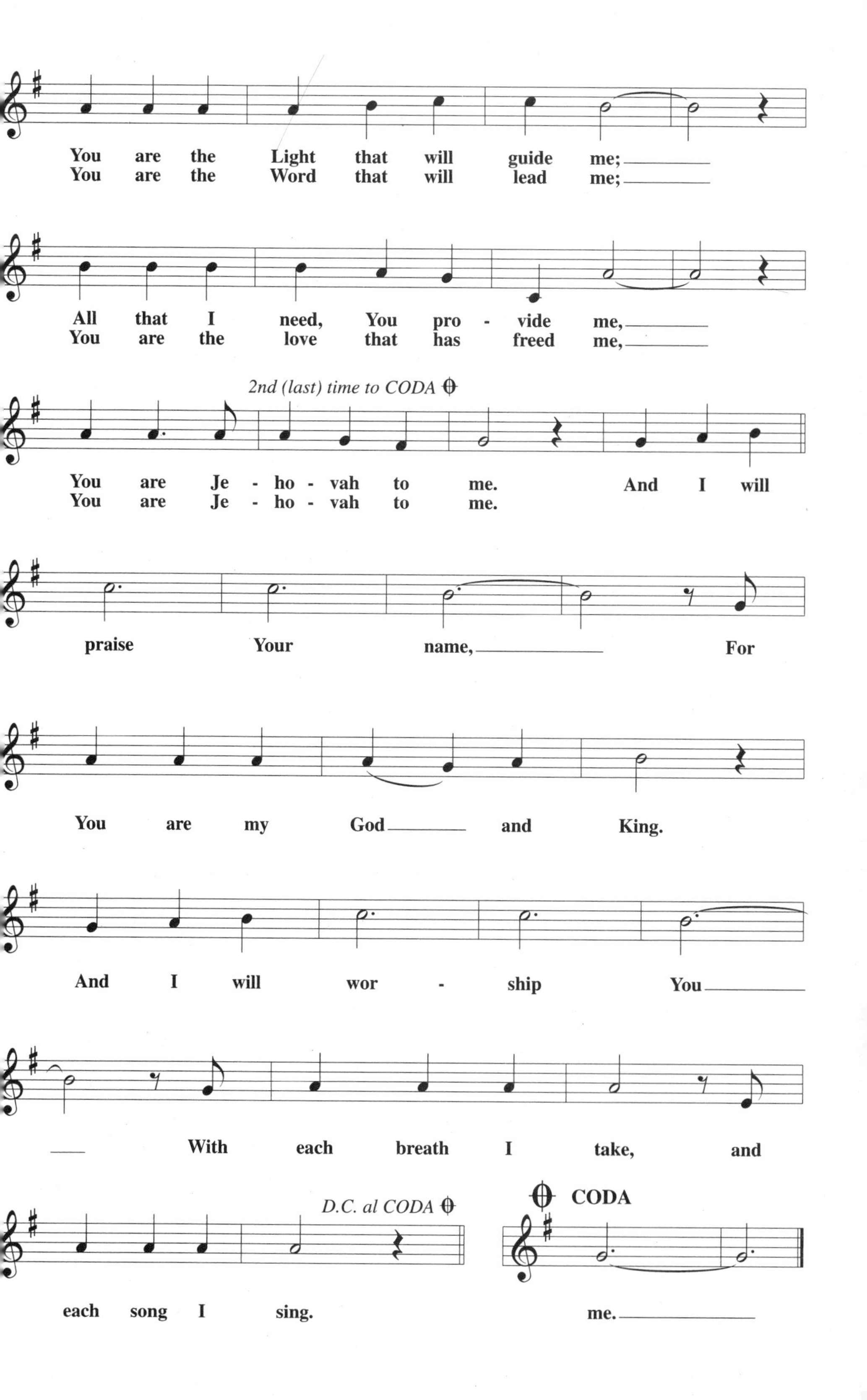

You are the Light that will guide me;_____
You are the Word that will lead me;_____

All that I need, You pro - vide me,_____
You are the love that has freed me,_____

2nd (last) time to CODA ⊕

You are Je - ho - vah to me. And I will
You are Je - ho - vah to me.

praise Your name,_____ For

You are my God_____ and King.

And I will wor - ship You_____

_____ With each breath I take, and

D.C. al CODA ⊕   ⊕ **CODA**

each song I sing.   me._____

232

I Am the God
That Healeth Thee

DON MOEN

DON MOEN

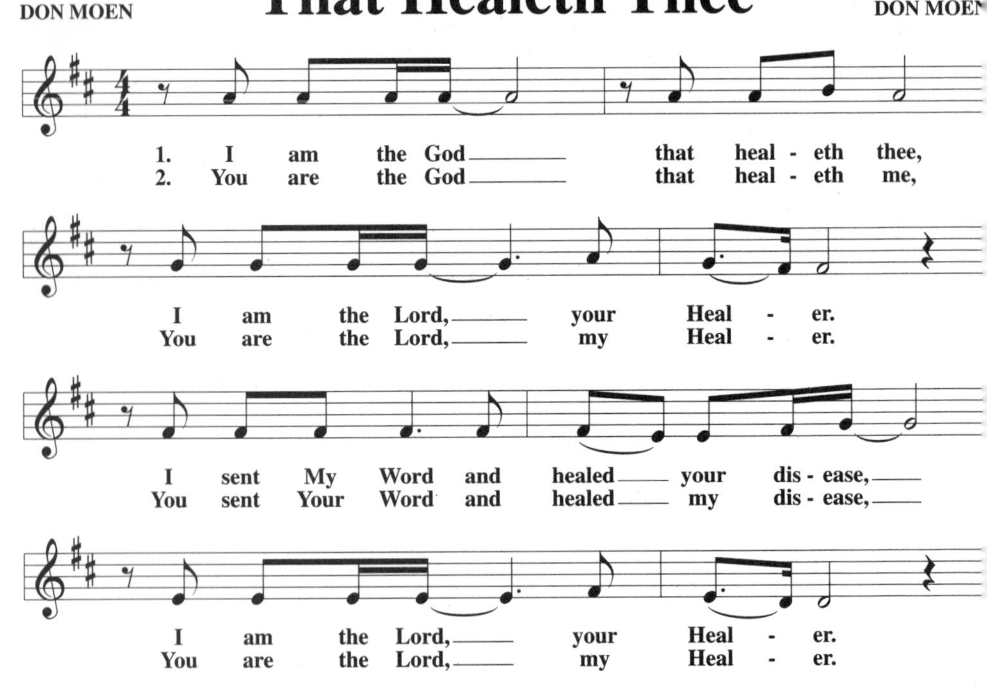

1. I am the God_____ that heal - eth thee,
2. You are the God_____ that heal - eth me,

I am the Lord,_____ your Heal - er.
You are the Lord,_____ my Heal - er.

I sent My Word and healed_____ your dis - ease,_____
You sent Your Word and healed_____ my dis - ease,_____

I am the Lord,_____ your Heal - er.
You are the Lord,_____ my Heal - er.

233

Sing unto the Lord

LEON PATILLO

LEON PATILLO
Arranged by Tom Fettke

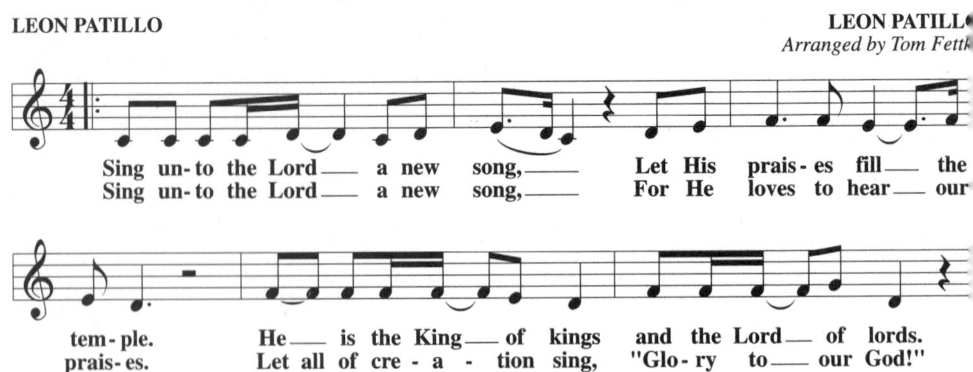

Sing un-to the Lord_____ a new song,_____ Let His prais - es fill_____ the
Sing un-to the Lord_____ a new song,_____ For He loves to hear_____ our

tem - ple. He_____ is the King_____ of kings and the Lord_____ of lords.
prais - es. Let all of cre - a - tion sing, "Glo - ry to_____ our God!"

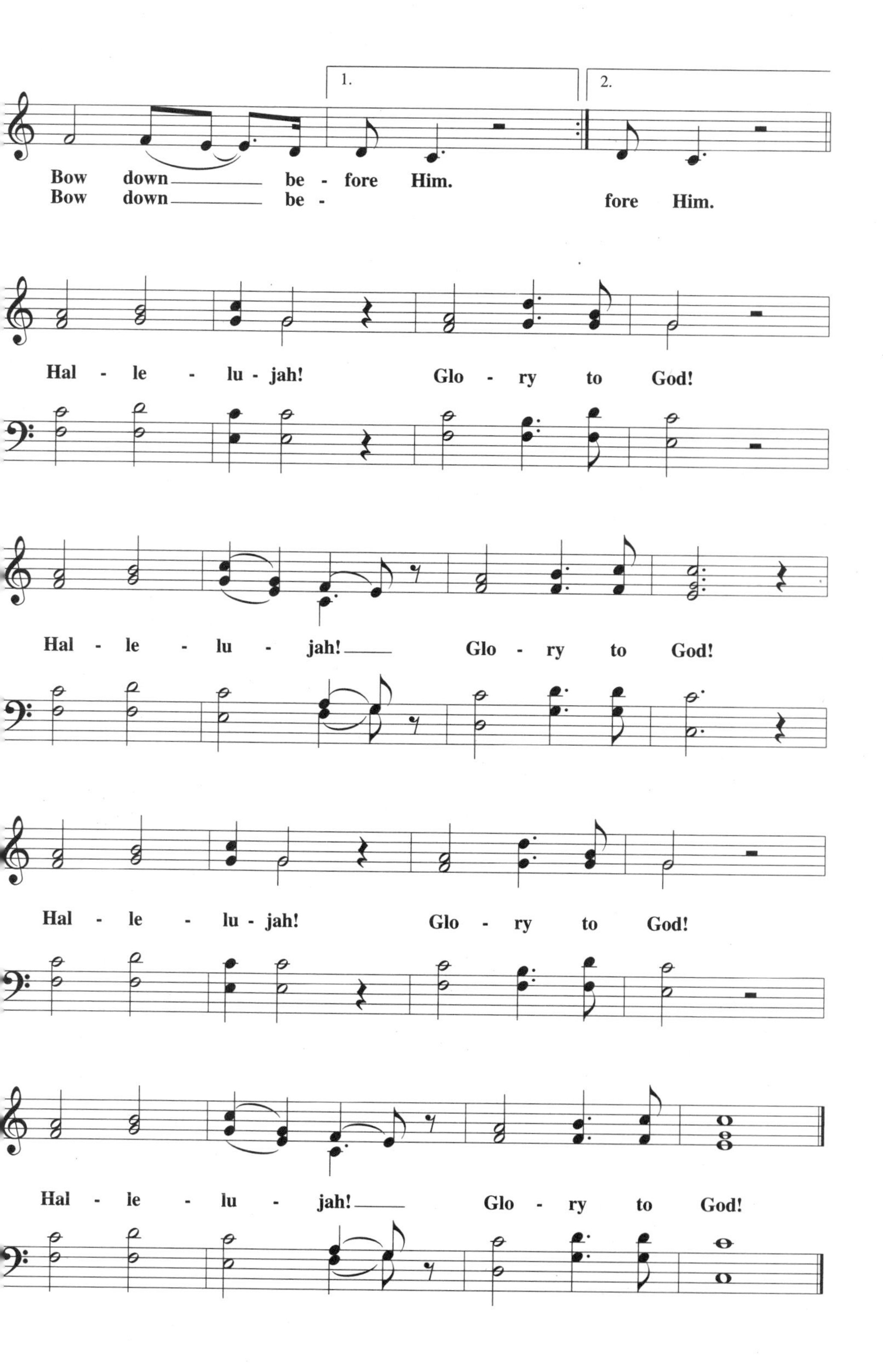

Bow down ——— be - fore Him.
Bow down ——— be -   fore Him.

Hal - le - lu - jah! Glo - ry to God!

Hal - le - lu - jah! ——— Glo - ry to God!

Hal - le - lu - jah! Glo - ry to God!

Hal - le - lu - jah! ——— Glo - ry to God!

234   At the Name of Jesus

DENNIS L. JERNIGAN   DENNIS L. JERNIGAN

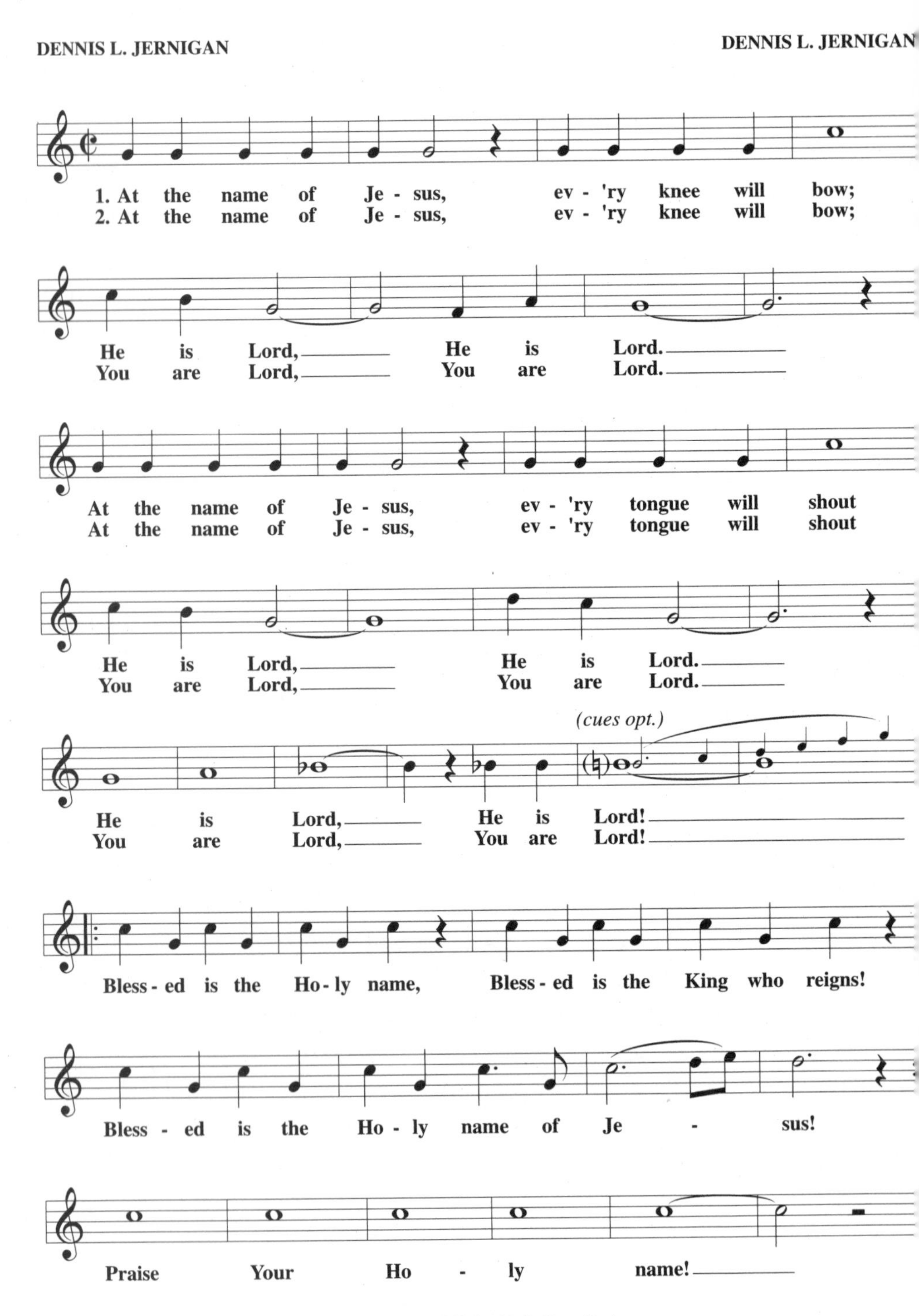

1. At the name of Je - sus,   ev - 'ry knee will bow;
2. At the name of Je - sus,   ev - 'ry knee will bow;

He is Lord,_____ He is Lord._____
You are Lord,_____ You are Lord._____

At the name of Je - sus,   ev - 'ry tongue will shout
At the name of Je - sus,   ev - 'ry tongue will shout

He is Lord,_____ He is Lord._____
You are Lord,_____ You are Lord._____

(cues opt.)

He is Lord,_____ He is Lord!_____
You are Lord,_____ You are Lord!_____

Bless - ed is the Ho - ly name, Bless - ed is the King who reigns!

Bless - ed is the Ho - ly name of Je - sus!

Praise Your Ho - ly name!_____

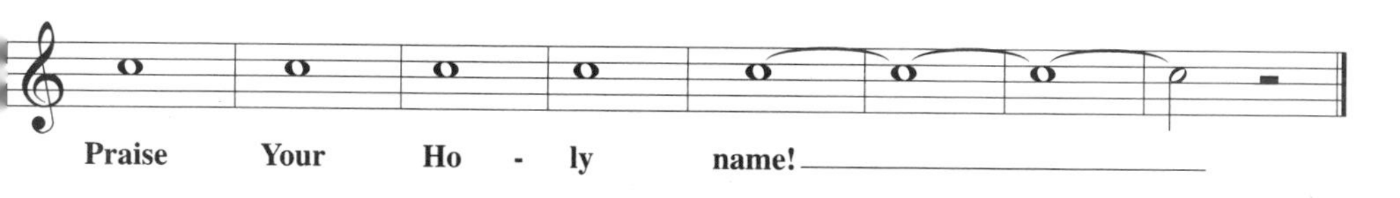

Praise Your Ho - ly name!

Let Your Spirit Rise within Me

235

RANDY SPEIR

RANDY SPEIR

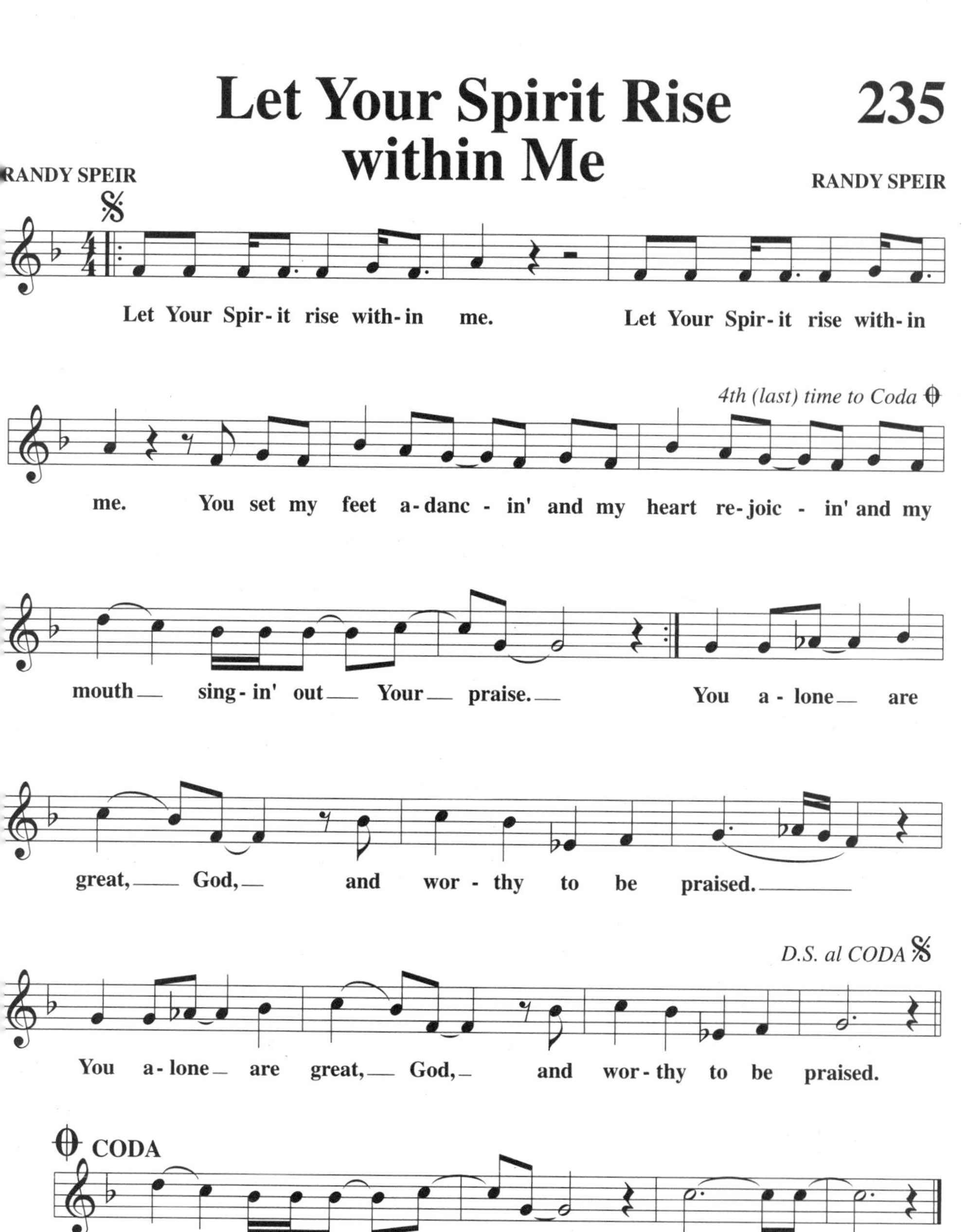

Let Your Spir - it rise with - in me. Let Your Spir - it rise with - in

4th (last) time to Coda ⊕

me. You set my feet a - danc - in' and my heart re - joic - in' and my

mouth— sing - in' out— Your— praise.— You a - lone— are

great,— God,— and wor - thy to be praised.—

D.S. al CODA 𝄋

You a - lone— are great,— God,— and wor - thy to be praised.

⊕ CODA

mouth— sing - in' out— Your— praise,— Your— praise.—

236

This Is the Day

PSALM 118:24

LES GARRETT

This is the day, this is the day that the Lord hath made, that the Lord hath made. We will re-joice, we will re-joice and be glad in it, and be glad in it. This is the day that the Lord hath made; We will re-joice and be glad in it. This is the day, this is the day that the Lord hath made.

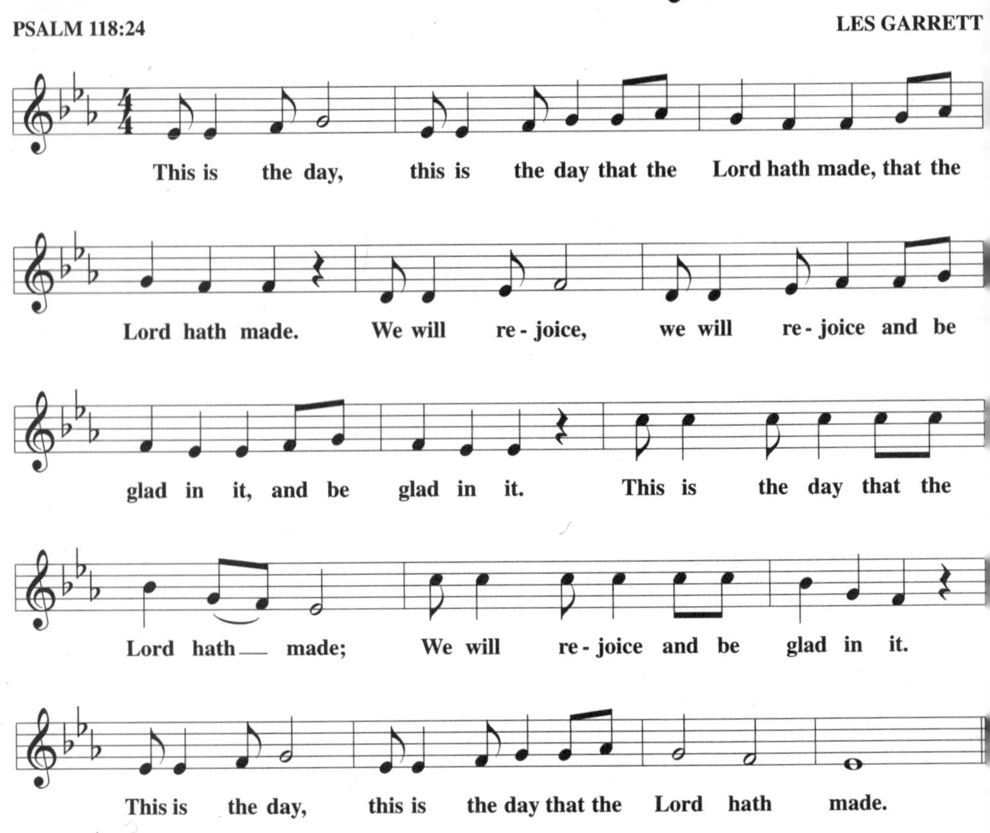

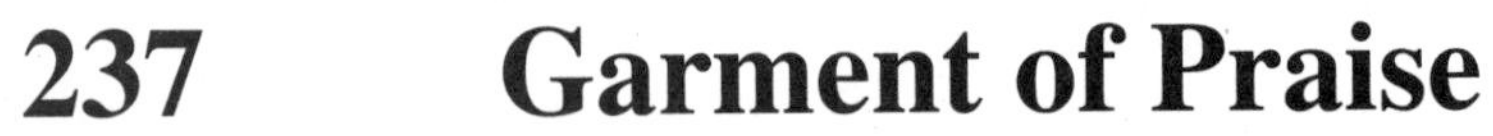

237

Garment of Praise

DAVID INGLES

DAVID INGLES

Put on the gar-ment of praise for the spir-it of heav-i-ness;— Lift up your voice to God. Praise with the Spir - it

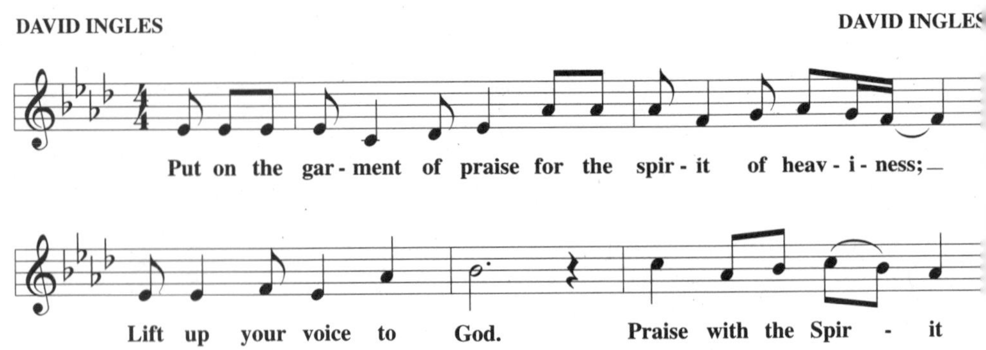

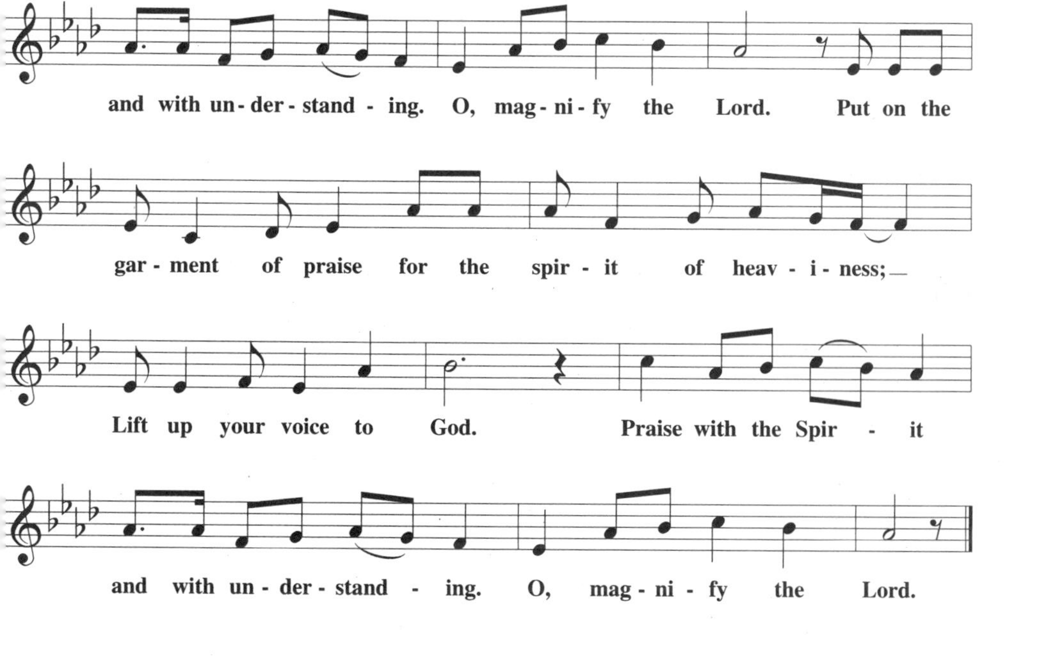

and with un - der - stand - ing. O, mag - ni - fy the Lord. Put on the

gar - ment of praise for the spir - it of heav - i - ness;—

Lift up your voice to God. Praise with the Spir - it

and with un - der - stand - ing. O, mag - ni - fy the Lord.

Let the Redeemed

238

WARD ELLIS

WARD ELLIS

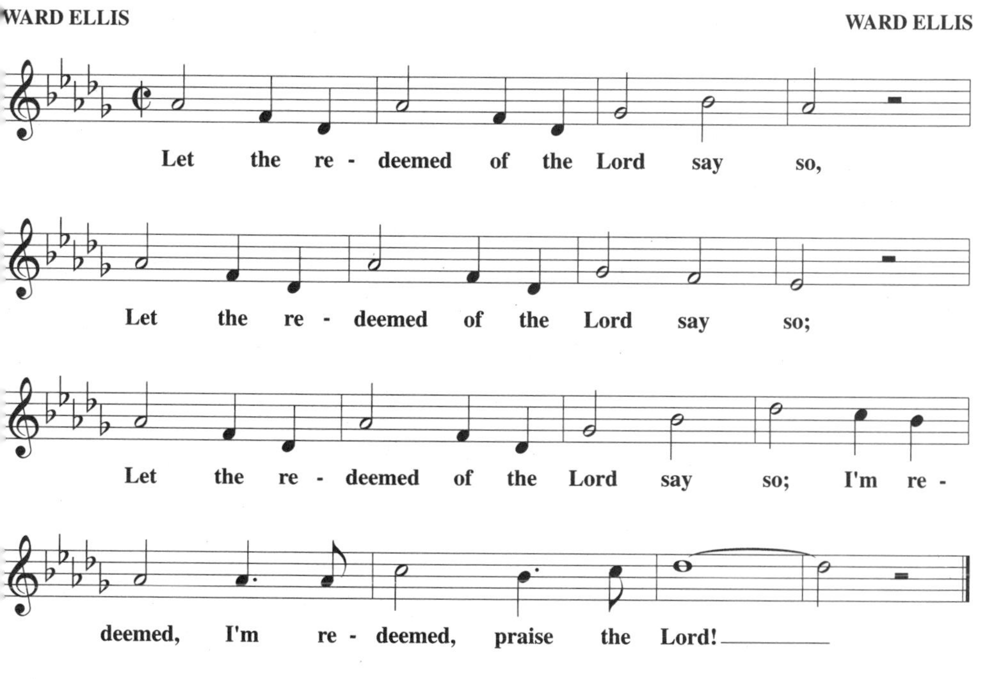

Let the re - deemed of the Lord say so,

Let the re - deemed of the Lord say so;

Let the re - deemed of the Lord say so; I'm re -

deemed, I'm re - deemed, praise the Lord!—

239 I Will Glorify

SAMMY DAVENPORT SAMMY DAVENPORT

I glo-ri-fy ___ Je-ho-vah, King of kings; ___ I bow be-fore the ho-ly Lamb of God. ___ I come in-to His pres-ence, and He fills me with His love; The Spir-it of the Lord is on us now. ___ I will glo-ri-fy ___ the Lord, ___ Praise Him in ___ His tem - ple; Mag-ni-fy ___ His name, ___ who reigns on high. ___ I will glo-ri-fy ___ the Lord, ___ Praise Him in ___ His tem - ple;

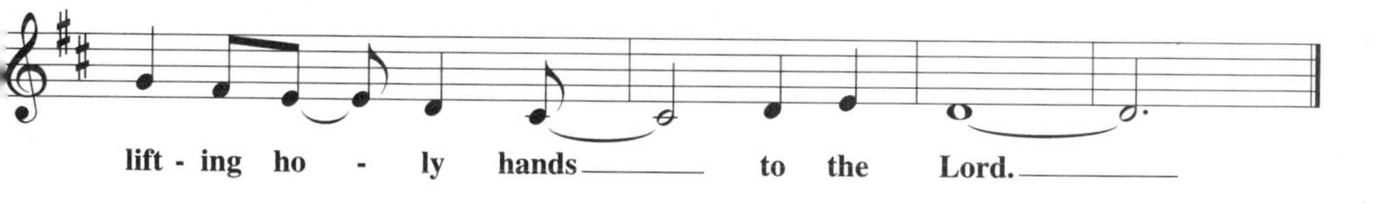

lift - ing ho - ly hands——— to the Lord.———

As We Gather

240

Words and Music by
MIKE FAYE and TOM COOMES

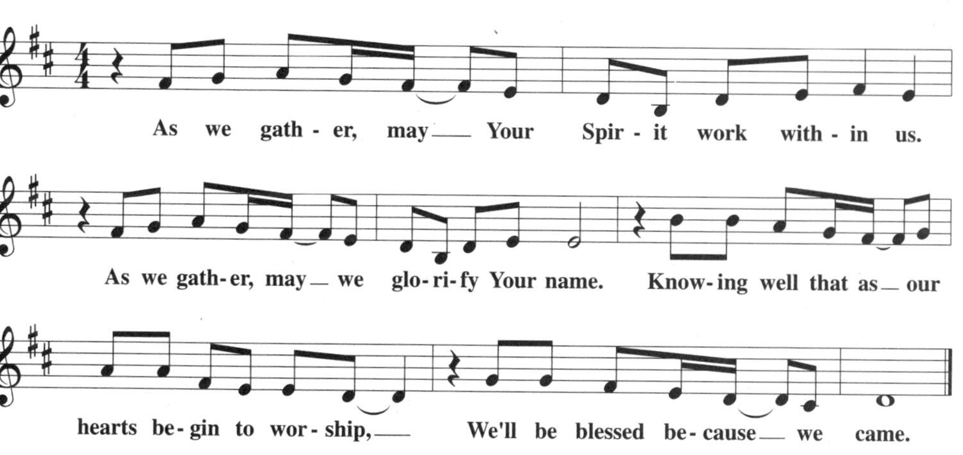

As we gath-er, may—— Your Spir-it work with-in us.

As we gath-er, may— we glo-ri-fy Your name. Know-ing well that as— our

hearts be-gin to wor-ship,——— We'll be blessed be-cause— we came.

See His Glory

241

ICH COOK

RICH COOK

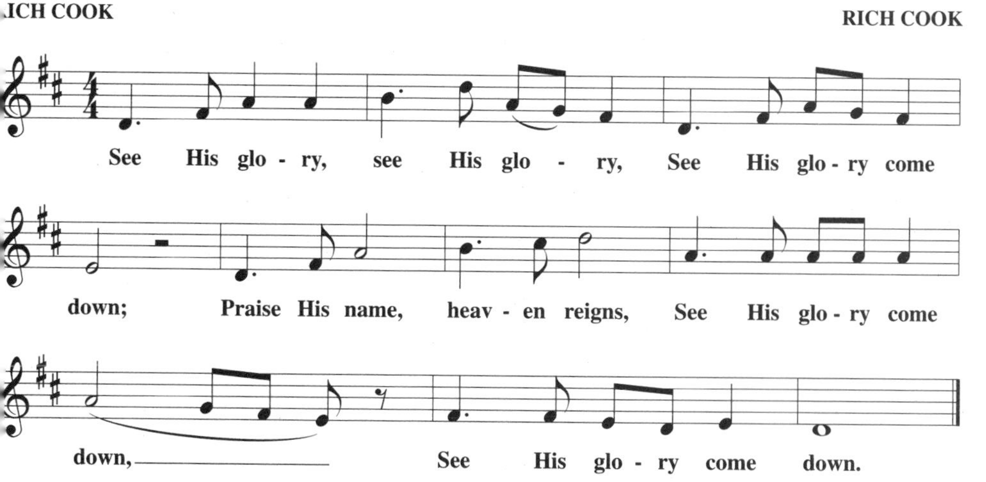

See His glo - ry, see His glo - ry, See His glo - ry come

down; Praise His name, heav - en reigns, See His glo - ry come

down,——————— See His glo - ry come down.

242 We Have Come into His House

BRUCE BALLINGER

BRUCE BALLINGE

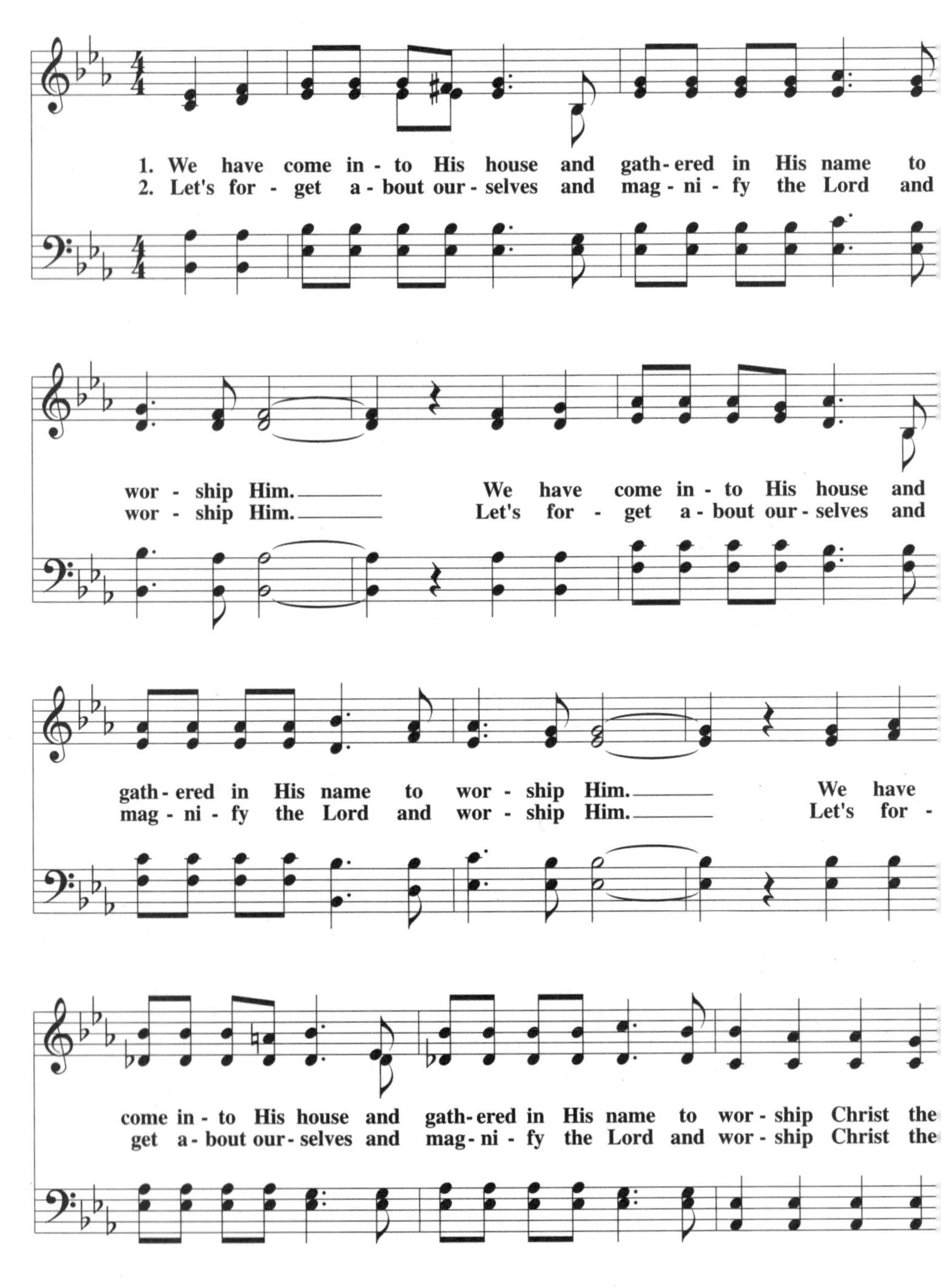

1. We have come in-to His house and gath-ered in His name to wor-ship Him._____ We have come in-to His house and gath-ered in His name to wor-ship Him._____ We have come in-to His house and gath-ered in His name to wor-ship Christ the

2. Let's for-get a-bout our-selves and mag-ni-fy the Lord and wor-ship Him._____ Let's for-get a-bout our-selves and mag-ni-fy the Lord and wor-ship Him._____ Let's for-get a-bout our-selves and mag-ni-fy the Lord and wor-ship Christ the

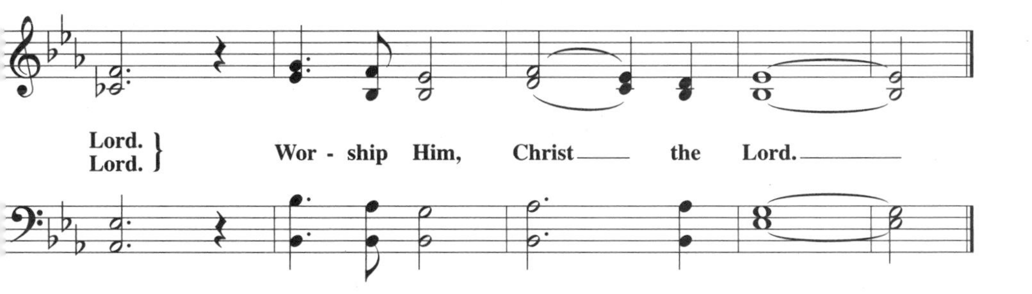

Lord. }
Lord. }
Wor - ship Him, Christ____ the Lord.____

Surely the Presence

243

LANNY WOLFE

LANNY WOLFE

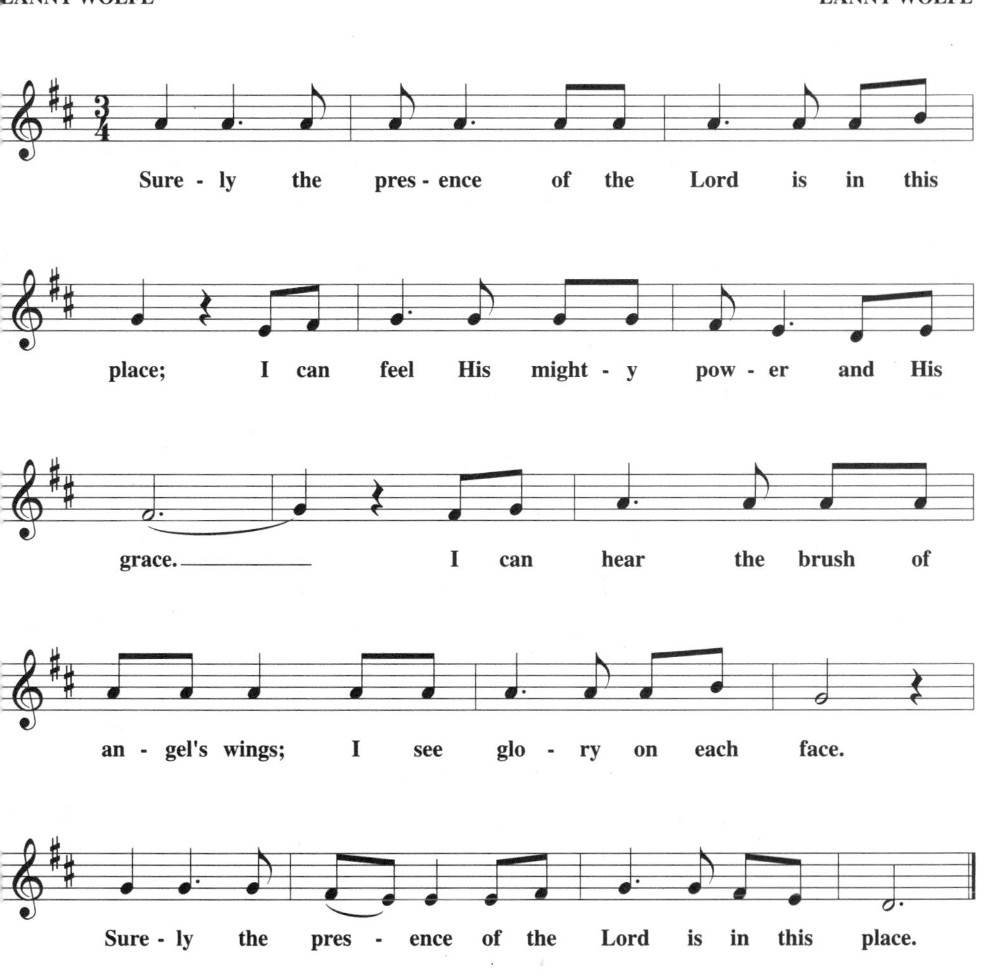

Sure - ly the pres - ence of the Lord is in this

place; I can feel His might - y pow - er and His

grace.____ I can hear the brush of

an - gel's wings; I see glo - ry on each face.

Sure - ly the pres - ence of the Lord is in this place.

244

Let's Just
Praise the Lord

GLORIA GAITHER and WILLIAM J. GAITHER   WILLIAM J. GAITHER

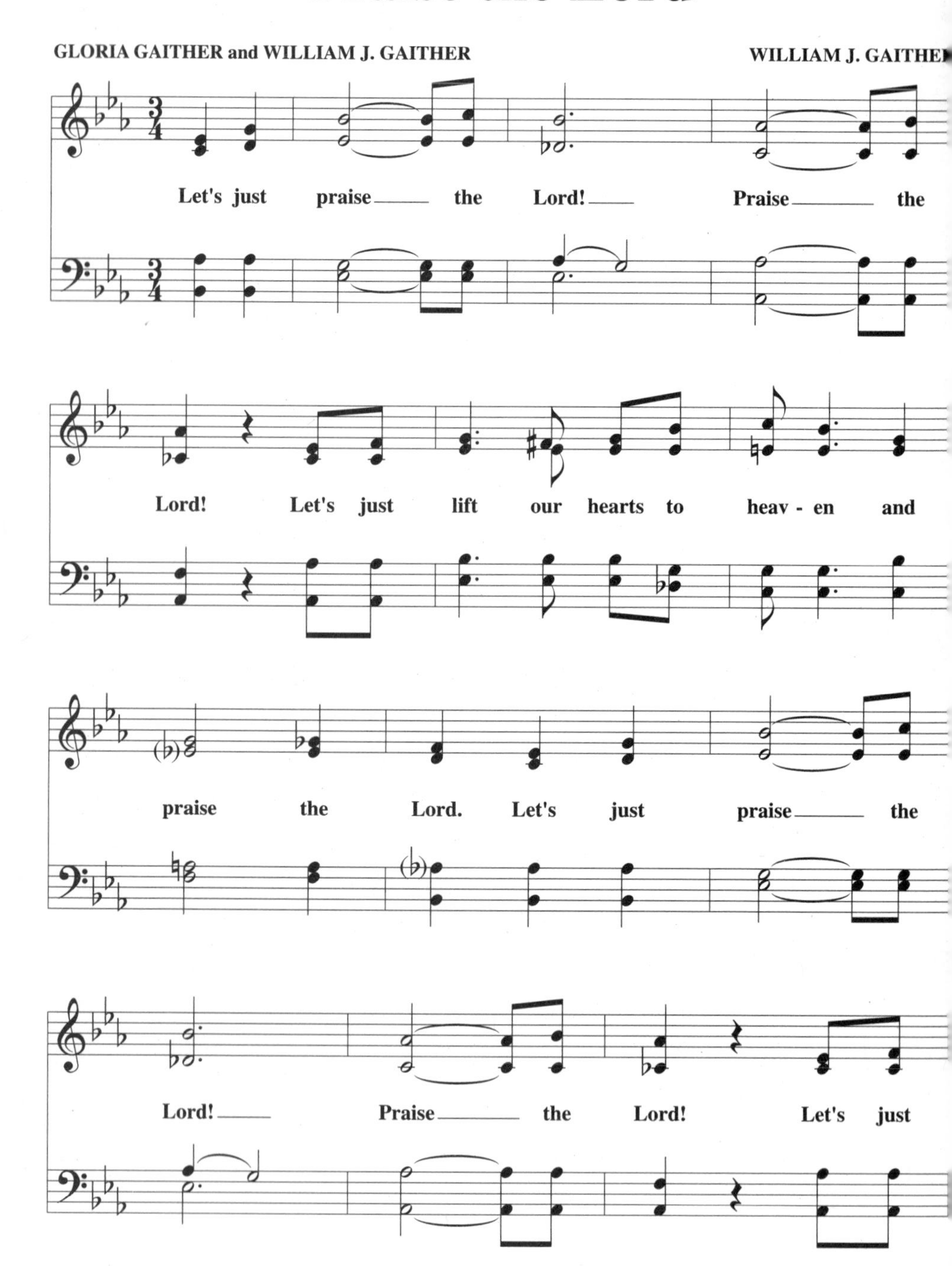

Let's just praise the Lord! Praise the Lord! Let's just lift our hearts to heav-en and praise the Lord. Let's just praise the Lord! Praise the Lord! Let's just

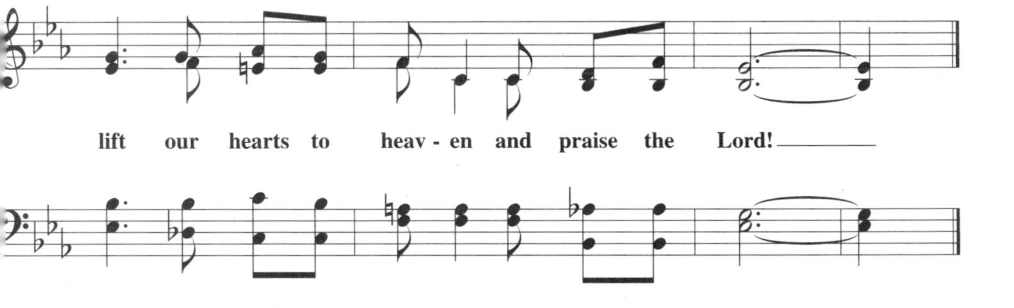

lift our hearts to heav-en and praise the Lord!_____

Come and Praise Him, Royal Priesthood

245

NDY CARTER

ANDY CARTER

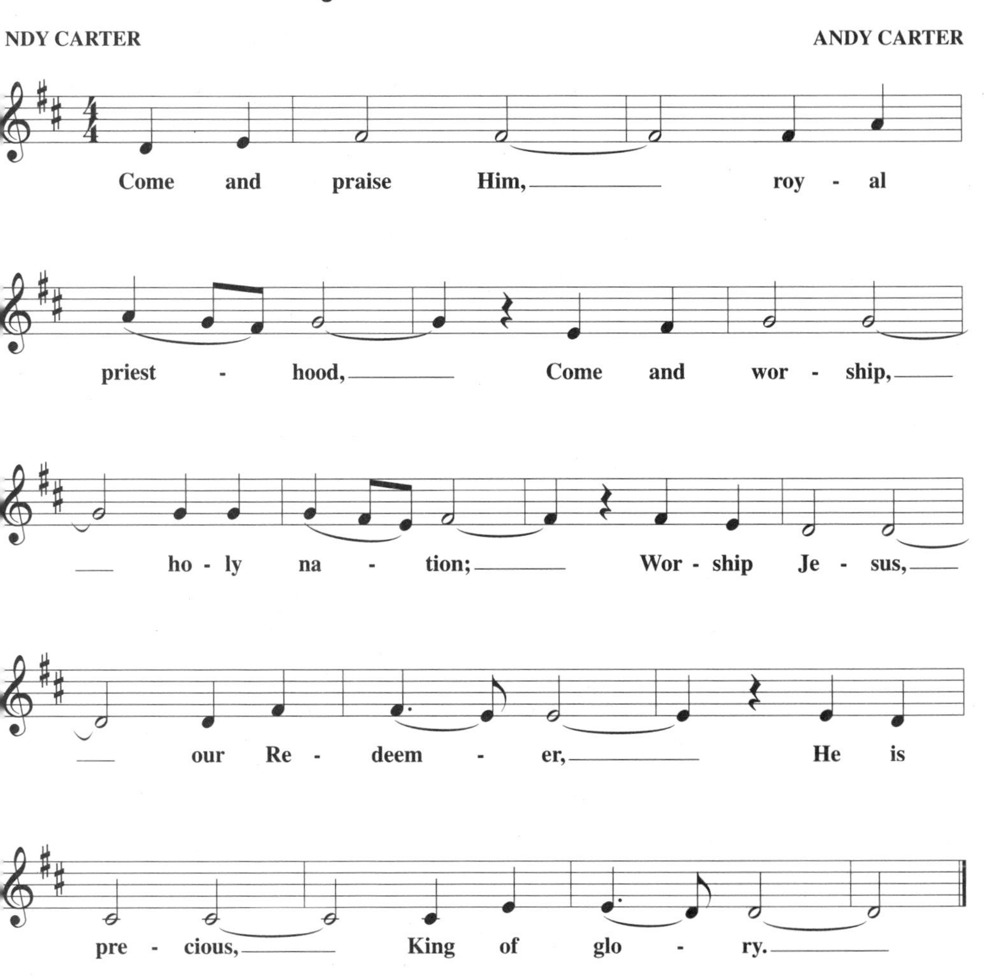

Come and praise Him,_____ roy - al

priest - hood,_____ Come and wor - ship,_____

____ ho - ly na - tion;_____ Wor - ship Je - sus,_____

____ our Re - deem - er,_____ He is

pre - cious,_____ King of glo - ry._____

246

Come, Let Us Worship and Bow Down

DAVE DOHERTY
Based on Psalm 95:6, 7

DAVE DOHERTY

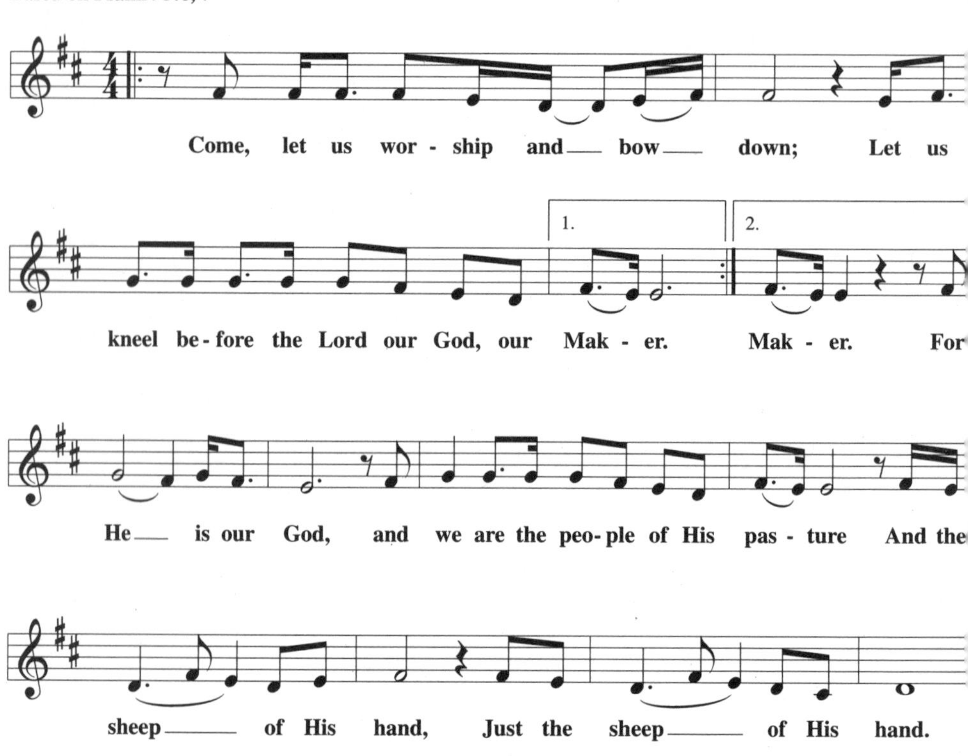

Come, let us wor - ship and bow down; Let us

kneel be - fore the Lord our God, our Mak - er. Mak - er. For

He is our God, and we are the peo - ple of His pas - ture And the

sheep of His hand, Just the sheep of His hand.

247

I Will Come and Bow Down

MARTIN NYSTROM

MARTIN NYSTROM

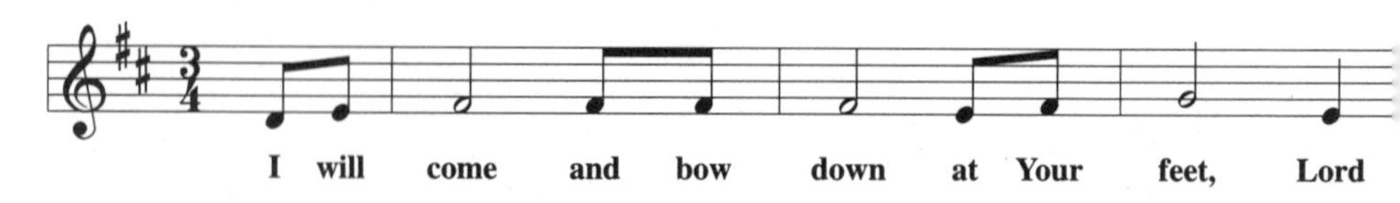

I will come and bow down at Your feet, Lord

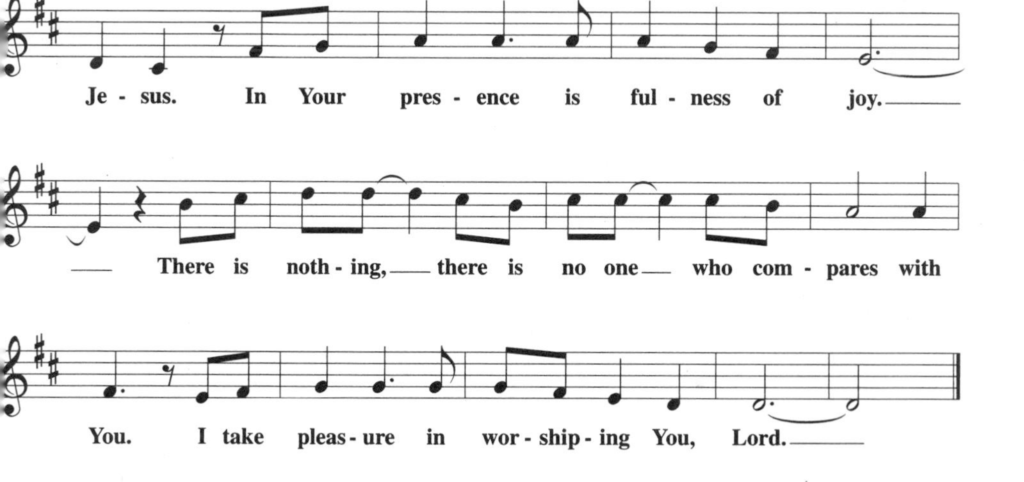

Je - sus. In Your pres - ence is ful - ness of joy.

There is noth - ing, — there is no one — who com - pares with

You. I take pleas - ure in wor - ship - ing You, Lord.

O Come, Let Us Adore Him 248

RADITIONAL

WADE'S *CANTUS DIVERSI*

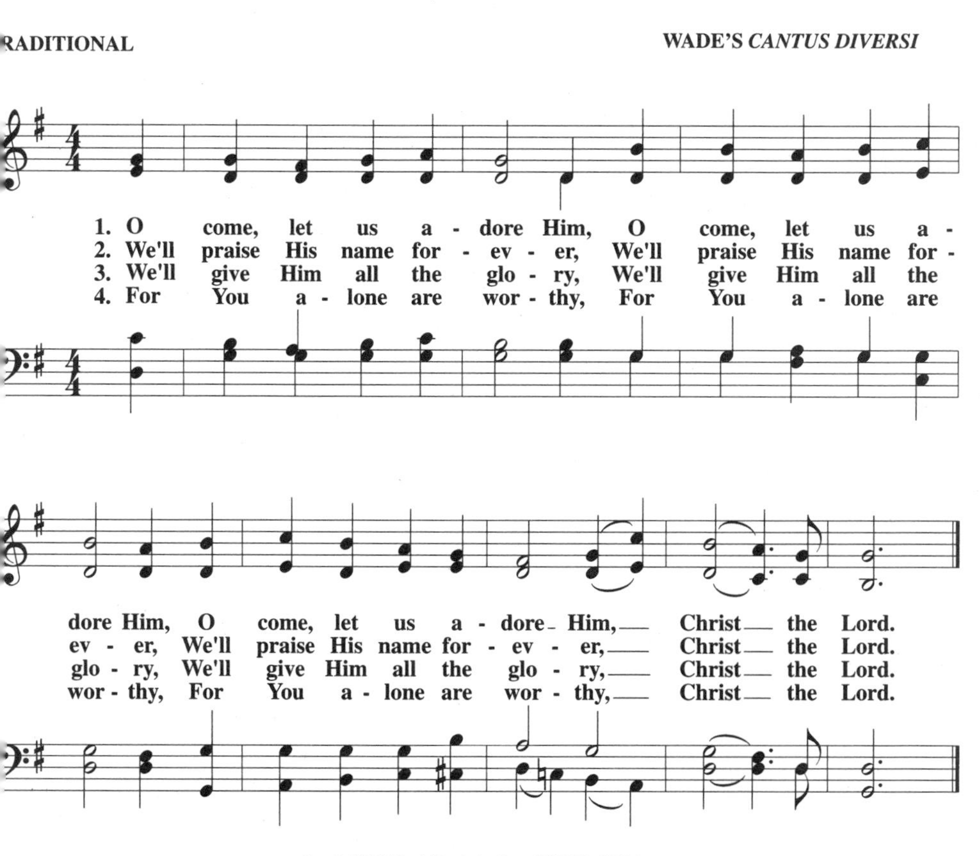

1. O come, let us a - dore Him, O come, let us a -
2. We'll praise His name for - ev - er, We'll praise His name for -
3. We'll give Him all the glo - ry, We'll give Him all the
4. For You a - lone are wor - thy, For You a - lone are

dore Him, O come, let us a - dore Him, — Christ — the Lord.
ev - er, We'll praise His name for - ev - er, — Christ — the Lord.
glo - ry, We'll give Him all the glo - ry, — Christ — the Lord.
wor - thy, For You a - lone are wor - thy, — Christ — the Lord.

249 Glorify the Lord

Words and Music b[y]
PAULA and ROBERT TIL[...]

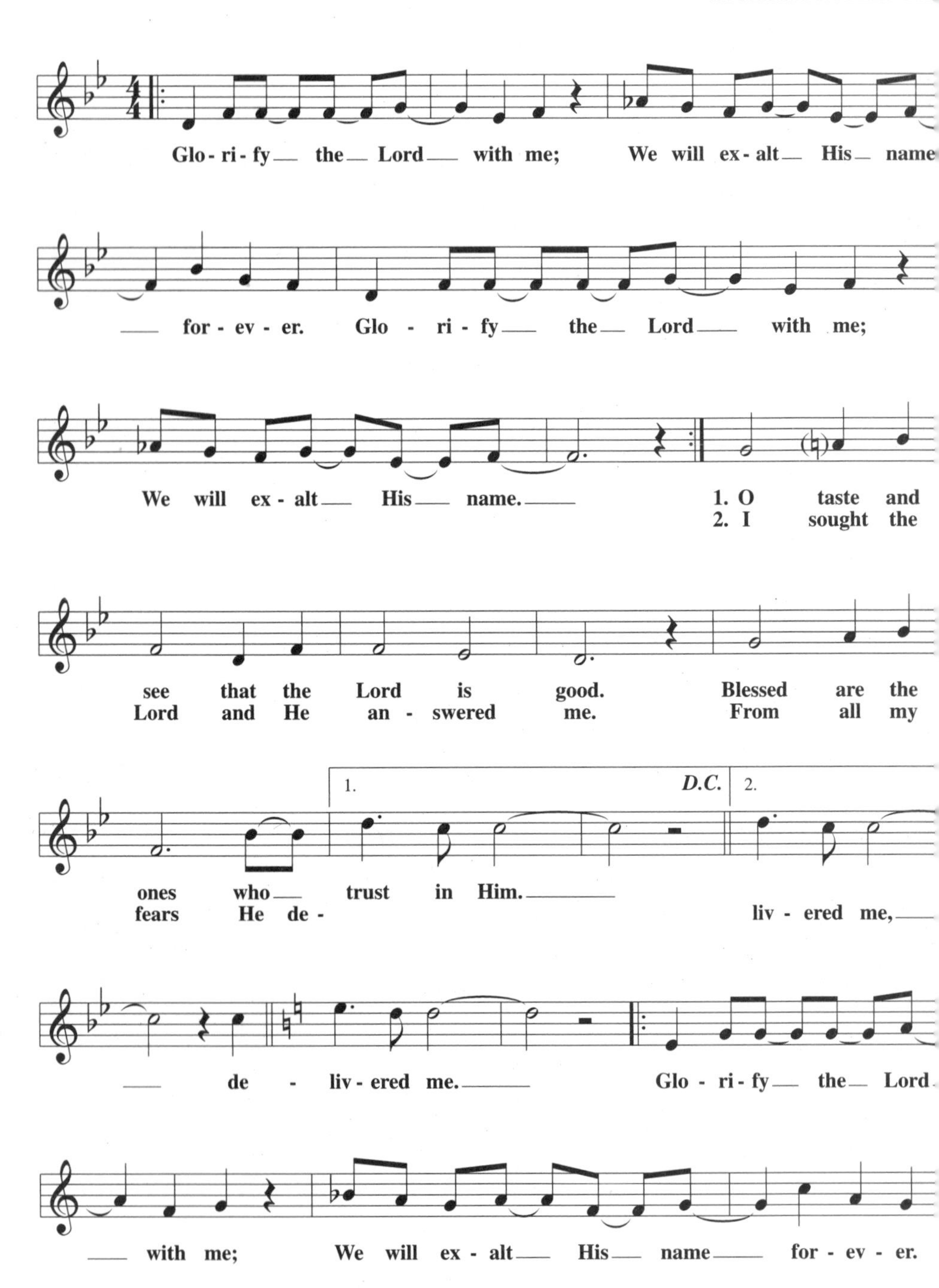

Glo - ri - fy — the — Lord — with me; We will ex - alt — His — name
— for - ev - er. Glo - ri - fy — the — Lord — with me;
We will ex - alt — His — name. —

1. O taste and
2. I sought the

see that the Lord is good. Blessed are the
Lord and He an - swered me. From all my

1.
ones who — trust in Him. —
fears He de - *D.C.* 2. liv - ered me,

— de - liv - ered me. — Glo - ri - fy — the Lord.

— with me; We will ex - alt — His — name — for - ev - er.

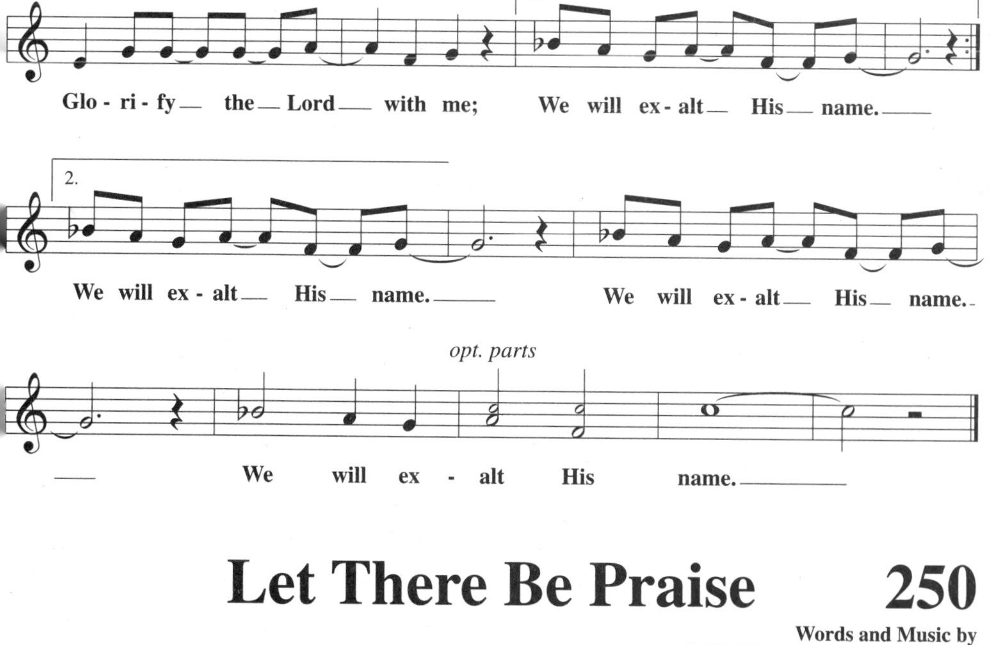

Glo - ri - fy — the — Lord — with me; We will ex - alt — His — name. —

We will ex - alt — His — name. — We will ex - alt — His — name. —

opt. parts

— We will ex - alt His name. —

Let There Be Praise 250

Words and Music by
MELODIE and DICK TUNNEY

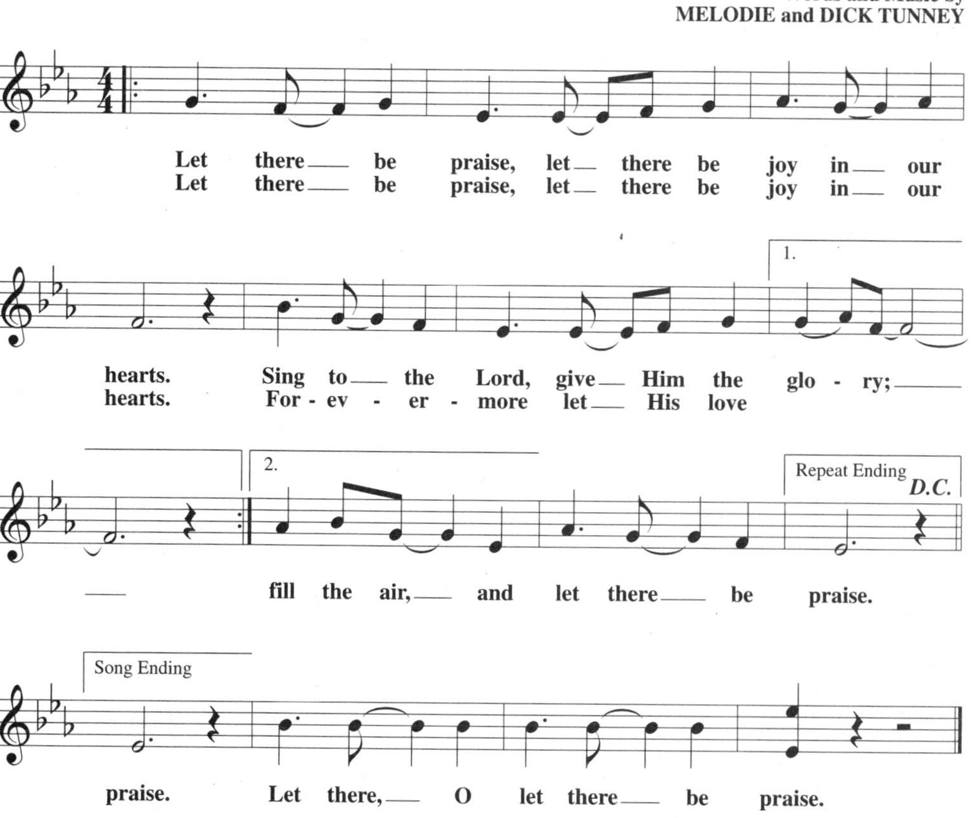

Let there — be praise, let — there be joy in — our
Let there — be praise, let — there be joy in — our

hearts. Sing to — the Lord, give — Him the glo - ry; —
hearts. For - ev - er - more let — His love

Repeat Ending
D.C.

— fill the air, — and let there — be praise.

Song Ending

praise. Let there, — O let there — be praise.

251
Let the Peace of Christ Rule in Your Heart

Colossians 3:15

DENNY CAGLE

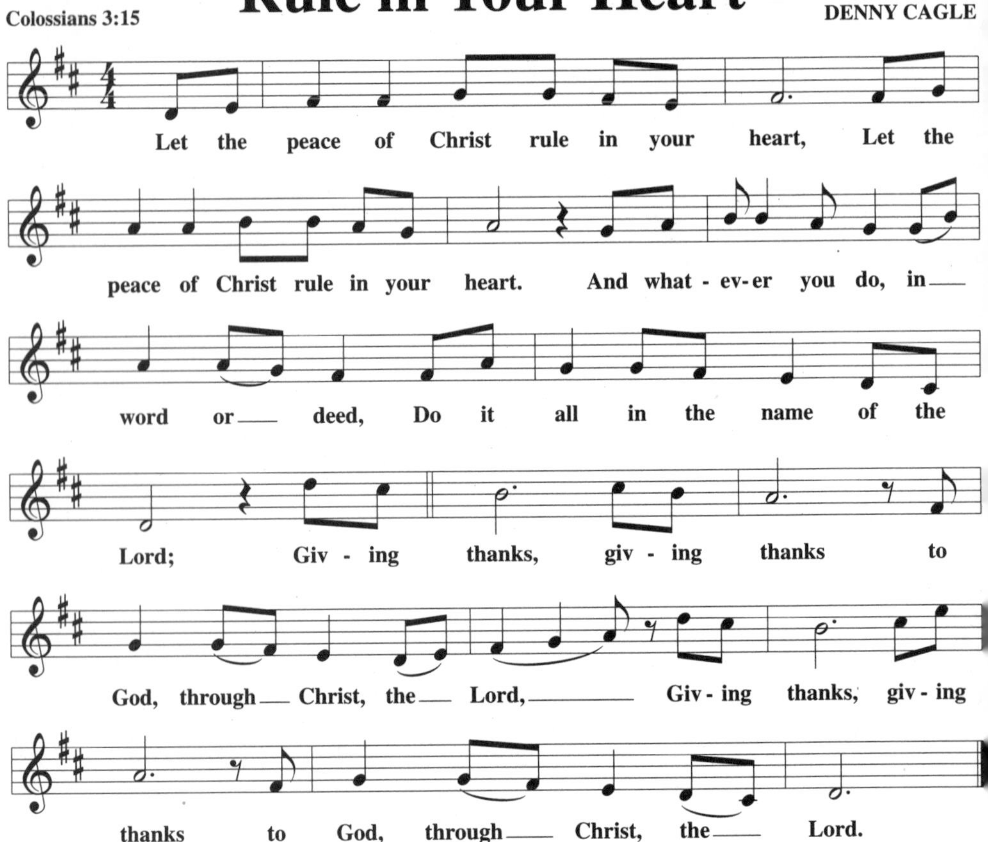

Let the peace of Christ rule in your heart, Let the
peace of Christ rule in your heart. And what-ev-er you do, in word or deed, Do it all in the name of the Lord; Giv - ing thanks, giv - ing thanks to God, through Christ, the Lord, Giv - ing thanks, giv - ing thanks to God, through Christ, the Lord.

252
Now unto the King Eternal

I Timothy 1:17

LORRAINE SONNENBERG

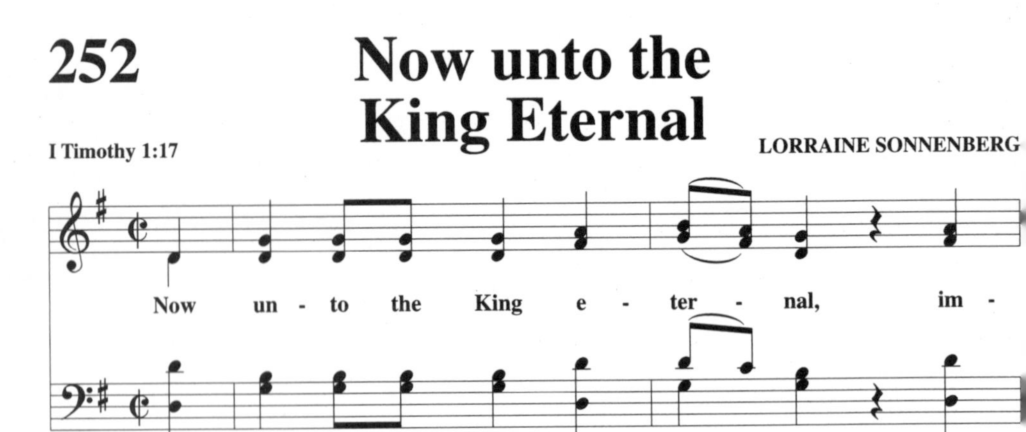

Now un - to the King e - ter - nal, im -

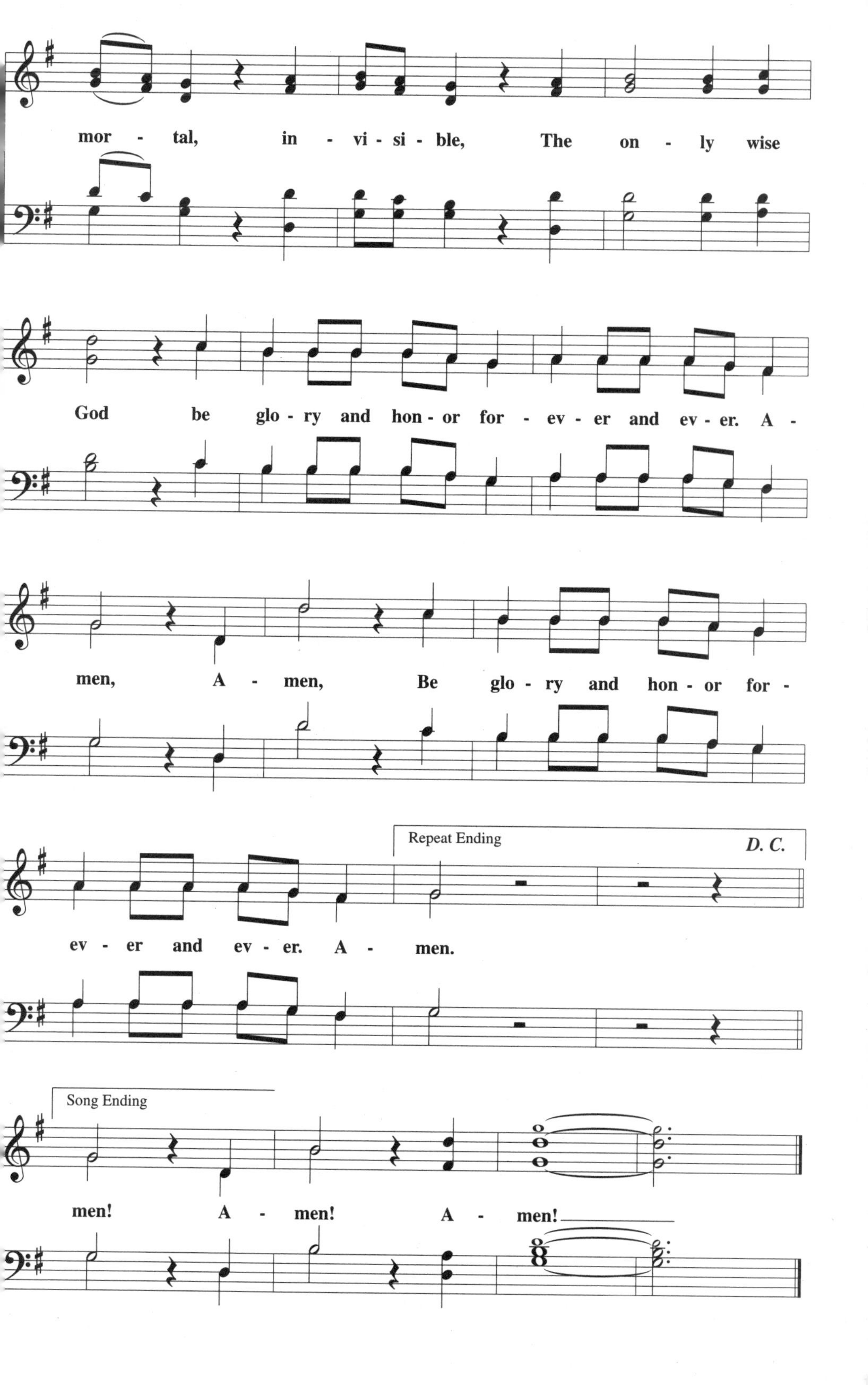
mor - tal, in - vi - si - ble, The on - ly wise
God be glo - ry and hon - or for - ev - er and ev - er. A -
men, A - men, Be glo - ry and hon - or for -
Repeat Ending
D. C.
ev - er and ev - er. A - men.
Song Ending
men! A - men! A - men!

253 Now unto Him

DAVID MORRIS
Based on Jude 24-25

DAVID MORRIS

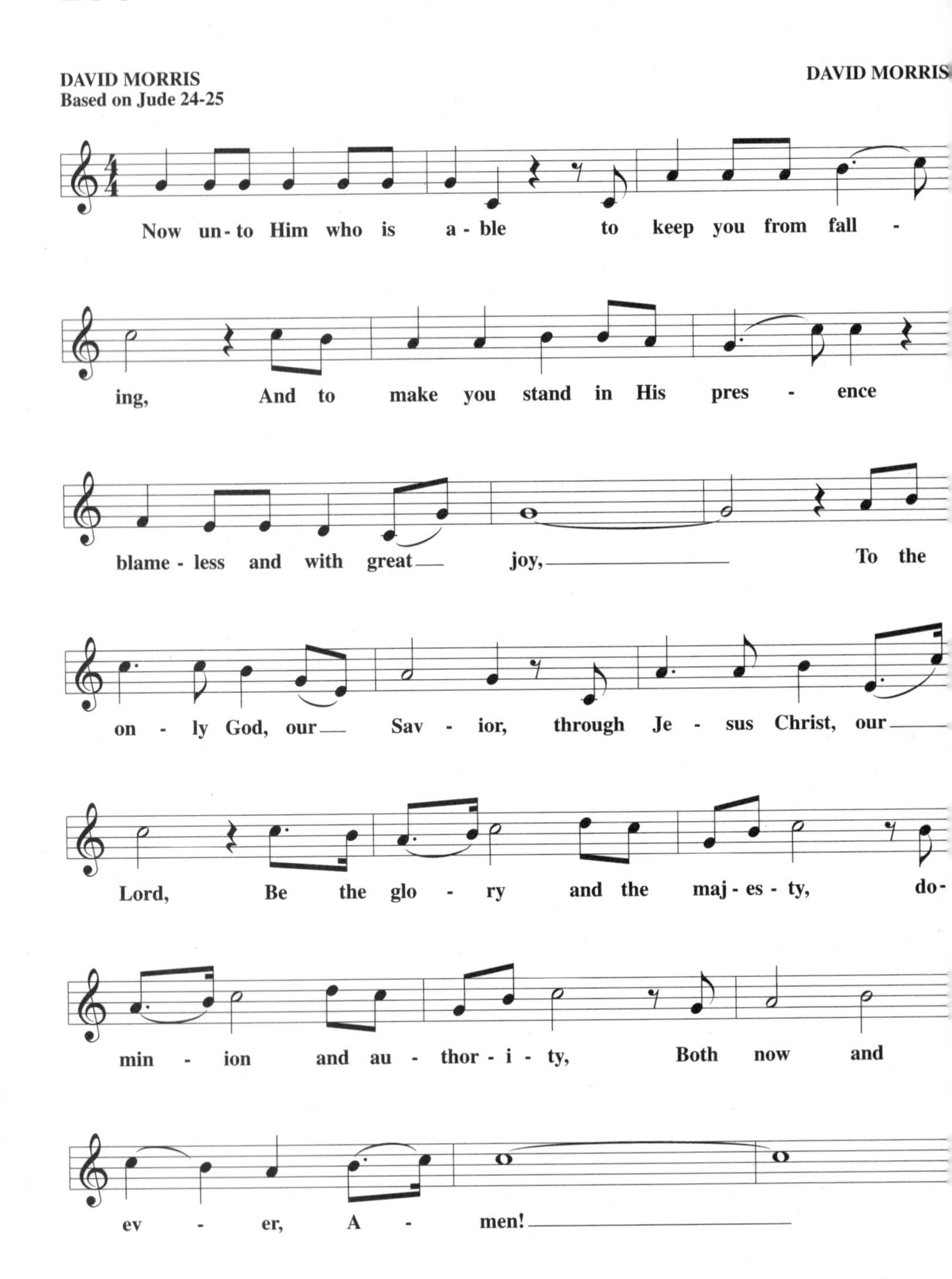

Now un-to Him who is a-ble to keep you from fall-ing, And to make you stand in His pres-ence blame-less and with great joy, To the on-ly God, our Sav-ior, through Je-sus Christ, our Lord, Be the glo-ry and the maj-es-ty, do-min-ion and au-thor-i-ty, Both now and ev-er, A-men!

COMPREHENSIVE PRODUCT LIST

PRODUCT	DESCRIPTION	PRODUCT #
Pew Edition	Softbound	301 0071 361
Pew Edition	Blue	301 0061 366
Pew Edition	Red	301 0062 362
Pew Edition	Brown	301 0063 369
Pew Edition	Gray	301 0064 365
Pew Edition	White	301 0065 361
Pew Edition	Green	301 0066 368
Pew Edition	Berry	301 0067 364
Pew Edition	Teal	301 0068 360
Pew Edition	Oyster	301 0069 367
Singer's Edition	Spiral	301 0055 366
Singer's Edition	Looseleaf	301 0056 362
Worship Planner Edition	Hard bound	301 0057 369
Worship Planner Edition	Leather bound	301 0058 365
Singalong Edition	Spiral	301 0203 497
Transparency Masters	Words Only	301 0059 361
Slides	Words Only	301 0060 36X

INSTRUMENTAL BOOKS

Conductor's Score	Book One	301 5031 317
Flute/Oboe/Melody	Book Two	301 5032 313
Bb Clarinet/Bass Clarinet	Book Three	301 5033 31X
Eb Alto Saxophone I,II	Book Four	301 5034 316
Bb Tenor Saxophone/ Baritone Treble Clef	Book Five	301 5035 312
F Horn I,II	Book Six	301 5036 319
Bb Trumpet I/Melody	Book Seven	301 5037 315
Bb Trumpet II,III	Book Eight	301 5038 311
Trombone I,II/Melody	Book Nine	301 5039 318
Violin I,II/Melody	Book Ten	301 5040 316
Viola/Melody	Book Eleven	301 5041 312
C Bass/Bass Trombone/ Tuba/Cello-Bass/Bassoon/ Baritone Saxophone	Book Twelve	301 5042 319
Percussion	Book Thirteen	301 5043 315
Synthesizer	Book Fourteen	301 5044 311
Master Rhythm	Book Fifteen	301 5045 318
Keyboard	Spiral	301 5046 314
Keyboard	Looseleaf	301 5049 313

ALPHABETICAL INDEX OF SONGS
Titles are in bold face type; First lines are in regular type.

INDEX OF SONGS

INDEX OF SONGS

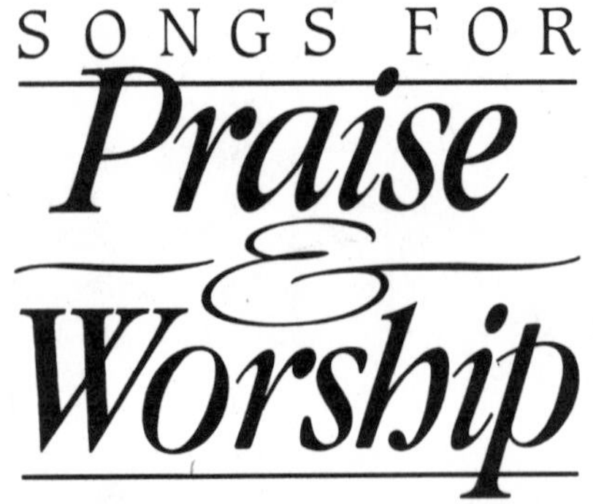

SONGS FOR

Praise & Worship